MARCELLINO'S
Restaurant
Report '96
NEW YORK CITY

Marcellino's Guides USA Inc.
340 East 52 Street
Suite 7E
New York, NY 10022
Tel: 212/752-5700
Fax: 212/752-4101

GARY KANE

Marcellino
Publisher

WELCOME

Dear Friends,

I'd like to welcome you to the first American edition of *Marcellino's Restaurant Report*. Although we've been publishing these guides in Europe since 1988, this is our first venture "abroad," and we're terribly excited about it. We chose New York City for our debut in large part because of the plethora of dining choices available here, which fits right into our motto — "taste the difference and enjoy."

Our task began in earnest last April 17th, when we "officially" put the wheels of production into motion. But in reality we began well before that. Months of research, thought and time went into the planning of our entry into the restaurant guide market. We didn't want to simply mimic what's already been done, but rather to make some innovative additions that would be most helpful to New York diners. As a result, we've taken a somewhat different approach by adding several new and unique features to our book.

We believe in neighborhoods, and as such, we've divided our book into geographical areas. We also believe that the consumer should be offered as much information as possible about each restaurant. That means not only do we rate them as to food, service and atmosphere, but we also provide vital information as to the type of cuisine, the form of payment accepted, fax numbers, the availability of takeout and/or delivery, and the specialties of each restaurant. We also offer maps and the appropriate coordinates, in an effort to make it easier to locate each restaurant.

Of course, one of the most important ingredients necessary to our success is your cooperation and participation. We invite you to be a part of our "team," to grow along with us, by offering your opinions which, after all, is what we're all about. Please take a look at page 9, and drop us a line, so you can be one of our surveyors.

And in the end, all we ask of you is to "taste the difference and enjoy!"

Marcellino & Team

October 15, 1995

GARY KANE

CONTENTS

DIRECTORY OF INDICES

Pages 255-302 contain indices listing the restaurants by alphabetical order, type of cuisine, and special interest.

HOW TO USE THIS GUIDE

RATING SCALE

We have created a rating system with the three most important ingredients, so to speak, of any restaurant: Food (**F**), Service (**S**) and Atmosphere (**A**). The rating is given on the Marcellino's scale:

0	1	2	3	4	5	6	7	8	9	10
disappointing		fair		good		very good		excellent		perfect

SYMBOLS

B	=	Breakfast		AE	=	American Express
L	=	Lunch		MC	=	Mastercard
D	=	Dinner		V	=	Visa
TO	=	Take Out available		D	=	Diners Club
D	=	Delivery available		DIS	=	Discover Card
		SPEC	=	Specialties		

COST

The **$** sign indicates the average cost of a dinner. It includes an appetizer (or dessert), an entree and an alcoholic beverage. Tax and tip are not included. New York sales tax is 8.25%. To decide the amount of the tip, a common practice in New York is to double the sales tax.

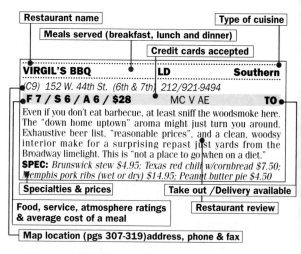

Restaurant name

Meals served (breakfast, lunch and dinner)

Credit cards accepted

Type of cuisine

VIRGIL'S BBQ   **LD**   **Southern**

(C9) 152 W. 44th St. (6th & 7th) 212/921-9494

F 7 / S 6 / A 6 / $28   MC V AE   **TO**

Even if you don't eat barbecue, at least sniff the woodsmoke here. The "down home uptown" aroma might just turn you around. Exhaustive beer list, "reasonable prices", and a clean, woodsy interior make for a surprising repast just yards from the Broadway limelight. This is "not a place to go when on a diet."
SPEC: *Brunswick stew $4.95; Texas red chili w/cornbread $7.50; Memphis pork ribs (wet or dry) $14.95; Peanut butter pie $4.50*

Specialties & prices

Take out /Delivery available

Food, service, atmosphere ratings & average cost of a meal

Restaurant review

Map location (pgs 307-319)address, phone & fax

TOP 10 RESTAURANTS

In each price category we have selected the 10 best restaurants based on the surveys that were returned to us. You will find the resulting charts on pages 17-25. In the margins throughout the book, you will find these logos next to restaurants listed in the "Ten Best" charts.

Top 10 $0-20	Top 10 $21-35	Top 10 $36-55	Top 10 $56+
Inexpensive	Moderate	Expensive	Very Expensive

The reviews in *Marcellino's Restaurant Report New York City '96* are based on the surveys returned to us by individuals who want to share their impressions about the restaurants they visit with you, the reader. Each restaurant was also checked by our team of researchers. Everyone can participate in Marcellino's review of restaurants. After all, the restaurant owner depends on you, the diner. And each year we will publish a new revised edition of *Marcellino's Restaurant Report New York City*.

Simply send us your name and address and we will send you a Survey Form in the Spring of 1996. If you want us to send a Survey Form to your friends, please include their name(s) and address(es) and a Survey Form will be on its way to them too!

Of course, if you review at least 10 restaurants your name will be listed in the next edition of *Marcellino's* (see page 13) and you will receive a free copy of the new guide. You will also receive a Marcellino's reviewer discount on additional copies.

Please send your Survey Form request to:

Marcellino's Guides USA Inc.
340 East 52nd Street
Suite 7E
New York, New York 10022

You can also contact us by calling our office at 212/752-6242, or by faxing your request to 212/752-4101.

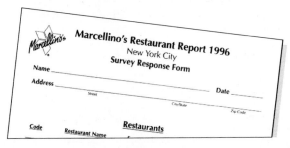

THE TEAM

Publisher	Marcellus Hudalla
Associate Publisher	Willem J. Remmelink
Editor-in-Chief	Charles Salzberg
Editors	Andrew F. Ackers
	Gail Eisenberg
	Brian Silverman
Editorial Assistants	Greg Longenhagen, John Espinosa
Art Director	Barbara Seitz
Advertising Director	Dori Bryant
Project Manager	Andrew F. Ackers
Research Editors	James Babbin, Donte Burse,
	Christina Chiu, Stanley Ely,
	Gail Eisenberg, Alexandra Flood,
	Ramona Flood, Naomi Helig,
	Jane Hodges, Ross Klavan,
	Kathryn Lancioni, Arthur Lindo,
	Ramsey Piazza, David Prior,
	Jocelyn Serio, Sarah Schenck,
	Brian Silverman, Alix Strauss,
	Cheryl Ursin, Geoffrey Welchman,
	Paige Wiiliams, Gunilla Wranne
Published by	Marcellino's Guides USA Inc.
	340 East 52 Street
	Suite 7E
	New York, NY 10022
	Tel: 212/752-5700
	Fax: 212/752-4101
ISBN	01-9648202-4-2

Every effort has been made to assure the accuracy and objectivity of all information in this guide, but neither the authors nor the publishers make any warranty, nor assume any responsibility with respect thereto.

The photographs used in this book were provided with permission from the restaurants or photographers.

SURVEYORS

Marcellino's would like to thank the following people who helped make this guide possible by completing a total of 1300 restaurant surveys.

A

Abrahamson, Mark
Ackerman, Daniel
Adams, Micheline
Adler, Paul
Al-Hamad, Ahmad
Albright, Jr., Don
Allison, Jane
Amgott, Madeline
Amparado, Keith,
Anderson, Robert
Angeles, Elaine
Angeli, Donna
Angelino, Frank
Angelino, Frank
Antreassian, Brenda
Armegol, Mary
Armstrong, Ann
Arnold, Mr. & Mrs. A.
Asperti, Ciro
Averrbach, Esther
Azizi, Efat

B

Baff, Marc Dana
Baldassare, Leslie
Baldwin, Janet
Banks, Nancy A.
Bark, Robert
Baron, Blake
Baron, Debbie
Barona, Maria
Barrios, Aguiar, Ricardo
Bassman, Mike
Basso, Anthony
Baum, Douglas
Beeck, Patricia
Beidner, Brad
Belanske, Ronald
Belth-Garbers, Bernice
Bendel, Peggy
Benyahia, Jean-Charles
Berg, Suzy
Berkley, Mari
Berman, Carol
Berris, Lee
Bettinger, Marc
Bevilacqua, Mauro,
Biederman, Barry
Bifulco, Tom
Bilenas, Jonas
Bini, Edmund
Binishi, Tomorr
Black, Deven
Black, Rhonda
Blatt, Lila S.
Blenzig, Lia
Bloch, John
Block, Aaron
Bogacz, Stephen
Boguslav, Donna
Bonilla-Camacho,
  Chastidy
Bookhardt, Fred B.
Bourne, Marie
Brandes, Barry
Brandonisio, Dominick
Brant, Campbell
Brassem, Julie
Bratyanski, Doris
Bratyanski, Mr. & Mrs. A
Bratyanski, R.
Brelesky, Gail
Brent, Harry
Brescia, Michael

Brisman, Deborah
Broussard, Tom
Brown, Anne
Brown, Kate
Brown, Sari
Bruce, Tammy
Brunetti, Philomena
Budge, Candace
Burger, Joanna
Burgos, Mirza
Burko, Helen
Byer, Deborah
Byer, Deborah

C

Cacioppo, Mary
Cage, Betty
Caldwell, Constance A.
Calimano, Maria
Cally, Mary
Cantone, Leona
Capria, Denise
Caracciolo, Theresa
Carr, Larry
Carson, Carolyn
Carter, Eric
Carter, Jr., J. S.
Casadona, Mark,
Casassola, Vitor
Castellano, Michael
Caswell, Nicole
Centeno, Jose
Chang, Wen-wen
Channing, Mark
Charne, Jeff
Chiappardi, Bob
Chonchol, Mr. & Mrs.
  Ralph
Chow, Seville
Christie, Bob
Clark, Brian W.
Coffey, Paul
Cohen, M.
Cohen, Marvin
Cohen, Nancy
Colure, Eileen
Connelly, Marjorie
Conway, George
Corcoran, Cindy
Cornet, Benoit
Cornez, Gerry
Cosentino, Chris
Cosgrone, Mark
Courrier, Norma
Courtenay, Jeanne
Crociata, Theresa
Csala, Margaret
Cucurullo, Renee
Cuyar, Karen

D

Da Silva, Virginia
Dahl, Erik
Datesh, Paula,
Davies, P. Vaughan
Davis, Kate Comstock
De Bari, Marcella
De Blasio, Edmund
De Francesco, Tom
De Jesus, F.
Decaro, Frank
DeCrette, Danielle
Defrin, Elin
Deichman, Ruth
Delaney, Teresa
Demarais, Ann

DeMuro, Susan
DeSalvo, Teresa
Dhoury, Julie
Diamond, Shari
Diamond, Shari
Dinoff, Addison
Doherty, John
Dolor, Stephanie
Domedion, D.,
Donis, Paula
Doyle, Maureen E.
Drelyos, Constantine
Dreyfus, Bendit
Drougas, Jim
Dunbar, Carol
Duncan, John
Duprey, Sherry

E

Eastract, Richard
Eddy, Don
Edwards, Seth
Egan, Amanda
Eilers, Gerald
Eisenhaver, Anita
Eliot, Fred
Elliott, Steve
Elstein, Stephen
Endo, Yuki
Eng, Debbie,
Eng, Elizabeth
Eng, Elsa
Engel, D.
Engel, Diana
Ensling, Jesse
Epstein, Cynthia
Esposito, Joseph
Etheridge, Jennifer
Everett, Mr.

F

Falco, Ciro
Falkoff, . Juli
Farley, Joey
Fass, Suzanne
Feightner, Kathryn
Feldeisen, Bruno
Feldman, Richard
Ferreras, Gloria
Ferrugio, Theresa
Fielding, Susan
Finch, Christi
Fioramonti, Frank
Fish, Jean Marie
Fiske, Lori
Fitzgerald, Saundra
Fontanilla, Edrex
Foo, Violet
Forman, Robin
Forminio, Donna
Foskey, Jay
France, James
Frank, Pamela
Frankel, Edwin
Franks, Claire
Franzetti, Mike
Freedman, Helen
Freedman, Ken
Freeman, Donnell
Frishberg, Aaron &
  Nancy
Fuchs, Carole

G

Galante, D.
Gandara, Siso

13

Gassin, Nancy
George, Matthew
Gerber, Evelyn & Charles
Gerber, Terry
German, Frederick
Giamundo, Christine
Gianfrancesco, Edward
Gillikin, Benjamin
Ginger, Lee Gretta
Glickman, Edwin
Globus, Rudo Dr.
Glotzer, Karen
Go Bio, Deanna
Gokcebay, Nazmiye
Goldstein, Sylvia
Gong, Lin
Gonsalves, Laurel
Goodwin, Jerry
Gorka, C.
Gotlin, Stanley
Granberg, Lorain
Green, Audrey
Greenberg, Jan
Greenberg, Kate,
Gross, Jennifer
Gross, Ruth & William
Grossberger, Bob
Gruber, Howard Dr
Grunebaum, Peter
Gura, Timothy

H

Hahn, Janine
Hamilton, Patricia
Hansen, G. W.
Hardoy, Jorgelina
Harris, Raymond
Harrison, Stan
Hay, Kathy
Hayes, Lateefa
Hayes, Victoria
Hemstead, Raymond
Hendra, Barbara
Herbat, Martin
Herz, Lisa
Higgins, James M.
Hill, Judith
Hiller, Robert
Hirschfeld, M.
Hirschorn, Deborah
Hittel, Ken
Holbrook, Harriet
Holmen, Robert
Hommel, Liz
Hommel, Liz
Horowitz, Mitchell
Howard, Christine
Hu, W. Bradford
Huang, Jenny
Hudson-Baron, Caryl
Hughes, Jane K.
Huppert, Joseph

I

Iannallo, Theresa
Ihle, Robert
Indyke, Perry
Ioannides, William
Iogha, Beth
Irizarry, Michelle
Israfil, Nabi
Ivanov, Sergey

J

Jacobson, Eric
James, April
Jawhi, Dana
John, Edith
Johnson, Harmer
Johnson, Kevin
Jones, Jennifer

K

Kane, Margot
Kanfer, Lillian
Kaplan, Allan
Karaszi, Gabriella
Katz, Leonard
Kaufman, Andrew
Kaufman, Leslie
Kearns, Elizabeth
Keenan, Claudia
Kennedy, H. Young
Kerrigan, Robert
Khoury, Julie
Kirschhoch, Deborah L.
Klausner, Jeremy
Klein, Michael
Klibanoff, Leonard
Koesther, Susan
Kolber, Billy
Kosa, John
Kramer, Robin
Kramer, Bennette
Krauthamer, Nina
Kravitz, Robin
Krugo Voy, Caludia
Kubiak, Margaret
Kufrin-Seltzer, Arna Lee
Kull, Rudi
Kwan, Toby

L

La Porta, Ann
La Scala, Nancy
Lalonde-Nespresso, Daniel
Landou, Bernard
Laney, Jack
Langley, Susan
Lappi, Sara
Leberfeld, Michelle
Lee, Brenda
Lee, Dennison
Lee, Lori
Leon, Ynes
Lerner, Susan
Leudesdorf, Frances
Levy, Jeffery
Liang, G. M.
Lo, Anita
Loffredo, Stephen & Thalia
Lohle, Virginia
Lortscher, M.D., Loren
Lukas, Wayne
Lusmil, Regina
Lynn, Aja

M

Machinist, Gabrielle
Mack, Christine
Madigan, Richard
Makhi, Abbas
Makouitzky, Joann,
Mancher, Diane
Mancini, Laura
Mangiaracina, Barbara
Manning, Ernestine
Marks, Elizabeth
Maropis, Patrick
Marra, Regina
Marro, G. S.
Martin, Carla
Mascio, Evelyn
Maslow, Jerry
Matis, Dr. & Mrs. J. D.
Mauroff, Mr. & Mrs. D.
Maxey, Barbara,
Mayer, Mrs. Robert
Mayhew, Elizabeth
McGorty, Fran
McKenney, Anne-Marie

McAvliffe, Gervais
McAward, Jeremiah
McCormack, D.
McDonald, Katherine V.
McDonald, Robert
McGinnis, Elizabeth
McGorty, Fran
McGraw, Kelly R.
McIntyre, John
McKenzie, Victoria
McLaughlin, Marrie
Meekins, Crystal
Mendez, Barbara
Merrels, Charles
Mersinger, Bill
Messana, Steve
Meyer, Jennifer
Michelena, Adaleza
Milewski, Yvonne
Miller, Jane
Monaco, Marie
Montag, Murray
Montemarano- Stein, Anita
Morales, Claire E. H.
Morales, Vernon
Morandi, Dominic
Morgan, Kathleen
Morgan, Maggie
Morikawa, Elaine
Morrow, Thomas O. J.
Mosca, Lucille
Mott, Hanno
Munro, Robert
Murphy, Diana

N

Neher, Sonja
Nelson, Aida
Nicolas, Corinne
Nonken, Marilyn
Nostrand, C. R. Van
Novacek, Laura
Nyilas, Robert

O

O'Berski, Mark
O'Brien, Julie
O'Neil, Nancy,
O'Rourke, Brian
O'berg, Nancy,
Oh, Albert
O'Kun, Jodi
Olsaver, Gary
Oltmans, Timothy
Oppenheim, Guy
Ortega, Darryl
Osnos, Noah
Owen, Harvey

P

Palasin, Ludmica
Palevsky, Joy
Palo, Frank
Panariello, Rose,
Parker, Audrey
Parmenter, Kay
Partilla, Karla
Pashliowsky, Alex
Patterson, Robert
Peck, Nikki
Pell, Jessica
Pensabene, Kim,
Perchuk, Florence
Perez, Wilfredo
Perinuzzi, Linda
Perkinson, Gary
Perrern, Richard
Pesky, Andrew
Petersen, M. J.
Peterson, Marian
Phillips, Kimberly
Pillai, Sathi

Pires, Helena
Piscitelli, Paul
Plastik, Harry
Pomeroy, Lee
Porter, Valerie
Porter, Regina
Portnoy, Mark
Posnack, Clare
Prioleau, Alison
Probert, Clare
Prsky, Andrew
Puleo, Frank
Putter, Felicia

Q

Quaknine, Lisa
Quinn, Irene

R

Rad, Juliet
Radulesco, Carla
Reddy, Mary
Reich, Paul
Reiner, Robert
Reinhardt, Barbara
Reiss, Bob
Remer, John
Resnick, Sybil
Reville, Amy
Reyes, Consuelo
Riccitelli, Leanna
Rico, George
Rie, Linda
Rineitant, Elaine
Ring, Nancy
Risco, Lisa
Rivera, Martha
Rizzo, Joe
Robb, P. D.
Robbins, Jack & Sonia
Roberts, Judith
Roberts, Stephen
Rodrigues, Steven
Rodriguez, Ydalia
Rodriquez, Iris
Roether, Eileen
Rogers, Robert
Rolihaus, Leah
Romano, Eleanor
Rondell, Susan
Roque, Tony
Rose, Alyce
Rosenau, Heidi
Rosenberg, Linda
Rosenblatt, Joan
Rosendin, Cece
Rosenthal, Alvin
Roser, Jonathan P.
Ross, Kenita
Rossi, JoAnn
Rothenberg, Donna
Rothschild, Stephanie
Rubin, Hal
Ruderman, Adam
Ruderman, Kitty
Russell, Leah
Russler, Diana
Rutigliano, Theresa

S

Sabata, Kenta
Sachs, Professor Leon
Saddie, Jill
Saiger, Aimee
Salerno, Vito
Salives, Harry
Salomon, Harvey
Salvo, Calogero
Samuel, Tanya
Sanchez, Wilma
Sandmeyer, April
Sapirstein, Monica

Sarns, Agnes
Sarver, Eugene Dr.
Schaper, Betsy
Scheetz, Janice
Scherber, A.
Schneider, Naomi
Schott, Christine
Schowalter, Tom
Schubert, Micki
Schutz, Jeane
Schwartz, John
Schwarz, Gloria
Sebren, Lee
Seidenberg, Beryl
Seidman, Lillian
Seto, Justin
Settanni, Kenneth &
  Ellen
Shalley, Eve
Shapiro, Dan
Sharkey, Brian
Shaver, Marian
Shaw, Cynthia
Shear, Esther
Sheffield, Edwin
Sheiner, Patricia
Sherman, Betsy
Sherwood, Peter
Shoukas, Denise
Shukovsky, Andrea
Sicard, Linda
Siehr, Pamela
Silk, Felice
Simmons, Noreen
Singer, Peter
Skinner, E. J.
Slater, Connie
Smith, Effie
Smith, George
Smith, Kate
Smith, Michael Steven
Smith, Scott
Smith, Elayne
Snider, Lee
Snyder, Murray
Snyder, Ronald
Sodano, Thomas
Soell, Emily
Somogy, V.
Spaleta, Jay
Spencer, Abigail
Spinelli, Phillip
Spodek, Walter
Spranger, Carol
Staiano, James
Stanley, Marilyn
Steele, Tom
Stein, Harriet
Steinberg, Roy
Stimler, Iru
Stone, Michelle
Stone, Sara
Strong, Monique
Strong, Monique
Sturdivant, Larry
Sukezane, Tomo
Sulsona, Shannon,
Sulyok, Teresa
Surles, Barbara
Susman, Rosanne
Swartz, Scott
Szilagyi, George
Szogyi, Alex

T

Tabs, Nancy
Takahashi, Midori
Tam, Chiu-muen
Taylor, Analiese
Taylor, B. Kim
Thompson, Allison

Thompson, David
Tomko, Janan
Toosie, Cristina
Torre, Michael
Torres, Jose
Torres, Norma
Torres, Ponciano
Tortora, Elvira
Tower, Erin
Tse, Wayne
Tuomey, Judith
Turkel, Ann
Turok, Brendy

U

Uzzo, Cheryl

V

Vargas, Diana
Vassallo, Mariano
Vastola, Thomas
Vaughan, Alexander
Velez-Lebron, Selena
Villani, Rocco
Volin, Judith

W

Wadsworth, Bill
Wallis, Bruce
Warren, Steven
Weed, Bet
Weinberg, Pamela
Weinberg, Pamela
Weiner, Beth
Weiner, Beth
Weinganten, Laurie
Welborn, Jr., John
Wells, Peter
Westenberger, Fritz
Westphal, Kirk
Whipple, George
Widdemo, Pamela
Wiener, Geri
Wiessler, Joel
Willams, Alpe
Williams, Julie
Wilsker, R
Wilson, Kenneth
Win, Kyimon
Wingard, D. F.
Winski, Paul
Withim, Gloria
Wofsey, Robert A.
Wolper, Marjorie
Womersley, Susan
Works, P. B.

Y

Yaari, Uzi
Yanghlin, Marnie
Yao, Stephanie
Yee, J.
Yin, Stanley
Young, Donna

Z

Zablow, Lori
Zacharow, Beaty
Zasauski, Jack
Zialcita, R. S.

*List may be incomplete
and does not include
those participants who
wished to remain
anonymous. Please
excuse any errors, addi-
tions or omissions.
Thank you.*

15

Introducing Membership Rewards.℠®

The Membership Rewards program gives you a world of choices. So...

If you can't find something you like here...

*Saks Fifth Avenue.
Caswell-Massey.
Timberland.
Filene's Basement.
One Step Ahead.
FTD Direct.*

Maybe you'll find it here.

*Tourneau.
Beverly Clark Collection.
Fortunoff.*

Or here.

*CompUSA.
Tower Records.
Nobody Beats The Wiz.
Waldenbooks.
NordicTrack.*

Or here.

*Hertz.
Budget Rent a Car.
National Car Rental.*

Or here.

*Delta Air Lines.
USAir.
Continental.
Southwest Airlines.
Swissair.
Austrian Airlines.
Sabena.
EL AL Israel Airlines.
Aeromexico.
Mexicana.*

Or here.

*Marriott.
ITT Sheraton.
Hilton.
Westin.
Renaissance.*

The Membership Rewards program turns every dollar you spend on the American Express® Card into rewards that you decide how to use. So you can go where you want, get what you like, and stay where you'd prefer to stay. It's up to you. To enroll, call 1-800-AXP-EARN.

TOP TEN

AWARDS

New Yorkers dine out frequently, some even daily. They can choose from many restaurants, cuisines, and price ranges, depending upon their mood and budget. Marcellino's honors the best restaurants, and the hard work of their chefs and service staff, from among those many diverse restaurants, and created awards in four price categories. On the following pages you will find the 10 best restaurants in each price category, offering you the finest dining values as chosen by our surveyors.

GARY KANE

Edmundo Grazon, Chef
Paula Toppani, Owner
Tanti Baci Caffe

TOP TEN **INEXPENSIVE**

The following list is the top ten restaurants in the $0-$20 price range category. The price includes an appetizer (or dessert), an entree and an alcoholic beverage. Tax and tip are not included.

Number	Restaurant	Page
1.	TANTI BACI CAFFE *Italian*	94
2.	O.G. *Asian*	68
3.	BELLISSIMA *Italian*	149
4.	BROOKLYN DINER *American*	200
5.	MOUSTACHE *Middle Eastern*	89
6.	BAR PITTI *Italian*	75
7.	GREAT JONES CAFE *Cajun*	64
8.	HAVELI *Indian*	64
9.	BELLA DONNA *Italian*	148
10.	PATSY'S *Pizzeria*	249

Top 10
$0-20
Inexpensive

Peter Hoffman, Owner/Chef (r)
David Worth, Chef de Cuisine (l)
Savoy

TOP TEN **MODERATE**

The following list is the top ten restaurants in the $21-$35 price range category. The price includes an appetizer (or dessert), an entree and an alcoholic beverage. Tax and tip are not included.

Number	Restaurant	Page
1.	SAVOY *Mediterranean*	55
2.	SALAAM BOMBAY *Indian*	42
3.	PAOLA'S *Italian*	172
4.	MAZZEI *Italian*	169
5.	HONMURA AN *Japanese*	49
6.	DUANE PARK CAFE *American*	39
7.	SUSHISAY *Japanese*	142
8.	GRAND CENTRAL OYSTER BAR & RESTAURANT *American*	107
9.	PIER 25A *Seafood*	253
10.	VILLA MOSCONI *Italian*	96

Top 10
$21-35

Moderate

James Henderson, Chef
One If By Land, Two If By Sea

GARY KANE

TOP TEN **EXPENSIVE**

The following list is the top ten restaurants in the $36-$55 price range category. The price includes an appetizer (or dessert), an entree and an alcoholic beverage. Tax and tip are not included.

Number	Restaurant	Page
1.	ONE IF BY LAND, TWO IF BY SEA *Mediterranean*	91
2.	NOBU *Japanese*	41
3.	RAPHAEL *French*	217
4.	PERIYALI *Greek*	194
5.	JUDSON GRILL *American/Continental*	208
6.	TWO TWO TWO *American*	242
7.	FOUR SEASONS–THE GRILL *Continental*	126
8.	UNION SQUARE CAFE *American*	117
9.	F.ILLI PONTE *Italian*	30
10.	CAPSOUTO FRERES *French*	38

Top 10 $36-55
Expensive

Gray Kunz, Chef
Lespinasse

TOP TEN **VERY EXPENSIVE**

The following list is the top ten restaurants in the $56+ price category. The price includes an appetizer (or dessert), an entree and an alcoholic beverage. Tax and tip are not included.

Number	Restaurant	Page	
			Top 10 $56+
1.	LESPINASSE *French Asian*	132	Very Expensive
2.	LA GRENOUILLE *French*	130	
3.	LES CÉLÉBRITÉS *French*	211	
4.	LA CARAVELLE *French*	209	
5.	FOUR SEASONS–THE POOL ROOM *Continental*	126	
6.	AUREOLE *American*	147	
7.	LE CIRQUE *French*	164	
8.	LE BERNARDIN *French*	210	
9.	CHANTERELLE *French*	38	
10.	BOULEY *French*	38	

LAST MINUTE NEWS

At press time these restaurants of note were due to open:

TRIBECA

Layla (211 W. Broadway; 212/431-0700) The latest entry in the Drew Nieporent/Robert De Niro restaurant sweepstakes. The cuisine is Middle-eastern and entertainment will be provided by belly dancers.

Mos'Quito (179 Franklin St.; 212/334-2397) Updated New Orleans cuisine, featuring French Creole dishes, served in a 2-level 200-seat space, spiced up with a sculpture garden and cascading waterfall out back.

TriBaKery (186 Franklin St.; 212/431-1114) Drew Nieporent, the Joyce Carol Oates of owner/chefs, opens this streamlined cafe offering home-baked pastries for breakfast, sandwiches, salads and pasta for lunch.

SOHO

Blue Ribbon Sushi (119 Sullivan St. bet. Spring & Prince; 212/343-0404) The owners of Blue Ribbon, Eric, Ellen and Bruce Bromberg, along with Toshi Ueki, open their long-awaited sushi bar.

Riodizio (417 Lafayette St. bet 4th & Astor Pl.; 212/529-1313) Chef Jamie Leeds from Cub Room adds an American slant to Sao Paulo cuisine.

WEST VILLAGE

13 Barrow (13 Barrow St. 212 727-1300) Guided by chef John Tesar, of the Hamptons Inn in Quogue, this Asian-Mediterranean restaurant will offer a raw bar, juice bar, and dinner served till 4am.

Village Grill (518 LaGuardia Pl. 212 228-1001) Actor Griffin Dunne and Conan O'Brien producer Jeff Ross, turn their attention to food, offering mussels and steak frites for under $15. Wash it down with a microbrewery selection of draft beers.

MIDTOWN WEST

La Cote Basque (60 W, 55th St. 212/688-6525) A new chef joins Jean Jacques Rachou when this renowned French restaurant reopens at its new location. The fabulous murals and paintings have been retained, but will it live up to its former reputation?

Pomp Duck and Circumstance (Dewitt Clinton Park, 11th Ave. & 53rd St.) Imported from Germany, this dinner-theater spectacle offers exotic dining under a plush tent as clowning restaurant staff interacts with audience-diners. The 3 1/2 hr. extravaganza includes cabaret as well as acrobatic acts. Fall through early Spring.

UPPER EAST SIDE

The Lobster Club (24 E. 80th St.) Arcadia owner Anne Rosenzweig's latest: a multi-cultural menu located in a townhouse duplex with fireplaces on each floor.

Willow (1022 Lex. Ave. 212/717-0703) In the former home of May We, the Table d'Hote owners open a 60-seat spot lined with 19th century paintings, offering creative organic cuisine.

There's also been a trend of late, of noted restaurants relocating. **Bouley's** lease is up soon and they will move, and it's rumored that **Le Cirque**, is also considering a move to the landmark Villard Houses in the Palace Hotel. So, keep an eye peeled.

Marcellino's

NEIGHBORHOODS

LOWER MANHATTAN

AU MANDARIN   LD   Chinese

(E3) 220 Vesey St. (#4 W.F.C.) 212/385-0313 Fax: 385-0412

F 6 / S 6 / A 4 / $25   MC V D AE DIS   **TO/D**

With branches in Frankfurt and Paris, Au Mandarin brings European sophistication, flair and elegance to the WTC area. The cuisine is beautifully prepared and presented. Courtyard seating or, for more formal dining, try the banquet rooms inside.
SPEC: *Honey shortribs $6.75; Popcorn baby shrimp $6.75; Beef tangerine $11.50; General Tso's chicken $9.75*

BENITO I   LD   Italian

(C4) 174 Mulberry St. (Broome & Grand) 212/226-9171

F 6 / S 6 / A 5 / $26   MC V D AE DIS   **TO**

The room is small, comfortable and free of the over-embellishments which typify neighborhood establishments. The Sicilian inspired menu features fresh ingredients served in unusual combinations. Smokers are welcome at the original Benito. But whatever you do, don't ask if Benito I is related to Benito II.
SPEC: *Artichoke stuffed w/pepato cheese $6; Spiedini alla Romana $6.50; Penne al portobello $12; Pollo Principessa $13*

BENITO II   LD   Italian

(C4) 163 Mulberry St. (Broome & Grand) 212/226-9012

F 6 / S 4 / A 6 / $21   Cash only   **TO**

With exposed brick walls, red-checked tablecloths and plastic lobsters on the wall, this is what might be considered a "typical" Italian restaurant. The owner greets you as if you're the last paying customer on earth, then gives you a waiter who can barely hide his disgust at your request for parmesan with your clam sauce.
SPEC: *Eggplant parmigiana $5.80; Spaghetti carbonara $9.85; Penne a la vodka $11; Cannoli Sicilian style $4.50; Zabaglione $4*

BIG WONG OF CHINATOWN   BLD   Chinese

(C4) 67 Mott St. (Canal) 212/964-1452

F 6 / S 6 / A 3 / $11   Cash only   **TO**

For a welcome change from dim sum, come here for breakfast and feast on congee pork and homemade fried bread. Food is served cafeteria style, and, much to the chagrin of many diners, you may wind up "sharing tables." Comments range from "not very friendly," to "sleazy but good, cheap eats." **Closed: Monday**
SPEC: *Combination beef, squid, pork $2.50; Roast pork $4.75; Chow fun $4.50; Beef nom (belly) $3*

BRIDGE CAFE   LD   American

(E4) 279 Water St. (Dover) 212/227-3344 Fax: 619-2368

F 6 / S 4 / A 4 / $27   MC V D AE   **TO**

Feel like a trip back in time? Well, try the Bridge Cafe which inhabits the oldest wood-frame building south of Canal St., circa 1801. The ceilings are tin, the floors slope, and that shadow you see is cast by the Brooklyn Bridge. Diners applaud the "great views," but some say the appetizers are better than the main courses." "Wine Discover Tuesday," means 30% off all bottled wine. Fridays and Saturdays, live jazz.
SPEC: *Grilled swordfish & eggplant $7.95; Curried lobster & spinach crepes $8.95; Soft shell crabs $17.95; Buffalo steak $18.50*

BURRITOVILLE   LD   Tex-Mex

(F4) 36 Water St. (N. of Broad St.) 212/747-1100 Fax: 747-0071
See review on page 77.

CANTON   LD   Chinese

(D4) 45 Division St. (Bowery & Market) 212/226-4441

F 8 / S 7 / A 3 / $21   Cash only   **TO**

This inviting Cantonese-style restaurant first opened in 1958, thus qualifying it as one of the oldest restaurants in Chinatown. Boasting patrons like I.M. Pei, who has frequented the eatery for 30 years, its decor is simple yet elegant: neutral tones and matching blue porcelain.
SPEC: *Dim sum $6.95; Lettuce wrap (prepared on request) $14.95; Special chicken $13.95; Peking duck (serves 4-6) $39.95*

CARMINE'S BAR & GRILL   LD   Italian

(E4) 140 Beekman St. (Front) 212/962-8606

F 6 / S 4 / A 4 / $21   MC V   **TO**

There's a definite rustic feel to this northern Italian restaurant. And with good reason. Located in an 1870 building with the original oak paneling and bar, complete with seafaring memorabilia, how could it be otherwise? The atmosphere is informal and friendly. The cuisine is "good, basic Italian," with emphasis on seafood.
SPEC: *Baked clams $5.45; Spaghetti w/red clam sauce $8.45; Fried calamari $9.95; Fried fillet of sole $9.95; Italian cheesecake $3.45*

COVE DINER   LD   Continental

(E2) 2 South End Ave. (W. Thames) 212/964-1500 Fax: 786-9546

F 4 / S 4 / A 4 / $23   MC V D AE DIS   **TO/D**

Pleasant, modern, contemporary setting, including scenic outdoor dining. A "nice neighborhood crowd." Moderate prices for good food, and friendly service. Could we ask for anything more? Well, maybe yes. But we'll gladly settle for this.
SPEC: *Buffalo wings $4.95; Chicken nuggets $4.95; Roasted stuffed chicken $10.95; Grilled jumbo shrimp $12.95; Pizzas $5.95-$7.95*

DONALD SACKS   LD   Amer/Continental

(E3) 220 Vesey St. (Courtyard W.F.C.) 212/619-4600 Fax: 732-6184

F 4 / S 6 / A 4 / $28   MC V D AE DIS   **TO/D**

A sunny, open, congenial place for lunch turns into a more intimate restaurant for dinner. The service is fast, efficient and friendly. Still, some diners find that it's a "get in and get out atmosphere." On a nice day, try the marble and brass courtyard of the World Financial Center.
SPEC: *Grilled chicken Caesar salad $14.95; Linguini primavera w/spring vegetables $10.50; Pizzas $8.75-$9.25; Chicken fajitas $12.95; White chocolate mousse cake $3.95*

EDO   LD   Japanese

(E3) 104 Washington St. (Rector St.) 212/344-2583 Fax: 732-9602

F 6 / S 7 / A 7 / $34   MC V D AE DIS   **TO/D**

Beautiful and roomy with contemporary Japanese decor, "and outstanding food and service," makes for a wonderful dining experience. Besides the dining rooms, there is a hibachi room, sushi bar and a cocktail lounge. No wonder it's a favorite with the business crowd craving raw fish instead of red meat. **Closed: Saturday & Sunday**
SPEC: *Yakitori $6.75; Tatsuta-age (deep fried chicken) $6.75; Sukiyaki $22; Shabu-Shabu $24*

0	1	2	3	4	5	6	7	8	9	10
disappointing		fair		good		very good		excellent		perfect

**Bobby Flay
Owner/chef of Mesa Grill and Bolo**

"**Nobu** is the most exciting restaurant to open in New York in the last five years. **Daniel** is the best upscale restaurant for special occasions. And **Blue Ribbon** is the best late night restaurant."

EDWARD MORAN BAR & GRILL   LD   American

(E2) 250 Vesey St. (#4 WFC on N. Cove Marina) 212/945-2255

F 4 / S 3 / A 5 / $23   MC V D AE DIS   **TO**

The atmosphere is pure Irish pub, but what sets Moran's apart from the rest is the terrace overlooking the harbor, the marina and the Lady with the Torch. On Thursday and Friday evenings it turns into a major singles scene. "So popular now they feel they no longer need good food or service to attract customers."
SPEC: *White New "Yawk" chowder $4.50; Chicken finger salad $6.95; Hamburger $8.95; Smoked sausage & peppers on Ciabotta bread $11.75; Brownie cheesecake $4.75*

Top 10 $36-55

Expensive

F.ILLI PONTE   LD   Italian

(D2) 39 Desbrosses (West & Washington) 212/226-4621

F 8 / S 7 / A 8 / $38   MC V D AE

A gorgeous family-owned and operated restaurant located in the historic Longshoreman's Hotel building. A sprawling complex that includes a casual brick oven pizza restaurant downstairs, with a formal dining room and separate cigar lounge upstairs—all with breathtaking views of the Hudson. Impeccable service and a cozy, refined atmosphere make this a wonderful place for a special occasion.
SPEC: *Angry lobster $20; Grilled veal chop w/seasonal vegetables $32; Pizza $8-$13; Profiterolles $8*

FINE & SCHAPIRO   BLD   Deli

(E3) 5 World Trade Center 212/775-7600
See review on page 229.

FLEDERMAUS CAFE   BLD   American

(E4) 1 Seaport Place (Front) 212/269-5890

F 4 / S 4 / A 4 / $16   MC V D AE   **TO**

This European-style outdoor cafe is located on the quaint, cobble-stoned plaza of the South St. Seaport. It's a great place to plop down, have a leisurely snack, or "late night coffee," and people-watch. Some suggest "getting rid of the plastic." Try the extensive coffee bar, or the soup and sandwich combo for $7.95.
SPEC: *Espresso & special coffees $4.95; Spicy chicken wings $5.50; Weisswurst (veal and pork sausage) $6.50; Linzer tart $3.95*

FRAUNCES TAVERN RESTAURANT   BLD   American

(F3) 54 Pearl St. (Broad St.) 212/269-0144 Fax: 269-3658

F 5 / S 6 / A 6 / $31   MC V D AE DIS

Old New York, doesn't get any older than Fraunces Tavern, which first opened its doors in 1792—think it was George Washington himself who hoisted the first tankard? Over the years this tavern may have taken a lickin' (a bomb went off there in the turbulent '70s), but it keeps on tickin'. Some diners consider it "a tourist trap," and "stuffy," while others applaud its "charming service."
Closed: Saturday & Sunday
SPEC: *Applewood smoked salmon spring roll $7.95; Grilled vegetable & goat cheese tart $5.95; Yankee pot roast $15.95; Beef Wellington $22.95; Walnut salmon $18.95*

FULTON ST. CAFE   LD   Seafood

(E4) 11 Fulton St. (Front) 212/227-2288

F 5 / S 5 / A 5 / $25   MC V D AE   **TO**

Another great people-watching vantage point on the cobblestoned Seaport promenade. Not particularly distinguished in terms of cuisine, but it does offer an oasis for tourists who want to take a load off. Particularly hectic during the lunch hour. At night it turns into a singles scene.

GIANNI'S   LD   Italian

(E4) 15 Fulton St. (So. St. Seaport) 212/608-7300

F 5 / S 5 / A 5 / $31   MC V D AE DIS

A popular hangout for the after-work, downtown crowd. It's a bright, open space with a good view of an historic seaport street, and the outdoor cafe is a great place for people watching.
SPEC: *Garlic bread w/gorgonzola sauce $6.50; Antipasto sampler $8.50; Crabcakes w/lobster sauce & orange oil $10.50; Grilled swordfish mignon $21*

GIOVANNI'S ATRIUM   LD   Italian

(E3) 100 Washington St. (Rector) 212/344-3777 Fax: 233-6547

F 6 / S 6 / A 7 / $36   MC V D AE DIS   **TO/D**

Lunchtime, Wall Streeters favor this Italian/Continental restaurant. At night, the clientele changes to neighborhood folk with their families. The decor is luxurious, with stone columns and exposed brick, with flowers abounding. But, "Beware of Greeks bearing gifts," because some diners find the food "mediocre." **Closed: Saturday and Sunday**
SPEC: *Hot antipasto $9.75; Zuppa di pesce $19.95; Surf & turf $23.25; Bistecca alla pizzaiola $20.50; Saltimboca-scarpariello $15.75*

GROTTA AZZURRA   LD   Italian

(C4) 387 Broome St. (Mulberry) 212/925-8775 Fax: 431-6701

F 6 / S 6 / A 6 / $29   Cash only

This basement level blue "cavern" has a diverse enough menu to please even the pickiest in your family. Possessed of "Old World charm and warmth," it's "noisy and close, but very Italy." Has a loyal following, attracted by the "good food." **Closed: July**
SPEC: *Spedini alla romana $8.95; Stuffed peppers $7.50; Chicken rollatine $16.95; Linguine & clams $11.95; Zambagliom $4.95*

HARBOUR LIGHTS   LD   American

(E4) Pier 17 So. St. Seaport (3rd Fl.) 212/227-2800

F 5 / S 6 / A 7 / $42   MC V D AE DIS

When we think South Street Seaport we think tourists and tacky souvenirs but Harbour Lights is different. This spacious, bright, restaurant, specializing in steaks and seafood, is popular with business people and the upscale tourist trade. Reactions range from "another tourist attraction," "awful," and "expensive" to "great place to take out of town guests."
SPEC: *Tuna steak $27; Charred Chicago strip steak $32*

HOULIHAN'S   LD   Amer/Continental

(E3) 196 Broadway (Fulton) 212/240-1280
(E4) 7 Hanover Square (Water) 212/483-8314
(F3) 50 Broad St. (Beaver) 212/483-8310
See review on page 230.

0	1	2	3	4	5	6	7	8	9	10
disappointing		fair		good		very good		excellent		perfect

HUDSON RIVER CLUB LD American

(E3) 250 Vesey St. (#4 W.F.C.) 212/786-1500 Fax: 406-1913

F 7 / S 7 / A 8 / $46   MC V D AE DIS

Boasting the world's largest selection of NY State wines, HRC also offers "great views" of the harbor, an "original, elegant, exquisite setting," and a staggering menu of American regional cuisine. It's not cheap—"you can smell the $ and power"— but you get what you pay for. If you arrive early, check out the busy bar scene specializing in rare spirits and beers.
SPEC: *Mint cured & apple smoked salmon Napoleon $16; Smoked quail salad $15; Venison chops $33; Smoked Catskill trout $2; Braised rabbit pot pie $27*

J.W.'s BLD American

(E3) 85 West St. (Albany-Marriot Financial) 212/385-4900

F 5 / S 7 / A 5 / $26   MC V D AE

The look is bright, modern and cheery. The cuisine, American, though there has been the recent addition of a "bistro-type" menu to the "Financial Grill" in the lobby, offering lighter, trendy items. If you're thirsty after eating, you might stop in next door to "Pugsley's" micro-brewery, serving 8 tap beers, as well as light snacks.
SPEC: *Breakfast buffet $14.95; Lunch buffet $13.95*

JACK'S PLACE LD Continental

(E2) 320 S. End Ave. (Albany & Liberty) 212/786-5225 Fax: 786-4951

F 4 / S 4 / A 4 / $23   MC V D AE DIS   **TO/D**

If you find yourself in the Battery Park City area, and your stomach's growling, but you're not quite sure for what, you'll probably find it at Jack's Place. The menu in this casual bar and grill offers a broad mix; from stir-fried vegetables to jambalaya, and the prices are reasonable. Check out the live band every Friday night.
SPEC: *Barbequed shrimp $8.95; Sizzling skillets w/chicken, beef or shrimp $10.95-$12.95; Chicken pot pie $9; Chocolate mousse cake $5.25*

JOHNNEY'S FISH GRILL LD Seafood

(E3) 250 Vesey St. (#4 WFC in Ctyd) 212/385-0333 Fax: 385-0510

F 7 / S 7 / A 6 / $25   MC V D AE DIS   **TO/D**

The look is New England Seafood House, and that's just what Johnney's delivers—"good, limited sushi" and reliable seafood at affordable prices. The service is as friendly as the atmosphere and the entrees are nicely prepared. Nothing special here, but if you live in the area you might try their $15 takeout dinner special.
Closed: Saturday and Sunday
SPEC: *Johnney's lobster bisque $4.75; Homemade gravlox $6.50; Louisiana Cajun catfish $11.25; Chicken pot pie $9.95*

LE PACTOLE BLD French

(E3) 225 Liberty St. (#2 WTC-West) 212/945-9444 Fax: 945-4367

F 7 / S 7 / A 8 / $48   MC V D AE   **TO/D**

Chef Andre Laurent, after 10 years at Raoul's, whips up incredibly creative and exquisite meals to the dramatic backdrop of magnificent sunsets sinking below N.J. The decor—modern rustic—complements the scene perfectly. The less formal, but still elegant, Cafe Bar area with a separate menu, also offers the same views.
Closed: Saturday
SPEC: *Sautéed scallops $15; Terrine of duckling $14; Filet of salmon $26; Duck breast $25; Warm apple tart $8; La Poire Fantaisie w/caramel mousse & raspberries $8*

MACMENAMIN'S IRISH PUB   LD   Irish-American

(E4) Pier 17 So. St. (3rd Fl.) 212/732-0007

F 4 / S 4 / A 2 / $16   MC V D AE   **TO**

Transplanted anywhere else, this would be your average neighborhood tavern serving the usual pub grub. But its location and outdoor deck on the East River with a view of the Seaport ships, makes it a desirable "hotspot for tourists and local business people." Offers a large variety of domestic and imported beers.

SPEC: *Mozzarella sticks $5.25; Chicken fingers $5.25; Hot turkey or roast beef dip $6.95; Fish 'n chips $5.95; Open Reuben $6.95*

MANDALAY KITCHEN   D   Burmese

(C4) 380 Broome St. (Mott & Mulberry) 212/226-4218 Fax: 219-9174

F 5 / S 6 / A 6 / $18   MC V D AE   **TO/D**

The design of this quaint "kitchen" loosely resembles a Burmese temple, though the food is what's closer to heavenly. Regardless of what entree you order, make sure to get a side of coconut rice and thousand layer pancake—a real Burmese delight. Comfortable and welcoming, people tend to linger after meals, so sit back and relax.

SPEC: *Golden Triangle (cooked potatoes wrapped in pastry shell) $3.50; Lemongrass chicken $7.95; Mixed seafood w/vegetables $11.50; Thousand layer pancake $2.50*

MORAN'S TOWNHOUSE   LD   Seafood

(E3) 103 Washington St. (Rector) 212/732-2020 Fax: 571-6091

F 6 / S 6 / A 6 / $28   MC V D AE DIS   **TO/D**

Housed in a former chapel built in 1897, Moran's has provided surf and turf for the downtown crowd for almost 40 years. The atmosphere reminds us of a private club, with wood panels, subdued lighting and 3 levels for dining. In the taproom there are six cable and satellite hooked monitors tuned to sporting events.

SPEC: *Chunky beef chili $5.95; Shrimp tempura $7.95; Shepherd's pie $12.95; ;Crab cakes $16.95; Lobster pasta $19.95*

NHA TRANG   LD   Vietnamese

(D4) 87 Baxter St. (Walker & Bayard) 212/233- 5948

F 6 / S 6 / A 4 / $12   Cash only   **TO**

Good, cheap Vietnamese food for an eclectic New York crowd. Wait for a table along with the people that make downtown interesting: artists, dancers, sailors, drag queens, Vietnamese and German tourists.

SPEC: *Special rice noodles w/beef bowl soup $4.50; Barbecued pork chop $6.50; Soft shell crab $10*

NORTH STAR PUB   LD   British

(E4) 93 South St. (Fulton) 212/509-6757

F 4 / S 6 / A 5 / $19   MC V D AE   **TO**

This traditional British pub is great for informal gatherings with friends. Steeped in Seaport atmosphere, it's located in a building that dates back to 1821. The food, "typical pub grub," is nothing to write home about, but they do offer more than 70 single malt Scotches and NO American beer. And to some, "food takes a backseat to having the best staff in the city."

SPEC: *Scotch egg $4.95; Ale-battered shrimp $7.95; Fish & chips $9.95; Bangers & mash $9.95; Shepherd's pie $9.50; Bread & single malt whisky pudding w/custard $4.50*

0	1	2	3	4	5	6	7	8	9	10
disappointing		fair		good		very good		excellent		perfect

PAPOO'S | LD | Italian

(E6) 129 Greenwich St. (Cedar & Rector) 212/964-4266 Fax: 732-1187

F 5 / S 5 / A 5 / $28   MC V D AE DIS   **TO/D**

Sounds like a restaurant for Nanook of the North, but it's pure Italian. Cozy, wood-paneled and intimate, this 40-year old, moderately priced, ristorante specializes in pasta dishes. A favorite for lunch with the lower Manhattan business crowd, who also stay after work and make up most of the dinner crowd. **Closed: Saturday and Sunday**

SPEC: *Stuffed eggplant roulettes $6.50; Penne marinara $12; Spaghetti putanesca $13; Rigatoni in Vodka sauce $13*

PATRISSY'S | LD | Italian

(E4) 98 Kenmare St. (Mulberry & Centre) 212/262-2888

F 7 / S 7 / A 7 / $34   MC V D AE DIS

This 19th century, "very excellent" Little Italy landmark was rescued from a disruptive sale by friendly, neighborhood business owner Arnold Migliaccio. With a history for interior design, he elegantly sponge painted light yellow, and open-aired a heretofore plain, fine food eatery. Smartly preserving the fine chef and very accommodating host, Patrissy's offers the same, familiar and authentic style, "fine Italian" food it served to patrons "for $1," over 100 years ago.

PIPELINE | LD | American

(E2) 2 World Financial (N. Cove Marina & Hudson) 212/945-3686

F 6 / S 4 / A 5 / $25   MC V D AE DIS   **TO/D**

Dining out should be fun and it is here, what with all the action going on. Thursday and Friday there's a major singles scene plus people watching if you're seated outdoors overlooking the marina. Saturdays and Sundays are "Kids Nights"—their dinner is $1.95 with the purchase of an adult entree. Our advice: bring a kid and split the check with 'em.

SPEC: *Chilled escarole vichyssoise $2.95; Stuffed jalapeños $6.95; Roasted garlic chicken $14.25; Santa Fe style BBQ babyback ribs $14.95*

S.P.Q.R

S.P.Q.R. | LD | Italian

(C4) 133 Mulberry St. (Hester & Grand) 212/925-3120 Fax: 925-2382

F 6 / S 6 / A 6 / $28   MC V D AE   **TO/D**

Handsome, with tall columns, mahogany walls, and red brick and wood floors, this comfortable restaurant is larger and more spacious than many like-cuisine neighbors. "Return to the past," in this "elegant slice of Little Italy" that to some offers "the best Italian" in the city.

SPEC: *Tripe in marinara sauce $6.50; Stuffed shells $12.50; Trout w/rosemary $14.50; Chocolate mousse cake $5.50*

SAMMY'S ROUMANIAN STEAK   D   Roumanian

(C4) 157 Christie St. (Delancey) 212/673-0330

F 6 / S 7 / A 5 / $34   MC V D AE

It's a basement bar mitzvah all year long. The menu requires a dictionary (provided), and you'll need a few visits to absorb it all. Every square inch of wall space is covered by photos of family and friends. A highlight is making your own egg cream at the table, complete with a half gallon of milk and your own vaudevillian seltzer bottle. It's "definitely not fine dining," but it is "major fun." And, "if you can get 6 or more people you'll want a Schmalz."
SPEC: *Chopped liver $6.95; Kishka $5.95; Shell steak $24.95; Veal cutlet breaded $24.95; Strudel $3.95; Rugelach (4) $3.95*

SAY ENG LOOK   LD   Chinese

(D4) 5 East Broadway (Chatham Square) 212/732-0796

F 6 / S 7 / A 3 / $16   MC V D AE   **TO**

Shanghai-style cuisine served here is different from most Cantonese/Chinatown restaurants. The seafood, especially fried roll fish, is all "first rate." Delicacies such as shark fin soup, live cartail and fillet of eel, are an integral part of Say Eng Look's unique menu.
SPEC: *Fried roll fish $11.95; Sesame crispy chicken $9.95; Chunk chicken w/spiced sauce $9.95*

SEQUOIA   LD   American

(E4) Pier 17, 89 Fulton St. (So. St. Seaport) 212/732-9090

F 4 / S 4 / A 5 / $32   MC V AE   **TO**

Offering outdoor deck dining on 2 floors, Sequoia overlooks the East River, Brooklyn Bridge and the Brooklyn waterfront. "Great seaport location—lousy service," is how one diner puts it. The feel is light, airy and modern. The food is well-presented and tasty. .
SPEC: *Duck & pinenut dumplings $6.95; Rainbow trout w/oysters & crabmeat $16.95; Sequoia cioppino P/A; Pan fried honey marinated pork chops $15.95*

SFUZZI   Italian

(E2) 2 World Financial 212/385-8080
See review on page 240.

SGARLATO'S CAFE   LD   Italian

(E4) Pier 17, So. St. Seaport (Promenade–3rd Fl.) 212/619-5226

F 4 / S 6 / A 4 / $28   MC V D AE

The views from the outdoor terrace of this Italian cafe are magnificent. But the view from inside the bright, airy room isn't bad either. Perhaps the "food's just okay," but to make up for it there's a large dessert menu and a surprisingly ample selection of cordials and liqueurs.
SPEC: *Pizzas for two $12.95-$16.95; Extensive international coffee selections*

SLOPPY LOUIE'S   LD   Seafood

(E4) 92 South St. (Fulton St.) 212/509-9694

F 5 / S 4 / A 5 / $30   MC V D AE   **TO**

Located in a landmark New York seaport building dating back to the 1850s, Sloppy Louie's is a landmark itself. Nothing to look at really—with tile floors and a tin roof—but if you stick to the seafood basics you'll do fine. As for the service, "too many apologies," is how one diner charitably puts it.
SPEC: *Baked clams (4) $1.95; Long Island clam chowder (cup) $2.65; Seafood combination $21.95; Bouillabaisse $19.95*

0	1	2	3	4	5	6	7	8	9	10
disappointing		fair		good		very good		excellent		perfect

ST. CHARLIE'S LD American

(E3) 4 Albany St. (Greenwich & Washington) 212/964-6940

F 3 / S 3 / A 3 / $26   MC V D AE DIS   **TO/D**

As the stock market goes, so goes St. Charlie's. That's because the crowd that gathers here is mostly from the financial community. Either they can dine in the main room, which is deemed "too dark," or if they're in a hurry to close that big deal, there's the cafe/sandwich bar for lighter fare. **Closed: Saturday & Sunday**

SPEC: *Arugula salad w/poached pears, beets & crumbled blue cheese $7; Roast salmon filet $18; Braised veal stew in Tuscan bread bowl $14*

STEAMER'S LANDING LD American

(E3) On the Esplanade (Liberty & Albany) 212/432-1451

F 6 / S 5 / A 7 / $30   MC V AE

Overlooking the Esplanade and the Hudson River, this is one of the most beautiful, romantic dining terraces in town. If you're lucky, the QE II will cruise by. Great people, sunset, dog and sailboat watching, too. While some find the food, "great, fresh, imaginative," to others it's a "view without portfolio."

SPEC: *New England clam & corn chowder $5.50; Escargot $7.25; Grilled salmon $17.50; Penne esplanade $13.50*

20 Mott Street

20 MOTT STREET BLD Chinese

(C4) 20 Mott St. (Bowery & Pell) 212/964-0380 Fax: 571-7697

F 7 / S 5 / A 5 / $25   MC V AE DIS   **TO**

An entire wall displays this restaurant's numerous reviews. And though the atmosphere may not be the most pleasant, it's "lively," and the food is likely some of "the best in Chinatown." If you like seafood, you're in the right place—you can choose from the tanks filled with lobster, striped bass, crab, eel, and clams. "Perfect for a Sunday brunch, and the best dim sum in NYC."

SPEC: *Braised shark's fin w/shredded chicken $14.50; Peking duck (2 courses) $32; Lobster w/ginger & scallion $18.95-$20.95*

WAVE LD Japanese

(E2) 21 South End Ave. (W. Thames) 212/240-9100 Fax: 240-9103

F 7 / S 6 / A 7 / $33   MC V D AE   **TO/D**

The view is spectacular from the outdoor terrace overlooking the New York harbor and the Statue of Liberty. Inside, the decor is Japanese modern. For lunch, try one of the four Express Bento box specials for $6.75. For dinner, dive into the far more comprehensive menu.

SPEC: *Yasai tempura $3.95; Broccoli kushizashi $3.95; Chicken teriyaki $8.95; Chicken katasu $8.95; Sushi deluxe $15*

WO HOP BLD Chinese

(C4) 17 Mott St. (Chatham Square) 212/267-2536

F 7 / S 6 / A 4 / $10   Cash only   **TO**

Knowing Wo Hop and its mouth-watering wonton soup and noodles is close by, makes serving on jury duty an almost pleasurable experience. Since this Cantonese-style restaurant is open 24 hours, the experience of having "great late night munchies," and walking up those steps to an early dawn, is one you'll never forget. "No atmosphere," but who cares, since "you can't beat the price."
SPEC: *Wonton soup $1.25; Roast pork $3.70; Chicken kow w/black-bean sauce $6.25; Crabs Cantonese style $6.50*

ZEN LD Chinese

(E2) 311 South End Ave. (Liberty & Albany) 212/432-3634

F 7 / S 7 / A 7 / $22   MC V D AE DIS   **TO/D**

Zen-like in decor. Sleek and modern. The service is friendly and this, coupled with consistently interesting dishes, and serene calmness perfect for intimate conversations, makes for an overall pleasant dining experience. However, it is "a bit pricey."
SPEC: *Shanghai spring roll $1.25; Braised bean curd w/black mushroom $7.95; Fried boneless chicken w/orange sauce $8.95*

TRIBECA

ACAPPELLA LD Italian

(D3) 1 Hudson St. (Chambers) 212/240-0163

F 7 / S 6 / A 6 / $35   MC V D AE

Formerly the home of One Hudson Cafe, this new downtown Italian bistro bodes well with diners. The atmosphere "is warm," and "they'll do anything to please you." Although a bit pricey for some dishes, the portions are large and the meals "excellent" and extremely satisfying.
SPEC: *Brisola $11; Minestrone soup $7; Fusilli Genovese $12; Suprema di pollo alla Alba $17.95*

AMERICAN RENAISSANCE D American

(C3) 260 W. Broadway (Amer Thread Bldg–S. of Canal) 212/343-0049

F 6 / S 6 / A 6 / $50   MC V D AE

Adds new flair to American cuisine. Housed in the historic American Thread building, it offers innovative cuisine for its hip, eclectic downtown crowd. The "unique decor" is "beautiful, warm and friendly." Chef Eric Blauberg, formerly of Colors, whips up fun, fanciful dishes. But some diners find the food "inconsistent," and service "slow."
SPEC: *Foie gras $16; Corn ravioli $16; Organic vegetarian tasting menu $55; Caribbean red snapper $25; Marinated young organic chicken $24*

ARQUA LD Italian

(C2) 281 Church St. (White) 212/334-1888

F 7 / S 7 / A 7 / $33   MC V D AE   **TO**

Sun-splashed painted walls and subdued lighting create an open, airy, spacious feel to this trendy Venetian Italian restaurant. The "excellent" cuisine is "true northern Italian." All pastas are hand-made on the premises. The service is applauded, but some think that there has been a noticeable "decline of late."
SPEC: *Carpaccio all'Arqua $10; Cozze con aglio e olio (mussels) $9; Gnocchi alla Padovana $16*

0	1	2	3	4	5	6	7	8	9	10
disappointing		fair		good		very good		excellent		perfect

BAROCCO LD Italian

(C3) 301 Church St. (Walker) 212/431-1445

F 7 / S 7 / A 7 / $34   MC V D AE   **TO**

Offering Tuscan cuisine, Barocco is a favorite with artists, writers and actors. It has a light, airy, trendy look. The "solid" menu is "interesting," the presentation creative and the service friendly. Some find the clientele "obnoxious," so if you'd rather stay home, try "Barocco Food To Go" at 297 Church or 121 Greenwich Street.
SPEC: *Gravlax $12; Garganelli w/octopus, tomato & black olive ragu $14; Zuppa di pesce $20; Roast loin of pork w/sautéed greens $16*

Top 10 $56+
Very Expensive

BOULEY LD French

(D2) 165 Duane St. (Greenwich & Hudson) 212/608-3852

F 8 / S 8 / A 8 / $75   MC V D AE DIS

Step into perfection. There's nothing this posh establishment hasn't thought of for your comfort. Entering the foyer, the senses are pampered with the sweet aroma of an orchard, and fresh flowers abound. David Bouley has paid attention to every detail from his savory delights to the lush yet simplistic mansion-like atmosphere. The food is organic French, and be prepared to plan ahead, since Bouley is booked weeks in advance. Diners rave about "The perfect meal," but complain about the "slow service" and the "arrogant and overbearing demeanor." (Bouley will move soon from their present location.) **Closed: Sunday**
SPEC: *Tasting menu dinner $75 (changes daily); Prix-fixe lunch $35*

BUBBY'S BLD Continental

(D2) 120 Hudson St. (N. Moore) 212/219-0666

F 6 / S 5 / A 6 / $14   MC V D AE   **TO/D**

Reminiscent of grandma's kitchen, this casual, "corner store," offers one of the best breakfasts in N.Y. The desserts and homemade sodas stand out. Comments range from "gives a lasting impression," to "OH, SO SLOW," and "very nice people, but they can't cook."
SPEC: *Black bean quesadilla $5.95; Turkey mole quesadilla $6.95; 1/2 Rosemary chicken $4.95; Mashed potatoes $2.95*

Top 10 $36-55
Expensive

CAPSOUTO FRERES LD French

(C2) 451 Washington St. (Watts) 212/966-4900

F 8 / S 7 / A 8 / $40   MC V D AE

Nestled amid the warehouses and barren streets of TriBeCa, this gem of a French bistro offers fanciful dining at reasonable prices. It's a "big, airy room," with high ceilings, fresh flowers and red brick walls. Diners rave about the "romantic atmosphere," and say it's "worth the trip downtown with a compass." **Closed: Monday lunch**
SPEC: *Smoked salmon w/caviar $12.50; Sole meuniere ou almandine $16.50; Grilled quails $18.50; Filet of beef $24*

Top 10 $56+
Very Expensive

CHANTERELLE LD French

(D2) 2 Harrison St. (Hudson) 212/966-6960

F 8 / S 8 / A 8 / $73   MC V AE

Any menu with a cute photo of a little girl, along with a wonderful quote from Allen Ginsberg on the front, is A-OK with us. And the food? Well that's more than A-OK. The decor is on the minimalist side, but the restaurant is "elegant" and roomy, with magnificent, massive floral arrangements throughout. The service is impeccable, the attention to detail, including meal presentation, is awesome. Gets many votes from diners as the "top restaurant in NYC."
Closed: Sunday and Monday for lunch
SPEC: *Assortment of raw fish $13.50; Potato ravioli in vegetable crêpe sauce $13.50; Braised free range chicken $18.50; Grilled Gulf shrimp in gazpacho sauce $21; Chocolate soufflé cake $10*

Chanterelle

DUANE PARK CAFE LD American

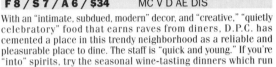

(D3) 157 Duane St. (W. B'way & Hudson St.) 212/732-5555

F 8 / S 7 / A 6 / $34   MC V D AE DIS

$21-35
Moderate

With an "intimate, subdued, modern" decor, and "creative," "quietly celebratory" food that earns raves from diners, D.P.C. has cemented a place in this trendy neighborhood as a reliable and pleasurable place to dine. The staff is "quick and young." If you're "into" spirits, try the seasonal wine-tasting dinners which run between $65 and $80. **Closed: Sunday**

SPEC: *Marinated Muscovy duck breast $9; Crispy skate $14; Pan blackened ribeye steak $23*

ECCO LD Italian

(D3) 124 Chambers St. (B'way & Church) 212/227-7074

F 6 / S 6 / A 6 / $37   MC V D AE   **TO**

The attractive turn-of-the-century saloon decor, with original fixtures, mahogany paneling, and hand-carved antique bar, lures them in. But it's the hearty Italian country fare that keeps them coming back. All of which might explain the big smile on the man on the menu cover. Diners call it a "beautiful place to celebrate an occasion." **Closed: Sunday**

SPEC: *Antipasto table $9.95; Pollo campagnola w/sausage, peppers, mushrooms & artichokes $15.95; Pizziola minute steak $21.95*

EL TEDDY'S LD Mexican

(C3) 219 W. Broadway (Franklin & White) 212/941-7070

F 6 / S 6 / A 7 / $28   MC V D AE

Get past the wild stained glass awning and enter the fun house-like maze. Move around and up to the bar where an energetic downtown crowd downs killer margaritas. Then, watching your step (and the way you look in the mirror), move to either a tiled dining room or one with Mexican Xmas decorations, and a fish tank. Finally, sit down and eat good, creative Mexican.

SPEC: *Bay scallop ceviche $7; Tres tamales $8; Smoked chicken & Coach farm goat cheese quesadilla $8; Duck confit tostada $8*

FRANKLIN STATION CAFE LD French

(D3) 222 W. Broadway (Franklin & N. Moore) 212/274-8525

F 6 / S 6 / A 6 / $17   MC V D AE   **TO/D**

On a corner in TriBeCa, beneath a rotating slide show and walls stripped to stone, flavorful "vrai French/Malay" food is served in this cozy bistro. The "super-nice" owners created an informal, intimate room in which they could serve food they wanted to eat. The result is a precious and inexpensive bistro, where fresh ingredients are used and the peanuts crushed daily for their chicken satay.

SPEC: *Noodles in peanut sauce $6; Curry chicken $6.95; Home baked ham sandwich $6.50; Mango tart $4.50*

0	1	2	3	4	5	6	7	8	9	10
disappointing		fair		good		very good		excellent		perfect

HERBAN KITCHEN BLD American

(C2) 290 Hudson St. (Spring St.) 212/627-2257 Fax: 627-2513

F 5 / S 6 / A 6 / $15 MC V AE DIS **TO/D**

A neighborhood newcomer offering organic food at reasonable prices. The rustic farmhouse decor, with baskets throughout and herbs hanging from the walls, reflects the food preparation philosophy: old-fashioned ingredients used to produce modern organic dishes that taste like mom's home cooking.
SPEC: *Grilled free range chicken $6.75; Pan pizza in rosemary crust w/portobello mushrooms & vegetables $6.95; Vegetarian grain burger $4.95*

J'AI ENVIE GALLERY & BASIC BISTRO LD French

(D3) 148 Chambers St. (W. B'way & Greenwich) 212/566-5544

F 4 / S 4 / A 5 / $35 MC V D AE DIS **TO/D**

A tiny, tranquil haven amidst the chaos of Chambers Street. The walls are enlivened with painting exhibits by local artists that change monthly. The food is nominally nouvelle French with liberal borrowing from Middle Eastern and Italian cuisine. The pastas are delicious, but the desserts taste like Sara Lee.
SPEC: *Calamari $6; Sculptured shrimp stuffed w/crab meat $18; Wild mushroom ravioli w/strips of sirloin $16*

LUPA LD Mediterranean

(D3) 277 Church St. (White & Franklin) 212/343-1035

F 5 / S 5 / A 5 / $30 MC V D AE **TO/D**

Named after the female wolf that saved Romulus and Remus, Lupa will rescue you from hunger pangs. There's a large front bar area with comfy chairs and a much sought-after sofa. The red and ochre washed walls create a "warm and intimate" atmosphere, though some of the original art on the walls is "ugly and distracting." Fortunately, the dining area has a more sedate feel. Live jazz Wednesdays and Thursdays.
SPEC: *Puff pastry stuffed w/wild mushrooms $7.50; Cassoulet of escargot $6.95; Fillet of salmon $15.50; Duck breast $17*

MONTRACHET D French

(C3) 239 West Broadway (Walker & White) 212/219-2777

F 8 / S 7 / A 7 / $55 AE

With TriBeCa Grill and Nobu, Montrachet represents Drew Nieporent's triumvirate. The food is "top rate," the ambiance understated. Patrons include Wall Streeters, as well as neighborhood writers, architects and artists, whose works grace the walls. The award-winning wine list is a knockout, offering many wines costing thousands of dollars. If you're a connoisseur, check out the half dozen wine dinners each year, costing from $125 to $650 per person. **Closed: Sunday**
SPEC: *Grilled quail salad $13; Wellfleet oysters w/Champagne sauce & caviar $14; Truffle crusted salmon $27; Pintade $29; Creme brulee $8; Banana & chocolate gratin on linzer crust $9*

NANCY WHISKEY LD American

(C3) 1 Lispenard St. (W. Broadway) 212/226-9943

F 4 / S 6 / A 4 / $10 MC V AE **TO**

A neighborhood joint where "everybody knows your name and they're always glad you came." Play table shuffleboard games, shoot the breeze with the working class characters that frequent the place, and order "one of the best burger and beer specials in the city."
SPEC: *Buffalo Chicken wings (12) $4.25; Shrimp Parmesan w/linguine $6.50; 1/2 lb burger w/fries $4*

NOBU   LD   Japanese

Top 10 $36-55

Expensive

(D2) 105 Hudson St. (Franklin) 212/219-0500 Fax: 219-1441

F 8 / S 9 / A 8 / $55   MC V D AE

Roe vs. Yellowtail. These are the trials and tribulations one must deal with when choosing delicacies at Nobu. The famous and fashionable have walked the hand-painted cherry blossom floor back to the translucent curtain which, when drawn, divides the dining room. Humor can be found in the David Rockwell designed chopstick-like chairs at the sushi bar. Super chef Nobu Matsuhisa is universally applauded for his "sublime" cuisine.

SPEC: *Omakase (chef's choice) lunch: $40; dinner $60 Sushi & sashimi $2.50-$8 each*

ODEON, THE   LD   French

(D3) 145 West Broadway (Thomas & Duane) 212/233-0507

F 7 / S 4 / A 7 / $27   MC V D AE

"As NY as ever," is this favorite for celebrities and big-name artists, who probably read about the steak frites and creme brulee long before their 15 minutes of fame rolled by. Still oozing "class and prestige," the original excessive 1980's playground of "Bright Lights, Big City," has matured into a consistently good restaurant—still the best place to go for a grilled lamb sandwich at 2:30 am.

SPEC: *Country salad $7.75; Crab & potato fritters w/cucumber salad $8.50; Steak au poivre $21; Grilled Louisiana shrimp $18; Creme brulee $4.75*

OTTOMANELLI'S CAFE   LD   Italian

(D3) 62 Reade St. (B'way & Church) 212/349-3430 Fax: 349-3432

F 4 / S 5 / A 2 / $14   MC V AE   **TO/D**

It began as a butcher shop and turned into...the burger/chicken/Italian food joint that devoured Manhattan. They all look pretty much the same and deliver reliable and consistent meals at reasonable prices a cut or two above fast food. **Closed: Saturday & Sunday**

SPEC: *Steakburger $4.95; Eggplant parmigiana $8.95; Atlantic Salmon $9.95; Steak a la pizzaiola $9.95; Chicken breast sandwich $7.50*

PIERINO   LD   Italian

(D3) 117 Reade St. (West B'way & Church) 212/513-0610

F 6 / S 5 / A 4 / $36   MC V D AE

Just another new TriBeCa eatery, or something special? Owners promise sumptuous meals and splendid service. So far, so good, as most seem impressed with the cuisine put out by the staff. We'll see...

SPEC: *Lunch: Fried calamari $7.95; Mussels $6.95; Penne alla vodka $11.95; Risotto w/mushrooms $14.95; Saltimbocca alla Romana $16.95*

RIVERRUN CAFE   LD   American

(D2) 176 Franklin St. (Hudson & Greenwich) 212/966-3894

F 5 / S 5 / A 4 / $22   MC V D AE DIS   **TO/D**

Squeezed between Nobu and TriBeCa Grill, this casual, turn-of-the-century pub with a "Cheers" like atmosphere, offers an earthy alternative to high trendiness. "Good, solid, old-fashioned American food." But some advise, "stick to burgers." With 15 micro-brews on tap to quench any thirst, and gallery wall space to satisfy the aesthetic, it's no wonder it's a favorite with locals.

SPEC: *Maryland crab cakes $6.25; Meatloaf w/mashed potatoes & vegetable $9.75; Clam bake for 2 $32; Key lime pie $4.25*

0	1	2	3	4	5	6	7	8	9	10
disappointing		fair		good		very good		excellent		perfect

Barbara Smith
Owner, B. Smith

Mad.61 is one of my favorites. It's got a great fun atmosphere, and it's always filled with interesting, fashionable people.

ROSEMARIE'S — LD — Italian

(D3) 145 Duane St. (West B'way & Church) 212/285-2610

F 6 / S 6 / A 6 / $35   MC V AE   **TO/D**

Although equipped with regulation exposed brick walls, it has none of the other elements that make it a cliché. Instead, the room exudes intimate sophistication with light soft enough to make anyone look good. Casual enough to dress comfortably, pretty enough to make it a night on the town. A romantic setting and a reputation for surprisingly good food. **Closed: Sunday**

SPEC: *Quail w/prosciutto & potato cake $10; Grilled veal sausage w/leeks & trumpet mushrooms; Red snapper $19; Ossobucco w/vegetable risotto $19*

Top 10 $21-35
Moderate

SALAAM BOMBAY — LD — Indian

(D2) 317 Greenwich St. (Reade & Duane) 212/226-9400

F 8 / S 7 / A 7 / $24   MC V D AE DIS

This "lovely spot" nestled in TriBeCa, lies far from the East Village's "Curry Lane." A gracious staff welcomes you into the gem-colored room and brings steaming dishes of "interesting and unusual food," cooked before your eyes in their Tandoori oven.

SPEC: *Fried dumplings stuffed w/fresh lentils $3.95; Skewered supremes of chicken, bell pepper & onions $5.95; Lamb marinated in yogurt, cooked in sealed pot $13.95*

SPAGHETTI WESTERN — LD — Italian

(D3) 59 Reade St. (B'way & Church) 212/513-1333

F 6 / S 5 / A 4 / $19   MC V D AE

Think Clint Eastwood as the cigar chomping, serape-wrapped Man With No Name. Now think grub. Somehow this bizarre combo of Italian and Mexican cuisine works. This restaurant/pub is as good a place as any to chow down, then chase it with their large variety of single malt Scotches.

SPEC: *Atomic wings $4.50; Gnocchi $8.95; Burritos $6.95-$8.95; Calamari fra diavolo w/black pasta $9.95; Chocolate mousse pie $3.25*

SPORTING CLUB, THE — LD — American

(D2) 99 Hudson St. (Franklin St.) 212/219-0900

F 4 / S 4 / A 4 / $20   MC V D AE DIS   **TO**

The quintessential sports bar—a playground for grownups. Five huge projection TVs, and several other monitors scattered throughout the 2-level, cavernous room; a large bar area; two pool tables, a basketball shoot game; celebrity auctions for sports charities and "the kind of food you'd expect in a stadium," with names like The Mark Spitz (chicken breast—get it?).

SPEC: *Mini chicken enchiladas $4.95; California sandwich (avocado, alfalfa sprouts & poached chicken) $7.95; The George Steinburger $5.95*

TRIBECA GRILL   LD   American

(D2) 375 Greenwich St. (Franklin) 212/941-3900

F 6 / S 6 / A 7 / $44   MC V D AE

Commonly linked with uncommon actor, Robert DeNiro, this film community favorite has more to offer than the star du jour. The late DeNiro, Sr.'s paintings grace the walls where exposed brick isn't adding to the homey atmosphere. The bar, last seen in all its grandeur at Maxwell's Plum, gives a repeat performance smack in the center of the room. "It's great for people watching." While some think it's "over-rated" and the most pretentious and disrespectful place in town."

SPEC: *Arugula salad $11; Seared tuna w/sesame noodles $13; Pan-seared red snapper $23; Herb crusted rack of lamb $26; Banana tart w/milk chocolate malt ice cream $7*

WALKER'S   LD   American

(D3) 16 N. Moore St. (Varick St.) 212/941-0142 Fax: 925-0796

F 4 / S 4 / A 4 / $21   MC V D AE   **TO**

Caters primarily to a downtown business crowd favoring the turn-of-the-century bar. Walker's offers a rather limited and run-of-the-mill menu of "good, basic pub food." But folks rave about the bar scene, which is lively with plenty of "downtown" ambiance. The service is "friendly and attentive." Live jazz every Sunday night.

SPEC: *Cowboy chili (bowl) $4.75; Quesadilla of the day $8.75; Mashed potatoes w/roasted garlic $3; Sirloin burger platter $7.25*

YAFFA TEA ROOM   BLD   Moroccan

(D2) 353 Greenwich St. (Harrison) 212/274-9403

F 6 / S 4 / A 8 / $22   V AE DIS   **TO**

If you're looking for a tranquil, soothing place to eat while having your Tarot cards read, this "wonderful little hideaway" is the place. The decor is described as "somewhere between Victorian and Turkish bath." The food is tasty, though some call the menu "boring," and there are dozens of teas to choose from. Sorry, no one to read the leaves.

SPEC: *Tapas $2.50-$4; Mediterranean platter $7.50; Chicken Dijon $11; Cous-cous royale (meat croquette, chicken, lamb & lamb sausage) $17*

ZUT   LD   French

(D3) 139 Duane St. (Church & W. B'way) 212/513-0505

F 7 / S 6 / A 4 / $33   MC V D AE   **TO**

Gosh! Zut is a find. This "terrific" newcomer seems to have developed a surer footing after a shaky start. The whimsical decor—old hats substitute for lamp shades—will put a smile on your face, while making you "feel like Alice in Wonderland." Features modern French cuisine, and "a weird sommelier." Standards like steak frites are joined by innovative dishes like a luscious goat cheese terrine with pink peppercorn and rhubarb sauce (it's a dessert!)

Closed: Sunday

SPEC: *Foie gras $14; Taboule $8; Bouillabaisse $21; Steak tartare $16; Plateau de mer (to share) $45*

ZUTTO   LD   Japanese

(D2) 77 Hudson St. (Jay & Harrison) 212/233-3287

F 7 / S 4 / A 6 / $29   MC V D AE

Diners can expect delicious food at reasonable prices. The sushi is out of this world—extremely fresh and beautifully presented. The crowd is young, casual and friendly; and there's also a very comfortable outdoor cafe.

0	1	2	3	4	5	6	7	8	9	10
disappointing		fair		good		very good		excellent		perfect

SOHO

AHNELL   LD   Italian

(B3) 177 Prince St. (Thompson & Sullivan) 212/254-1260

F 5 / S 5 / A 6 / $35   MC V AE   **TO**

A "chic," "in" spot for the fashionable, hip downtown crowd. The warm, paneled rooms with large oak bar in a turn of the century building, add to the fantasy that you, too, can be one of the "beautiful" people. For some, it "used to be good, but now the food is terrible."
SPEC: *Antipasto all'Italiana $12; Bresaola $10; Risottos $16-$18; Monkfish w/asparagus/ parmigiano in lemon sauce $15*

AMICI MIEI   LD   Italian

(B3) 475 W. Broadway (Houston) 212/533-1933 Fax: 387-0875

F 6 / S 6 / A 7 / $24   MC V D AE   **TO**

You'll appreciate the gallery look to this quintessential Soho restaurant: lofty and open with sparsely decorated walls of artwork. The enclosed, comfortable patio is the largest in a neighborhood known for its open air dining. Some diners say, "good location —average food," but a "fun place to go."
SPEC: *Polenta Toscana con ragu' di funghi $10; Tuna carpaccio $14; Grilled breast of chicken $15; Tiramisu $5.50*

BALUCHI'S   LD   Indian

(C3) 193 Spring St. (Sullivan & Thompson) 212/226-2828

F 6 / S 4 / A 4 / $24   MC V D AE   **TO/D**

A cozy haven amidst the bustle of Soho. Gracious service and beautiful decor—the tables are made from antique Punjabi doors and the tableware is handwrought burnished copper—complement the rich, subtle flavors of the food. Worth a visit just to see the manager, A.J., a charming cross between Elvis and Elvira, with his streaked bouffant hairdo, chunky gold jewelry, and electric blue shirt.
SPEC: *Malai kebab (chicken marinated w/cream, fresh ginger & garlic) $6.95; Chicken tikka masala $10.95; Whole pompano fish $14.95*

Barolo

BAROLO   LD   Italian

(C3) 398 W. Broadway (Spring and Broome) 212/226-1102

F 6 / S 6 / A 8 / $44   MC V D AE

The rich gold walls of this elegant restaurant compliment the overall simple, yet sophisticated "perfect" design. If weather allows, don't miss sitting in the spacious garden large enough to hold a few cherry blossom trees. Intimate it's not—the noise level is rather high—and some suggest that it's "better at night." The food has "some misses, but more hits."
SPEC: *Sea scallops w/white beans $10.50; Quail w/portobello mushrooms $9.50; Steamed red snapper $20; Sea bass baked in salt $23*

BERRY'S — LD — Amer/Continental

(C3)180 Spring St. (Thompson) 212/226-4394

F 6 / S 5 / A 7 / $28   MC V D AE DIS

Located in a turn-of-the-century building, this small, intimate space, with tin ceilings and Victorian decor, offers casual elegance in a homey atmosphere. The chefs are an amalgam of Belgian and Louisianan, resulting in "an eclectic and interesting menu." Sunday nights offer acoustic entertainment.

SPEC: *Lunch: Caesar salad $6.25; Spring navarin of lamb $8.75; Salmon cakes $10; Flourless chocolate & mocha cake $5.50*

BLUE RIBBON — D — American

(B3) 97 Sullivan St. (Prince & Spring) 212/274-0404

F 8 / S 7 / A 7 / $36   MC V AE

This dark and stylish and oh, so hip that "it hurts," Soho night spot serves the gamut in game—everything from sweetbreads to skate to rack-o-lamb and there's a fresh seafood bar. Flavors are smoky, sides are hearty and high fiber. The wine list is extensive and the patrons in the bar region are stylish. Diners deplore "long waits," and "crowded" interior. It's rumored the food's so good that chefs from other restaurants meet here after work.
Closed: Monday

SPEC: *Grilled shrimp remoulade $8.50; Foie gras terrine $14.50; Pigeon $24; Paella basquez $20; Chocolate bruno $6.50*

BOOM — LD — Continental

(C3) 152 Spring St. (W. B'way & Wooster) 212/431-3663 Fax: 431-3643

F 7 / S 5 / A 6 / $37   D AE

A restaurant staff with attitude is so 1980s! And the Boom staff has a special way of making their very-trendy crowd understand that they are replaceable. The crowd is primarily pseudo-hip Europeans and the room resembles a decayed European boudoir. "Wildest menu in town." "Fantastic food, but 'BOOM' goes the check with wine prices."

SPEC: *Eel & bamboo heart spicy & sour soup $7.50; Filipino sweet potato & shrimp fritters $8.50; Roasted duck breast $20*

BOX BAR — LD — Continental

(C3) 337 W. Broadway (Grand & Broome) 212/966-2626

F 4 / S 4 / A 3 / $20   MC V AE

A restaurant for those who've never been to NY, or any big city, and want to sit within a 4 block radius packed with restaurants just like Box Bar, crammed with people just like themselves. Not for people looking for a unique meal, interesting staff and crowd, or for a refreshing and unusual environment. "Lunch okay, dinner too noisy."

SPEC: *Fish fondue $12; Chinoise fondue $1; Creme brulee $5.50; Fruit tarte $5.50*

BROOME STREET BAR — LD — American

(C3) 363 W. Broadway (Broome) 212/925-2086

F 5 / S 5 / A 6 / $14   MC V D   **TO**

No discrimination here. Everyone is welcome and at one time or another anyone who's spent time in Soho has spent time at this "great, old-time saloon." Blackboards line the walls displaying the menu specials and the roomy bar invites you to eat, drink and, most importantly, be merry. "Early SoHo and still fun."

SPEC: *Super nachos $6.50; Knockwurst chili dog $5.50; Cheeseburger $6.25; Mediterranean salad $8*

0	1	2	3	4	5	6	7	8	9	10
disappointing		fair		good		very good		excellent		perfect

CAFE GITAINE   BLD   Mediterranean

(B4) 242 Mott St. (Houston & Prince) 212/334-9552

F 6 / S 6 / A 6 / $14   Cash only

Slip out of crowded SoHo onto Mott Street, where this cozy, chic cafe serves light French/Mediterranean fare in a "Godard film-like setting." Relax over a cafe au lait and a novel, because you'll want to stay well into the evening.

SPEC: *Cous-Cous and chicken $7.95; Smoked salmon $7.50; Noodles w/shitake mushrooms, mango & marinated tuna $8.95; Lemonade $2; Chocolate fudge tartlet $1.50*

CAFE NOIR   LD   French

(C3) 32 Grand St. (Thompson St.) 212/431-7910 Fax: 431-3781

F 7 / S 7 / A 8 / $27   AE

From the decor to the cuisine, this is truly a French bistro in Morocco, circa 1950. Even the "best music in town"—traditional jazz—and the menu design furthers the illusion. Diners run the gamut from NY and abroad, attracted by the lazily enticing atmosphere, the great "energy," and the menu which changes monthly.

SPEC: *Tuna carpaccio $7.50; Homemade pate w/port & brandy $5; Steamed mussels in lemon grass $13; Grilled chicken brochette $14*

CAFE NOVECENTO   BLD   Spanish

(C3) 343 W. Broadway (Grand & Broome) 212/925-4706

F 6 / S 6 / A 6 / $18   MC V D AE

There were so many people crammed in for late night parties here that owners had to book a permanent party room a few blocks away, on Varick Street. Nevertheless, this "cozy" bistro with a strong Spanish touch, still rocks nightly until 4am, with a mostly Latin crowd.

SPEC: *Seafood salad (marinated shrimps, mussels & squid) $8; Grilled tuna w/vinaigrette & capers $12; Flan caramel $4.75*

CAFFE DI NONNA   LD   Mediterranean

(C3) 104 Grand St. (Mercer) 212/925-5488

F 6 / S 7 / A 8 / $23   MC V   **TO/D**

If you're looking for "true European atmosphere," look no further. In a 1925 landmark building, on a less-traveled corner, sip one of 20 wines by the glass at the copper bar; or savor tasty seafood stew in the restful ambiance of flickering, green candles at your table.

SPEC: *Calamari w/tomato, rice, peas $5.25; Sautéed portobello & shitake mushrooms w/mesclun $5.75; Tagliolini w/portobello mushrooms $10.95*

CASCABEL   D   American

(C3) 218 Lafayette St. (Spring & Broome) 212/431-7300

F 7 / S 6 / A 7 / $40   MC V D AE

"Wonderful decor, inventive cuisine," "All you can say is, 'Oh, my God! It's great," say many diners. While others deplore "slow service" and "horrible clientele." Still, it's a safe bet for out-of-town guests and a special night out.

SPEC: *Ragout of mussels $8; Strudel of game bird $9; Braised lamb shank $23; Tuna seared rare $24; Frozen hazelnut mousse w/chocolate and caramel $8*

CUB ROOM | LD | American

(B3) 131 Sullivan St. (Prince) 212/677-4100 Fax: 228-3425

F 7 / S 6 / A 7 / $39   AE   **TO**

An "in spot," with "good buzz." The bar and lounge area are filled with an eclectic mix of fine vintage furniture, surrounded by glass doors opening onto the street. You'll find the space so refreshing you may opt to stay in the smoking section even if you detest smoke! The elegant dining room, as well as the attached cafe, are also very popular. "The menu is different from others," but some think the "food is a bit too tricky for its own good."

SPEC: *Lobster salad $12.50; Salmon Caesar $9; Cub steak $28; Alaskan King Ivory salmon $26*

CUPPING ROOM, THE | BLD | Continental

(C3) 359 W. Broadway (Broome) 212/925-2898 Fax: 966-5609

F 7 / S 7 / A 7 / $36   MC V D AE DIS   **TO/D**

Hey, ever order fiddlehead ferns? Or Chicken-of-the-wood mushrooms? You find them offered on this eclectic and staggeringly delicious menu. The space is large, "nice, airy," and diverse. Live jazz music Fridays and Saturdays, and a constantly welcoming staff make this a place to return to, for a new experience each visit.

SPEC: *Steamed mussels w/white wine & garlic $8.95; Sizzling garlic prawns $9.95; Grilled American lamb chops $17.95; Chicken moutard $15.95*

CYBER CAFE | BLD | American

(B3) 273 Lafayette St. (Prince) 212/334-5140 Fax: 772-0946

F 6 / S 6 / A 6 / $10   MC V AE DIS

This Soho spot eased into its dark neighborhood without much ado and is slowly taking over the corner. Built with enough wiring for 100s of multimedia work stations, and with printing, faxing and other services, it may sound like Kinko's with eats. The collegiate staff is strung out, but savvy, and the high ceilings and comfy chairs make this a homey spot. Food, though strictly cafe, is good and abundant. Visitors can play with software from the library.

DIVA | LD | Italian

(C3) 341 W. Broadway (Broome & Grand) 212/941-9024

F 6 / S 8 / A 8 / $29   MC V AE   **TO**

Elegant in design, this restaurant oozes ambiance. It's romantically lit, with tall red candles held by nude goddess figurines, and rust-red walls. A trendy "in spot," you can enjoy a pre-dinner drink at the bar, which extends along the length of the restaurant.

SPEC: *Bruschetta Toscana $6; Grilled eggplant $9; Spaghetti aifrutti di mare $14; Grilled chicken breast $15; Seared beef tenderloin $22*

FANELLI'S CAFE | BLD | American

(B3) 94 Prince St. (Mercer) 212/226-9412

F 5 / S 6 / A 7 / $15   Cash only   **TO**

With a liquor license that dates back to 1872, this is one of the oldest restaurants in Manhattan. Nothing has been restored, including the painted over tin walls and the black, antique bar, which faces photographs and posters of various boxers from the early years. "Very decent bar food, lively crowd."

SPEC: *New England clam chowder $3.95; Pizza $7.95; Linguini $6.75-$8.75; Southern fried chicken $10.95*

0	1	2	3	4	5	6	7	8	9	10
disappointing		fair		good		very good		excellent		perfect

Felix

FELIX   LD   French

(C3) 340 W. Broadway (Grand) 212/431-0021

F 6 / S 6 / A 7 / $32   AE

This oh-so-cool Grand Street bistro offers the following: gallic non-chalance; ceilings for days and off-white tin walls; banks of glass doors (yes, they're French, too); sprouting tables onto the sidewalk; and a superciliousness we'd think by now should have worn off. Airy and very French, the food runs from "good to fantastic." So we will forgive the attitude...for now.

SPEC: *Steamed mussels $8; Escargots $8; Bouillabaisse "Felix" $21; Grilled tuna, foie gras, mesclun, balsamic vinegar, crunchy vegetables $24*

5 & 10 NO EXAGGERATION   D   Continental

(C3) 77 Greene St. (Spring & Broome) 212/925-7414 Fax: 989-0949

F 5 / S 6 / A 7 / $22   MC V D AE

The owner has spent a lot of time filling his restaurant with big band era antiques and bumper cars. We only wish the menu was as carefully and lovingly thought out. When pasta St. Tropez shares a page with chicken burritos and blackened fish du jour, thoughts of Houlihans come to mind. Enjoy the jazz music and a cocktail at the bar and save dinner for later.

SPEC: *Fried calamari $7.25*

FRONTIERE   LD   Continental

(B2) 199 Prince St. (6th & MacDougal) 212/387-0898

F 7 / S 7 / A 7 / $34   MC V D AE

When you enter this Northern Italian/French provincial restaurant it's as if they were expecting you. Open bottles of wine on the table and black olives on the bar. Exposed brick, subdued lighting and reflections from mirror art and the zinc bar make for a very romantic setting. Comments range from "perfect" to "reliable."
Closed: Sunday

SPEC: *Asparagus & prosciutto crostini $11; Grilled stuffed squid $8; Grilled poussin $18; Crispy red snapper $26*

5 & 10 No Exaggeration

HONMURA AN
LD — **Japanese**

(B3) 170 Mercer St. (Houston) 212/334-5253

F 8 / S 7 / A 6 / $34   MC V D AE

A high-style Japanese restaurant on the brink of Soho's gallery row, that's a gallery unto itself. Specialties are homemade soba and udon noodles, as well as tempura made with huge prawns imported from Tokyo. "A great dining experience." **Closed: Monday**

SPEC: *Carpaccio-style Japanese roast beef $8; Soba topped w/button mushrooms $10.75; Cold Udon noodle $11.95; Soba shiruko (soba dumplings in sweet red bean soup) $6*

I Tre Merli

I TRE MERLI
LD — **Italian**

(B3) 463 W. Broadway (Houston & Prince) 212/254-8699

F 7 / S 6 / A 7 / $27   MC V D AE   **TO**

What was once an abandoned warehouse, as evidenced by the painted graffiti still apparent on the exposed red brick walls, is now a fashionable Soho eatery. Racks of wine bottles are artfully stacked against the walls, and the dim lighting is perfect for a romantic evening. And the food? Well, it's known as some of the finest in Soho.

SPEC: *Minestrone al pesto $7.50; Funghi alla Genovese con polenta $8.50; Cold braised veal w/tuna-caper sauce $13; Lobster ravioli $13*

IL CORALLO TRATTORIA
LD — **Italian**

(B3) 176 Prince St. (Thompson & Sullivan) 212/941-7119

F 6 / S 6 / A 6 / $22   Cash only   **TO/D**

This petite "inexpensive pasta boutique," has great pizzas and pastas. Photos of Italian street scenes, as well as imitation hand-drawn maps, decorate the light yellow walls. A pleasant change of pace from the usual trendy, over-priced Soho eateries.

SPEC: *Antipasto mozzarella $5; Crostini pomodoro $5.25; Black taglierini $9.95; Pizzas $6-$9.95*

JERRY'S
BLD — **American**

(B3) 101 Prince St. (Mercer & Greene) 212/966-9464 Fax: 219-9179

F 7 / S 6 / A 6 / $23   MC V AE   **TO/D**

Lunch is bustling here, packed with your average über-cool Soho types (along with some regular folk, too.) Brunch is the same, but with fewer jackets. Breakfast is "superb" and a cup o' joe won't disappoint. This casual, American diner has become a fashionable neighborhood staple with "good crowd-watching."

SPEC: *Caesar salad $5; Wild mushroom & fontina omelette $7; Sliced chicken breast w/roasted tomato mayonnaise on semolina $7; Grilled tangerine marinated chicken $9*

0	1	2	3	4	5	6	7	8	9	10
disappointing		fair		good		very good		excellent		perfect

Jerry's

KELLEY AND PING · LD · Asian

(B3) 127 Greene St. (Prince & Houston) 212/228-1212

F 6 / S 5 / A 6 / $25   MC V D AE   **TO/D**

The atmosphere is pure Soho: funky and offbeat. The ceilings are high, and when you enter you can't help but "taste" the tempting aromas. During the day, you can purchase Asian groceries and housewares and lunch is cafeteria-style. At night, all that changes as it turns into a "hip" place to meet and eat. "Interesting combinations," and "impressive tea selection."

SPEC: *Asian noodle soup $.95-$7.50; Spring rolls $5.25; Whole fish (fried or steamed) w/tamarind ginger sauce $16.95*

KIN KHAO · D · Thai

(C3) 171 Spring St. (W. B'way & Thompson) 212/966-3939

F 7 / S 6 / A 7 / $27   MC V AE

A chic, downtown "in spot," where the traditional Thai decor adds to the exotic, romantic appeal. The owners also own Kelley & Ping, a few blocks away. The genuine Thai dishes are "exquisite." To enjoy them fully, order sticky rice, which few Thai restaurants in the city go to the trouble of preparing. Comments range from "best Thai," to "worst Thai." Yer pays yer money, yer takes yer cherce.

SPEC: *Hot & sour prawn salad $7.50; Green papaya, green beans & tomatoes $5.95; Fried whole fish $17.95; Massaman kari $10.50*

KITCHEN CLUB · LD · Continental

(B4) 30 Prince St. (Mott) 212/274-0025

F 7 / S 6 / A 6 / $29   Cash only

Offbeat and "quirky," this European restaurant with a Japanese twist is one of the best kept secrets in the city. You'll be welcomed with a "chopstick" setting, school chairs, and the scent of incense that purifies the room. Designed by the owner, the walls display her eclectic collection of photographs and mirrors, while turquoise velour curtains drape the doorways. **Closed: Monday**

SPEC: *Mushroom dumplings $8; Organic greens w/house dressing $6; Spring baby lambchops $20; Mushroom medley $15*

KWANZAA · D · Amer/Soul

(B3) 19 Cleveland Pl. (Spring) 212/941-6095 Fax: 941-5728

F 7 / S 7 / A 8 / $21   MC V D AE DIS   **TO**

In this Afro-centric decorated hot spot, birthdays and other occasions are celebrated with drum music and song. Kwanzaa, Swahili for "first fruits of the harvest," delivers international soul food that lives up to the expectations of its name. Though open only for dinner, there is a Sunday jazz brunch, and on Friday nights it becomes a comedy club.

SPEC: *Maryland crab cakes $8.95; Jerk chicken wings $5.95; Bahanian coconut jumbo shrimp $16.95; Southern fried chicken $10.95*

L'ECOLE LD French

(C3) 462 Broadway (Grand) 212/219-3300 Fax: 274-1258

F 7 / S 6 / A 6 / $28 MC V D AE **TO**

As the home of the French Culinary Institute, this is unique among dining establishments. The dining room is the classroom, and patrons are subjects for experiments in the world of culinary delights. "Student chefs produce great food," in sometimes "small portions." But most pronounce the results "gems"
Closed: Sunday
SPEC: *Prix-fixe 5 course dinner: Poached filet of trout; Porkchop w/mushroom duxelles; Salmon cakes; Boneless breast of roasted duck; Sea scallops $22*

LA DOLCE VITA LD Italian

(C3) 195 Spring St. (Thompson & Sullivan) 212/431-1315

F 6 / S 6 / A 7 / $22 AE **TO**

A simple set-up with consistently quality food at very reasonable prices. The staff is helpful and anxious to please. Nothing special, but La Dolce Vita does offer unpretentious, dependable dining. "Frank Sinatra, candle light, Chianti."
SPEC: *Roasted garlic $4.50; Mussels Marco Polo $5.75; Penne w/artichoke hearts & roasted peppers $9.95; Capellini w/clams & hot sausage $12.50*

LA JUMELLE D French

(C3) 55 Grand St. (W. B'way & Wooster) 212/941-9651

F 6 / S 6 / A 6 / $24 MC V

A turn toward the east from crowded W. Broadway onto this quieter enclave on Grand, transports you to a bistro you might encounter ,driving through the French heartland. The authentic chairs, plankboard floors and vintage signs all point to this as being "the real thing." And if you're hungry at 3am, there's plenty of time to spare, since the kitchen's open till 4.
SPEC: *Endive roquefort $6; Steak au poivre $15; Chicken in mustard sauce $13; Couscous $13*

LE GAMIN CAFE BLD French

(B2) 50 MacDougal St. (Houston & Prince) 212/254-4678

F 5 / S 4 / A 5 / $12 Cash only

Crepes and coffee served by genuine Parisians. Plan to spend some time, bring a book, your laptop, or peruse the plentiful international magazines lining the wall. The place is small, the outdoor cafe, smaller—only three tables. But if you can score one, you've scored big. "Fun, unpretentious." "Great coffee," but "too smoky."
SPEC: *Les crêpes sucree $4.50; Crepe filled w/fresh orange w/caramel sauce $6; Cappuccino $2.50; Cafe Au Lait $2.75*

LE PESCADOU LD French

(B2) 18 King St. (6th Ave.) 212/924-3434 Fax: 924-2366

F 7 / S 7 / A 7 / $30 MC AE

"Cool Euro-Parisian feel and crowd, transported to St. Germaine," is how one diner describes this bistro. Come for the excellent fresh seafood, "frolicking in lush tomato sauce" or "swimming in a wave of garlic and oil atop a sea of homemade linguini," as the menu promises. Not for the minimally decorated, comparatively small space.
SPEC: *Grilled seafood sausage $8.25; Bouillabaisse $21; Whole striped bass broiled w/fennel & pernod flambé $19.25*

0	1	2	3	4	5	6	7	8	9	10
disappointing	fair			good		very good		excellent		perfect

LUCKY STRIKE   LD   American

(C3) 59 Grand St.   (Wooster & W. B'way) 212/941-0479

F 6 / S 5 / A 6 / $25   MC V D AE

It's got all the elements of an "in," "happening place," including a "clueless waitstaff and leggy lovelies." With its wood plank floor, tin walls, beamed supports, large copper bar, and reasonably priced food, it's no wonder this spot has a reputation as an "excellent late night hang." A D.J. takes over every night from 10:30 till closing.

SPEC: *Crab cake w/cucumber salad $8; Carpaccio on arugula $7.50; Bruschetta $5; Steak au poivre $15; Marinated tuna & ginger sandwich $9.50; Creme caramel $5*

LUPE'S EAST L.A. KITCHEN   LD   Mexican

(C3) 110 6th Ave. (Wells & Broome) 212/966-1326

F 7 / S 7 / A 4 / $14   Cash only   **TO/D**

Clean, but sparsely decorated, this storefront restaurant displays various "Mexico" posters that come alive when the food is served onto the hand-painted tables. The fact that it's little more than a dive is mitigated by the authentic Mexican food and the offer of "good, cheap eats."

SPEC: *Cazuelitas $3.75; Chili Colorado $6.95; Burritos $6.50-$7.95; Taquito platter $7.25; Coconut flan $2.50*

M & R BAR   D   American

(B4) 264 Elizabeth St. (Houston & Prince) 212/226-0559

F 6 / S 4 / A 4 / $22   MC V

The menu is too young to make a definitive judgment. But a "bland fish stew" indicates the night would be better spent with a stiff cocktail in the Parisian brothel atmosphere of the brick-red back room.

SPEC: *San Francisco cioppino fish stew $10.50; Maple creme brulee $4.50*

MANHATTAN BISTRO   BLD   French

(B3) 129 Spring St. (Wooster & Greene) 212/966-3459

F 6 / S 4 / A 4 / $25   MC V AE   **TO/D**

It's difficult to say who eats here since it often looks abandoned. There are many French bistros in Soho with charming atmospheres and welcoming maitre d's, but Manhattan Bistro doesn't seem to be one of them. The only outstanding feature here is an extraordinarily large security camera pointed ominously at the bartender.

SPEC: *Mousse de foie gras au porto $6; Tatare de saumon $7.50; Steak au poivre $16; Paillard de poulet aux herbes $12*

MATCH   LD   American

(B3) 160 Mercer St. (Hudson & Prince) 212/343-0020 Fax: 343-0241

F 7 / S 7 / A 9 / $29   MC V AE   **TO**

This suave, "chic," "in spot" is frequented by all kinds of high-profile people. Artsy and hip, there's banquette seating with a small balcony area for musicians and bands. Downstairs there's a smoking lounge area with a DJ every night. A small sushi bar complements the main menu. And get this—it's open until 4am, just in case you've got a bad case of insomnia.

SPEC: *Potato chive dumplings $5.50; Grilled oysters $5.50; Roast duck $18.75; Szechuan steak au poivre $19; Match brulee $6; White chocolate cheesecake $6*

MEZZOGIORNO   LD   Italian

(C3) 195 Spring St. (Sullivan) 212/334-2112 Fax: 941-6294

F 7 / S 6 / A 6 / $32   Cash only

Eye-catching and thought provoking "box art" from the diary of artist Firenze Pontorno lines the walls and the ceiling. His paintings were heavily influenced by what he ate so he would have loved dining at Mezzogiorno, not only for the food but for the hip crowd that gathers here. "Excellent brick oven pizza." But some think it's "going downhill."

SPEC: *Grilled seafood combination $16; Homemade noodles $14; Penne alla bisanzio $13; Sirloin steak $20*

N   D   Spanish

(C3) 33 Crosby St. (Broome & Grand) 212/431-1315

F 5 / S 5 / A 7 / $21   Cash only

This "very dark," popular oasis in a relatively secluded area of Soho serves authentic tapas. "Do you know what kind of bill you run up eating nothing you remember?" The atmosphere is nothing special, though it has attracted a loyal neighborhood following. "Great for a date you like, when you don't want to eat much and want to get a good buzz."

SPEC: *Gazpacho $4; Chopped mushrooms w/white wine, cognac, garlic, onion & red pepper $4.50; Boquerones (anchovies) $4; Baby clams $6*

NACHO MAMA'S BREWERY   LD   Mexican

(B3) 40-42 Thompson St. (West B'way) 212/925-8966

F 4 / S 6 / A 6 / $14   MC V AE   **TO/D**

The former home of the Manhattan Brewing Company has now been updated with live music and an inexpensive and dependable menu, much like Nacho Mama's uptown. English style ales remain, along with some new recipes which you can sample during the $2 Happy Hour.

SPEC: *Mexican buffalo wings $5.95; Roasted eggplant Mexicana $3.95; Enchilada fajita $7.95; Enchilada loco (steak or grilled chicken) $8.95*

NICK AND EDDIE   LD   American

(C3) 203 Spring St. (Sullivan) 212/219-9090 Fax: 219-9210

F 6 / S 6 / A 6 / $30   MC V AE

The food is "consistently sumptuous." The bar is "cozy." The prices reasonable. The service user-friendly. The ambiance casual yet romantic (in large part due to the dim lighting). All of which makes this "solid" American-bistro a favorite among the downtown crowd. Good idea to make reservations.

SPEC: *Potato pancakes w/onion applesauce $6; Roasted chicken breast $14.50; Honey-glazed catfish $16; Banana bread w/ice cream $6*

OMEN   D   Japanese

(B3) 113 Thompson St. (Prince & Spring) 212/925-8923

F 8 / S 6 / A 7 / $30   AE

With 2 other locations in Kyoto, this is "a little slice of Japan" right here in NY. The decor is simple and peaceful Japanese, but with the building's roots as a parsonage showing through handsome exposed brick walls. The beautiful artwork is a family tradition, done by the owner's father. "Always a pleasure," it offers "a good variety menu of excellent meals."

SPEC: *House salad $6.25; Peanut ae (spinach & scallops w/peanut cream) $6.50; Tuna steak w/ginger $12.50; Soba $7.50; Salmon & endive teriyaki $16; Acorn squash $9.50*

0	1	2	3	4	5	6	7	8	9	10
disappointing		fair		good		very good		excellent		perfect

PENANG   LD   Asian

(B3) 109 Spring St. (Greene & Mercer) 212/274-8883 Fax: 925-8530

F 8 / S 7 / A 8 / $25   MC V AE

Malaysian with a jungle decor. One seating area has rope nets cordoning it off from the back "forest" area, where there's a small waterfall. Serves "flavorful dishes," emphasizing sweet and peanutty tastes. A bar near the front is also quite "stylish."
SPEC: *Po-piah spring rolls $5.95; Flat noodles w/shrimps, squid, eggs, chives & bean sprouts $7.95; Pompano w/black bean sauce $16.95; Ice kacang w/ice cream $5.50*

PIETRO VANESSA   LD   Italian

(C4) 23 Cleveland Place (Spring & Kenmare) 212/226-9764

F 6 / S 5 / A 6 / $20   MC V AE   **TO**

On a breezy summer night the garden is among the most romantic spots in the city. Think European on a first date. The service can be "dreamy" as well, but it's all part of the charm. "Cheap but good Italian". Bring some friends, or one, sit in the garden, and plan to spend a few hours.
SPEC: *Carciofi funghi $5.25; Veal pizzaiola $9.95; Seafood combination over pasta $12; Gnocchi w/meat sauce $8.95*

DONTE BURSE

Savoy

ROCKY'S ITALIAN RESTAURANT   LD   Italian

(C4) 45 Spring St. (Mulberry) 212/274-0936

F 6 / S 7 / A 3 / $21   MC V D AE DIS   **TO/D**

This "unassuming, down-to-earth" family-run restaurant at the edge of Soho provides inexpensive, but good, hearty meals. Nothing to write home about as far as ambiance, but let's just say that it isn't so much the garnish that counts here, but the taste.
SPEC: *Garlic bread w/mozzarella $3.50; Potato croquette $3; Baked ziti w/eggplant $9.95; Broiled veal chops $14.95; Italian cheesecake $3.50*

SAVORE   LD   Italian

(B3) 200 Spring St. (Sullivan) 212/431-1212 Fax: 431-1218

F 6 / S 6 / A 6 / $31   MC V AE

The space is small, but the walls and stone floor put us in mind of the sunny climate of Tuscany. Which makes sense, since the cuisine showcases a contemporary Tuscan menu—"sort of healthy Italian"— with dishes inspired by Renaissance taste. "Wear black for good service," suggests one regular diner. And why not? This is New York.
SPEC: *Sautéed monkfish w/artichoke heart $12; Corn mousse w/wild boar sauce $10; Pasta rolled w/crab meat $13; Maremma-style wild boar $17*

SAVOY   LD   Mediterranean

Top 10 $21-35   Moderate

(B3) 70 Prince St. (Crosby) 212/219-8570

F 8 / S 7 / A 8 / $33   MC V AE

In the 5 years that it's been open, Savoy has earned a well-deserved reputation as a "gem," a "treasure" that serves interesting and tasty American/Mediterranean fare. The decor is "interesting," without being distracting. The working fireplace warms the room and the heart. The menu changes seasonally.

SPEC: *Marinated bluefish $8; Crab rolls $9; Penne w/rabbit, chanterelles, corn & walnut crumbs $17; Salt crusted baked duck $19.50*

SOHO KITCHEN AND BAR   LD   American

(B3) 103 Greene St. (Prince & Spring) 212/925-1866

F 5 / S 4 / A 5 / $18   MC V D AE   **TO**

If you can't choose from the 400 wines by the glass, 15 draught and 35 bottled beers, we suggest you kick back and have a soda and a Thai chicken pizza instead. Diners applaud the "excellent wine bar," and the "interesting art," but find the food "uninspiring." "A good first date spot."

SPEC: *Thai chicken pizza $10.50; Three cheese pizza $8.75*

Souen

SOUEN   LD   Asian

(B2) 210 6th Ave. (Prince) 212/807-7421 Fax: 627-4309

F 5 / S 4 / A 4 / $15   MC V D AE

Many people equate natural, healthy, organic macrobiotic food with no flavor, but for many Souen puts the lie to this myth. For others, though, it's "over-rated" and "needs an upscale revision." The decor, bright, airy and plant-filled, promotes a feeling of well-being and contentment without any of the dreaded New Age weirdness.

SPEC: *Seitan $6; Tempeh $6; Sole $12.50; Soba gomoku $8.50; Souen tempura $10.50; Tofu pie $4; Fruit crunch $3.75*

SPRING STREET NATURAL   LD   Vegetarian

(B3) 62 Spring St. (Lafayette) 212/966-0290 Fax: 966-4254

F 6 / S 5 / A 6 / $27   MC V D AE   **TO**

Pseudo-hip yet Zen-like, this open and airy restaurant filled with leafy potted plants and wooden tables is famous for its natural, healthy food. "Hearty minus the subtlety." The vegetarian dishes are prepared with organic ingredients only. "Nice portions...naturally balanced dishes."

SPEC: *Grilled calamari $6.75; Crisp marinated Tempeh $7; Jumbo shrimp $16; Organic rice and vegetable dinner $8*

0	1	2	3	4	5	6	7	8	9	10
disappointing		fair		good		very good		excellent		perfect

55

T SALON LD Amer/Continental

(B3) 142 Mercer St. (Prince) 212/925-3700

F 7 / S 6 / A 8 / $36 MC V AE

Fragrant with over 450 exotic teas— "a wonderful aroma to tickle the nose"— this elegant "salon" is frequented by gallery and model-types. Offering a range of dishes from jambalaya to Shanghai chicken salad— "and great sushi"— all the food is prepared according to the Ancient Art of Tea. This means there's tea in some form in every dish. "In the winter you need to know this place."

SPEC: Risotto w/seafood $18; Philippine Victorian garden rotisserie chicken $14; Grilled Santa Fe shrimp salad $16; Earl Grey chocolate cake $7

TASCA DO PORTO Latin

(C3) 525 Broome St. (Thompson & Sullivan) 212/343-2321

F 6 / S 5 / A 7 / $30 MC V D AE DIS

As Manhattan's only Portuguese tapas bar, this has the potential to be a great place for food and fun. The problem is location—a basement in Soho. It's got "an interesting, dark rustic atmosphere," and offers "nice jazz." But be careful of the Tapas style: a little bit can cost an awful lot.

SPEC: Paella stuffed squid $7; Chicken in clay pot $16; Filet mignon w/mango sauce $24

Tennessee Mountain

TENNESSEE MOUNTAIN LD American

(C3) 143 Spring St. (Wooster) 212/431-3993 Fax: 966-4393

F 7 / S 5 / A 5 / $22 MC V D AE **TO/D**

Probably the only place in Soho where your barbecue sauce smeared face won't elicit a second glance. Tennessee Mountain defies the laws of the neighborhood by offering "good, fun food" in an unpretentious atmosphere.

SPEC: Texas egg rolls $4.50; Chili fries $4.50; Barbecued special ribs $15.95 ; Hickory smoked ribs $12.50 $15.95; Chocolate mud pie $4.50

THREE DEGREES NORTH D Asian

(B2) 210 Spring St. (6th Ave.) 212/274-0505

F 7 / S 7 / A 9 / $25 MC V D AE DIS **TO**

Exotic and soothing, you'll enjoy the Eastern influenced design and the rich colors and tapestries of this Malaysian restaurant. The intimate banquettes are lined with pillows, and from the ceiling hang cone-paper lanterns. There's a cool blue lounge area, and a precious porch surrounded by bamboo trees.
Closed: Sunday
SPEC: Tuna $7; Cod $14; Beef $15; Coconut rice semolin cake w/mango $5; Armagnac chocolate mousse cake w/banana $6

TOUKIE'S LD Southern

(B2) 220 W. Houston St. (6th & Varick) 212/255-1411 Fax: 255-0924

F 4 / S 6 / A 6 / $37 MC V D AE

With ex-model Toukie Smith as its owner, this cutesy bistro features innovative combinations of Southwest cuisine. The combination of lavish red leather banquettes with red rose petals adorning table tops make this an interesting place to visit. The food, however, is "inconsistent."

SPEC: *Dee's crazy corn $5.25; Vegetarian pasta $13.50; Bob's ribs $14.95; Chic Chi Bunda (deep fried chicken) $13.75*

VUCCIRIA LD Italian

(B3) 422 W. Broadway (Prince & Spring) 212/941-5811

F 6 / S 6 / A 7 / $33 MC V D AE

If you're looking for a hearty meal in a romantic setting, this is the place. With a mural that depicts Palermo, it offers some of the finest Sicilian dishes at strikingly reasonable prices, Vucciria specializes in pasta, but save room for the desserts.

SPEC: *Pasta con sarde $13.50; Caponata $7.50; Involtini alla Siciliana (stuffed veal) $16.50*

WICKERS D Continental

(C3) 43 Crosby St. (Spring & Broome) 212/274-1404

F 5 / S 5 / A 6 MC V D AE DIS

"Like dinner at a friend's loft." The long, dark space is brightened by a rotating art exhibit, which includes the tables painted by local artists. No bottled beers; the owners wouldn't serve the preservatives—tap only!

SPEC: *Country pate $7; Roast pork $12; Vegetable platter $11; Chocolate truffle cake $4.50; Almond raspberry tart $4.50*

Zoë

ZOË LD American

(B3) 90 Prince St. (B'way & Mercer) 212/966-6722 Fax: 966-6718

F 8 / S 7 / A 7 / $36 MC V D AE DIS

An example of how presentation—both the decor and the design of the food itself—can distinguish a restaurant. "Pricey, but elegant." "The food tastes as wonderful as it looks," too! There are vividly colored walls, sponge painted green, blue, peach and yellow, as well as mosaic tiles, and terra-cotta columns. "Best scotch selection in the city." A treat for all the senses! A great plus is the owners' dedication to their diners' well-being.

SPEC: *Calamari w/Vietnamese dipping sauce $8.75; Salmon w/Moroccan spices $19.75; BBQ pork chop $18.50; Mochacinno pudding $7*

0	1	2	3	4	5	6	7	8	9	10
disappointing		fair		good		very good		excellent		perfect

EAST VILLAGE

@ CAFE   LD   Continental

(A4) 2 St. Mark's Place (3rd & 4th Aves.) 212/ 979 54-39

F 5 / S 5 / A 6 / $12   MC V D AE   **TO**

Most restaurants put condiments or flowers on the table, but here you get a Mac or PC. Staff can be multi-task, taking orders from the eclectic "global" menu, which offers light meals and a full bar, while also untangling you from the World Wide Web. Fun for a first date, or for the technically intimidated. You can video-chat live with other cyber cafe gnoshers and collegiate hacks on 5 special "CU-see me" hook-ups, check e-mail, write a novel, or surf deep into cyberspace, while munching on a German sausage.

SPEC: *Kappa maki (cucumber wrapped in rice & seaweed) $2.95; Mandarin spring roll $3.95; Ramen $6.50; Irish chicken pot pie $7.95; German sausage w/sauerkraut $7.95*

ACME BAR & GRILL   LD   Cajun

(B3) 9 Great Jones St. (Broadway & Lafayette) 212/420-1934

F 5 / S 5 / A 5 / $25   MC V D DIS   **TO**

Feels like a pit stop on a steamy road trip down south: stumble out of the Chevy, and into the local diner where you devour southern fried chicken and gulp lemonade. Hundreds of bottles of hot sauces line the ledge of the wall beside the tables. "Good cheap eats." "Fun, greasy, but great." A favorite haunt of NYU students. Downstairs, on many nights, there's live music. "If you can't make it south, this is the next best thing."

SPEC: *Crabcake $8.50; Catfish fingers $8.50; Blackened catfish $9.50 (lunch) $12.95 (dinner); Southern Fried chicken $7.95 (lunch) $11.50 (dinner)*

ANARCHY CAFE   LD   Italian

(A4) 27 3rd. Ave. (9th and St Marks Pl) 212/475-1270

F 6 / S 6 / A 6 / $24   AE   **TO**

New Age club and classic Italian restaurant rolled into one, makes this cafe truly anarchistic in plan and design. The food is fresh—the buffalo mozzarella flown in from Naples twice a week! World/acid jazz bands, as well as Latino, flamenco, and middle-eastern music, after midnight—and, in case you're dining alone and didn't bring a book to read, classic Italian films are projected on the back wall for you to watch. Fun, but at least one dissenter says, "Loud, rude, not worth the price."

SPEC: *Buffalo mozzarella $11; Lobster w/black linguini w/squid sauce $19; Pappardella porcini mushrooms $17;Tiramisu $5*

ANGELICA KITCHEN   LD   Vegetarian

(A4) 300 E. 12th St. (1st & 2nd) 212/228-2909

F 7 / S 6 / A 7 / $14   Cash only   **TO/D**

This popular vegan eatery offers more interesting choices than others of its ilk. Its consistently fresh, tasty creations elicit comments like "best organic/veggie in town," "feels like you're outside NYC," and "one of a kind; you won't believe what they do without meat." And the light, airy, natural ambiance, with soft music playing only adds to the experience.

SPEC: *Sea Caesar salad $5.25; Pickle plate $1.75; Three bean chili $6.25; Dragon bowl (rice, beans, tofu, sea vegetable, vegetable) $8*

ANGRY MONK, THE   D   Tibetan

(B4) 96 2nd Ave. (5th & 6th) 212/979-9202

F 5 / S 7 / A 7 / $20   MC V AE   **TO/D**

Delight in freshly prepared momos (dumplings) as a portrait of the Dalai Lama serenely watches over this delicately decorated restaurant. The name makes reference to the events occurring in Tibet today. "Unique, very friendly," "cozy and accommodating." Vegetarian or not, there are plenty of dishes to choose from.

SPEC: *Sheymo dumplings $7.50; Chasha khaka chili chicken $9.50; Shata fried sliced beef $12; Deysee steamed white rice $4.50; Gyako for 4 people $58*

AVENUE A   D   Japanese

(A5) 103 Ave. A (6th & 7th) 212/982-8109 Fax: 529-5143

F 6 / S 5 / A 3 / $17   MC V AE   **TO**

Known for their elaborate and colorful sushi which has been called "the best in town." You get an all-around unique experience in this "fun atmosphere." Black, splatter-painted walled cavern filled with artsy design paintings. Get there around 6 if you want to watch some Japanese cartoons (in English), or later for a loud D.J. music scene.

SPEC: *Panic roll $5.25; Oyster boister $5.75; Tempura soba $8.50; Beef teriyaki $10.25 Flaming tempura Alaska $4.75*

BABY JAKE'S   LD   Cajun

(B4) 141 1st Ave. (1st & 2nd) 212/254-2229

F 6 / S 5 / A 5 / $20   AE

When southern hospitality meets East Village funk, the result is "good cheap Cajun" barbecue and surly service, in a crowded diner. Baby Jake, whoever he may be, crawls towards the more curious dishes from down south. Sides are unusual and desserts make up for what the grilled entrees cut down on.

SPEC: *New Orleans muffalattas (chicken breast w/olive salad, smoked mozzarella & roasted peppers) $6.95; Salmon fajitas $11.95; Peanut butter pie $3.50*

Bayamo

BAYAMO   LD   Chino/Latino

(B4) 704 Broadway (N. of 4th St.) 212/475-5151 Fax: 475-8738

F 6 / S 6 / A 6 / $23   MC V D AE   **TO**

In this high energy restaurant, there's a diverse mix of pseudo-oriental papier-maché sculptures set against a vibrant, tropical Palm Beach background. The portions are big and satisfying. "A fun place," with a "wide menu." "Nice for the family." If you visit Tuesday night, get your blood moving again with some Mambo, or watch the scene from the balcony.

SPEC: *Cuban popcorn $5.95; Chicken fondue $11.95; Caribbean shrimp & swordfish brochettes $15.95; Mango margaritas/daiquiris $5; Habana banana $5.95*

0	1	2	3	4	5	6	~ 7	8	9	10
disappointing		fair		good		very good		excellent		perfect

BBQ LD Southwestern

(A4) 132 2nd Ave. (St. Mark's Pl.) 212/777-5574

F 5 / S 5 / A 4 / $14 MC V AE **TO/D**

This branch of Dallas BBQ isn't much to look at, but it delivers the goods. In this case, Texas-style barbecue, "at a great bargain." It differs somewhat from its uptown cousins in that its ambiance is spartan, "a slop house," to some, and diners are an eclectic mix of downtown denizens and uptown visitors—"young, young, young."

SPEC: *Texas fried wings $4.95; Vegetable tempura $2.95; Bar-B-Q roast beef $7.95; Rotisserie chicken (1/2) $4.95; Baby back ribs $8.95*

BENNY'S BURRITOS LD Mexican

(A5) 93 Avenue A (6th) 212/254-3286
See review on page 76.

Boca Chica

BOCA CHICA D Latin

(B4) 13 1st Ave. (1st & Houston) 212/473-0108

F 6 / S 5 / A 5 / $20 MC V AE DIS **TO**

The funky, downtown kitchen delivers sincere, reasonably-priced S. American dishes and stiff drinks like the Caipirinha ("country bumpkin") made with Brazilian sugar cane brandy. If drinks don't floor you, Mambo Kings tunes and food served in this always hopping, wildly painted dinner spot will. Crowd ranges from "fakes, rich people who feel like slumming," to hip downtowners looking for "fun."

SPEC: *South American bouillabaisse $9.95; Sweet corn soufflé topped chicken, raisin & tomatoes $10.50; Seafood in coconut spicy sauce Bahian style $14.50*

BOWERY BAR LD American

(B4) 40 East 4th St. Bowery 212/475-2220 Fax: 475-9269

F 5 / S 4 / A 6 / $22 MC V AE **TO**

Management lobbied long and hard with East Villagers to convert this old gas station into one of the most pretentious American bistros in NY. Tragically cool bouncers appeared to screen neighbors without the right glam quotient. Make it through the limos and Range Rovers stationed outside, and you'll sample fine continental cuisine. A walled-in patio dining area separates the chichi from the nose-pierced of NYU and the Bowery homeless. But architecture can't belie history. Someone once pumped petrol here.

SPEC: *Mussels Provencal $7.50; Fennel & orange salad $6; Grilled tuna w/bok choy and soy sake glaze $16; Grilled lamb kebabs $15.50*

Boy George
Singer

"I'm a vegan, and either I'll cook for myself, or when I'm in New York, I'll eat at **Souen**. And, if I can't get out, I'll order in from there at least once a day. The food is impeccable, unusual, and always tasty."

BRISCOLA   D   Italian

(A4) 65 4th Ave. (9th & 10th) 212/254-1940 Fax: 979-5725

F 7 / S 7 / A 7 / $26   MC V AE   **TO**

In honor of the name "briscola,"—an Italian deck of playing cards—the pink walls of this restaurant are appropriately decorated with different playing cards. There's a mural in the back room, as well as an elegant bar area. Catering to a selective clientele, you'll enjoy the quieter side of the East Village if you dine here.
Closed: Sunday
SPEC: *Eggplant w/capers $5.95; Mussels in white wine $5.95; Codfish filet $16.50; Linguine w/cuttlefish in black ink sauce $13.75; Homemade gelati $4.75*

BURRITOVILLE   LD   Tex-Mex

(A4) 141 2nd Ave. (8th & 9th) 212/260-3300
See review on page 77.

CAFE CENTOSETTE   LD   Italian

(A4) 107 3rd Ave. (13th) 212/420-5933

F 6 / S 6 / A 6 / $18   MC V AE

This warm, woodsy bistro brings a welcome touch of backstreet Rome to the uninspired edge of the East Village. Inside, among original oils that are for sale and change monthly, an arty neighborhood comes for tasty Italian dishes, none over $10.
SPEC: *Insalata exotica $6.25; Chicken masala $8.75; Chicken artichoke $8.75; Cappuccino mousse $4.50; Italian cheesecake $4*

CAFE ORLIN   BLD   American

(A4) 41 St. Marks Pl. (1st & 2nd) 212/777-1447 Fax: 228-7931

F 5 / S 6 / A 8 / $15   Cash only   **TO**

A casual downtown cafe, just a block away from the noisier part of St. Marks Place. It's like going to visit your grandparents in the country: "quiet and refined." The outdoor cafe gives this a laid-back, "metropolitan feel," making it a great place to sit and decompress from the pulse of the city.
SPEC: *Humus plate $3.95; Grilled salmon $8.95; Linguine gorgonzola $6.25*

CAFE TABAC   LD   American

(A4) 232 East 9th St. (2nd & 3rd) 212/674-7072 Fax: 388-9703

F 7 / S 7 / A 8 / $35   MV V AE   **TO**

Elegantly candlelit throughout, this upscale American bistro draws famous models, writers, and artists. You can do more than eat and gawk at this trendy "in spot," since there's a pinball machine on the main floor, and a place to shoot pool upstairs in "the back room." But to his credit, owner Roy Liebenthal, hasn't been satisfied to simply create a "hot" eatery "to be seen" at, but in hiring chef Robert Ginsberg, he's made certain the food is up to snuff. On Mondays there's a DJ and Sunday night is for women only.
SPEC: *Leg of lamb croustade $10; Pan fried oysters $10; Pan roasted red snapper $19.50; Shredded duck $19*

0	1	2	3	4	5	6	7	8	9	10
disappointing		fair		good		very good		excellent		perfect

CASANIS — LD — French

(B4) 54 E. 1st St. (1st & 2nd) 212/777-1589

F 7 / S 6 / A 6 / $27   AE

"J'aime beaucoup!" A cute, little French bistro that serves ample portions of comfort food. "Every neighborhood needs one," exclaim many New Yorkers. A wonderful spot in warm weather when the front doors are thrown open, the sun filters in through side windows, and a special cocktail is served from a hollowed watermelon cask. The menu changes daily and can be hit-or-miss. Check out the adorable bathroom.

SPEC: *Mussels marinara $6; Escargot w/garlic $6; Red snapper $16; Maigret et confit de canard $16; Tarte tatin $5*

CHRISTINE'S — BLD — Polish

(A4) 208 1st Ave. (12th & 13th) 212/254-2474

F 7 / S 6 / A 5 / $12   Cash only   TO/D

The food, service and prices make up for the lack of decor in this restaurant that looks like a "diner" but feels like home. The cuisine is Polish, but one little Polish girl wants her birthday party at Christine's because "they have the best hamburgers."

SPEC: *Blintzes, potato pancakes and pierogi 1/2 order $4.75, whole order $7.50; Stuffed cabbage $8.95*

CIRCA — D — Mediterranean

(A4) 103 2nd Ave. (6th & 7th) 212/777-4120 Fax: 677-0405

F 7 / S 6 / A 7 / $27   MC V D AE

Warmed by the gold-painted walls and velour-upholstered booths, lamps hanging over the bar seem on the verge of flowering. The table-tops are finished copper and the stained glass at the back of the room, and candleholders on each table add a touch of color. "The owners are young and attentive," but the place has become an "ultra-hip hangout for models and celebrities desperately holding onto their 15 minutes of fame."

SPEC: *Citrus cornmeal calamari $6.50; Pizzas $9-$10; Circa vegan $12; Lobster risotto $16; Steak frites $17*

CUCINA DI PESCE — D — Italian

(B4) 87 E. 4th St. (2nd & 3rd) 212/260-6800

F 7 / S 7 / A 6 / $19   Cash only   TO

Free "great mussels" at the bar while you wait. Already we like it. And so, evidently, do lots of others, as evidenced by the "long waits." The atmosphere is classy yet comfortable, and the outdoor cafe is strategically placed for some great East Village people watching.

SPEC: *Baked stuffed clams $5.95; Sicilian lasagna $7.95; Stuffed brook trout $9.95; Grilled salmon $9.95; Fusilli al pesto $6.95*

DALLAS BBQ — LD — American

(A3) 21 University Pl. (Washington Square Park) 212/674-4450

See review on page 227.

DANAL — BLD — American

(A4) 90 E. 10th St. (3rd & 4th) 212/982-6930

F 6 / S 6 / A 7 / $24   MC V D AE

"A homey, neighborhood place," Danal serves contemporary American and Mediterranean cuisine. The atmosphere is "cozy, casual" and "unpretentious," with fresh flowers and a (fake) fireplace. A great place to have brunch or dinner on a winter's day; or you can dine in the tiny garden during summer.

SPEC: *Artichoke & parmesan cheese tart $9; Smoked Norwegian salmon $12; Pear tarte tatin $4.50*

DOJO   LD   Japanese

(A4) 24-26 St. Mark's Place (2nd & 3rd) 212/674-9821
See review on page 83.

FEZ   D   American

(B3) 380 Lafayette St. (Great Jones & 4th) 212/533-2680

F 7 / S 7 / A 8 / $20   MC V D AE

Rub shoulders with a diverse New York crowd in this hip, Moroccan cocktail lounge. Enter through Time Cafe. If you're hungry, order from the limited menu derived from that restaurant. "Interesting architecture," and a "great place for dates." Live and unusual performances of music, poetry or jazz every night.
SPEC: *Margherita Pizza $9.75*

FIRST   D   American

(B4) 87 1st Ave. (5th & 6th) 212/674-3823 Fax: 674-8010

F 7 / S 6 / A 7 / $30   MC V AE   **TO**

That this way-hip continental late night spot is in a dubious corner of the East Village makes entering its dark and metallic atmosphere all the more of a treat. The mixed crowd comes for "inner city flavors," good foreign beers, and a return to the meat dominated menu, which includes roast suckling pig, a Sunday-only treat. Diners find the service "fun, with good energy," and there's a "great mix of customers."
SPEC: *Corn soup $6; Grilled ratatouille pizza $7.50; Sixth Street salmon $14; Braised lamb shank $14*

FLAMINGO EAST   D   Amer/Continental

(A4) 219 2nd Ave. (13th & 14th) 212/533-2860 Fax: 477-4550

F 7 / S 7 / A 8 / $30   MC V D AE

Glamorous and trendy, this 2-level restaurant was built in the 1800s. The downstairs is decorated with a tasteful eye for art deco; the upstairs gallery space is a reminder of this country's classic, aristocratic past. "Check out the bar up there." "Great energy." A "fun crowd" of the young, hip and artistic, with most showing up after 9. **Closed: Monday in summer**
SPEC: *Fried calamari $6; Grilled calamari salad $6.50; Grilled tuna $17.50; Sirloin steak frites $16.75*

GANDHI   LD   Indian

(A4) 345-347 E. 6th St. (1st) 212/614-9718

F 6 / S 6 / A 6 / $12   MC V AE   **TO/D**

This low-priced restaurant offers a wide variety of lamb, chicken and other dishes "with distinctive sauces." Though Gandhi might not be the best on the block, its decor —dark and elegant— good prices, diligent service, and south Indian specialties put it a cut above the rest and leave little to complain about.
SPEC: *Samosa $1.75; Tandoori chicken $6.95; Lamb tikka musallam $7.50; Sada Dosa (rice & lentil crepe) $5.95*

GLOBAL 33   D   Tapas

(B4) 93 2nd Ave. (5th & 6th) 212/477-8427

F 6 / S 6 / A 8 / $16   DIS

A popular "dark, postmodern tapas bar" that caters to late night diners with funky clothes and "dos." Revelers sip pricey elixirs (the house margarita is "Mexican prozac") and eat small portions of Mediterranean-inspired new American cuisine for a snack or combined as courses of a substantial meal. Framed cartoons behind the bar are eye-catching and quirky.
SPEC: *Global pizza $4.95; Bruschetta plate $4.50; Steak marinated in Barolo $8.95; Spanish spiced meatballs $5.50*

0	1	2	3	4	5	6	7	8	9	10
disappointing		fair		good		very good		excellent		perfect

GREAT JONES CAFE   D   Cajun

Top 10 $0-20   Inexpensive

(B3) 54 Great Jones St. (Lafayette & Bowery) 212/674-9304

F 7 / S 6 / A 6 / $19   Cash only

Eat a little better and be a little more comfortable here than at most places. The food and local crowd are as familiar as the atmosphere—"unpretentious and lots of fun." Menu changes daily, as the chef works with whatever's fresh at the moment. The crowd is eclectic, from underground filmmakers to writers and artists, without a tourist in sight. "Best brunch in NY!"
SPEC: *Cajun popcorn $6.25; Pork chop w/apricot glaze $11.95; Soft-shell crab po' boy $8.95; Key lime Pie $3.95*

HAVELI   LD   Indian

Top 10 $0-20   Inexpensive

(B4) 100 2nd Ave. (5th & 6th) 212/982-0533 Fax: 533-2676

F 7 / S 6 / A 6 / $19   MC V AE DIS   **TO/D**

"Contemporary East meets West." Lush mango and honeydew colored walls, simplified Moghul architecture, and small lanterns on the tables, factor into this spot's exotic and romantic appeal. From the balcony, look down at other diners and musicians playing sitar or tabla. "The only excellent downtown Indian." Definitely a step up in class and sophistication from the plethora of other Indian restaurants in the neighborhood.
SPEC: *Chana Chat (chick peas, potatoes & onions) $2.95; Shrimp curry $10.50; Rasmali $2.50; Gulab Jaman $2.50*

IN PADELLA   LD   Italian

(A4) 145 2nd Ave. (9th) 212/598-9800

F 6 / S 7 / A 7 / $20   Cash only   **TO**

Exposed brick walls, tiled floors, flower arrangements, stacked wine bottles and antique furniture scattered throughout. It adds up to a "neighborhood favorite" with charming ambiance. Dining areas separated by heavy maroon bordered black curtains, and "nice sidewalk seating." The food is good, the prices reasonable, the crowd young and knowing.

INDOCHINE   D   Vietnamese

(B3) 430 Lafayette St. (Astor & 4th) 212/505-5111 Fax: 477-0397

F 7 / S 6 / A 7 / $29   MC V D AE   **TO/D**

The grand aunt of the trendy Asian restaurant movement in downtown Manhattan, as the "Asian Odeon" continues to draw fashionable crowds, while serving "delicious," unusual French/Vietnamese fare. So cool and sophisticated, you want to be dressed in designer clothes and look good while dining here.
SPEC: *Ca Chien Xa (crispy whole sea bass w/lemon grass) $17.75; Nhom Sath Ko (salad of sliced beef w/lemon grass & basil) $10.75*

INTERNET CAFE, THE   LD   American

(A4) 82 E. 3rd St. (1st & 2nd) 212/614-0747

F 5 / S 5 / A 5 / $15   MC V AE   **TO**

This "cyber-cafe" (http://www.bigmagic.com) is a coffee bar on the outside; but inside, amidst books and arcana, sit 3 hulking computers and dozens of latte-swillers with laptops plugged into tableside ports. A "server" doesn't bring you cappuccino or a turkey and chipolte sandwich—it dishes up e-mail or lessons on the Net. Good jazz on the stereo, late hours, beer and wine and the smartest wait staff in New York asks, can I help you.
SPEC: *Muffins 2 for $3; Scones $2; Fresh turkey w/chipolte mayonnaise on baguette $10; Vegan sandwich $10; Brownies $2.50*

JOHN'S   D   Italian

(A4) 302 E. 12th St (1st & 2nd) 212/475-9531

F 6 / S 5 / A 5 / $24   Cash only   **TO/D**

A narrow room adorned with mirrors, frescoes of Italian landscapes, multi-colored tile floors, and a wonderful altar of "more candles and dripping dried wax than at St. Peter's." Tables are packed so tightly you can't help meet your neighbors. Great place to laugh with friends over Chianti, while eating pasta from heaped platters.

SPEC: *Marinated & grilled portobello mushrooms $8.95; Sautéed fresh tomatoes $12.95; Chicken arreganata 10.95; Homemade cakes $5*

DONTE BURSE

Jules

JULES   LD   French

(A4) 65 St. Marks Pl. (1st & 2nd) 212/477-5560

F 7 / S 6 / A 6 / $28   DIS   **TO**

This "Left Bank or Marais bistro" claims the East Village reflects its personality, while others argue that its personality has rubbed off on the neighborhood. The feel and food is sophisticated, the ambiance ultra cool,—some call it "the most atmospheric in town" —the clientele (writers, artists, musicians) hip and accomplished. Live jazz every night.

SPEC: *Snails in garlic parsley butter $6.50; Vegetarian couscous $13; Paella $14.50; Roasted leg of lamb $15.50*

KATZ'S DELI   BLD   Deli

(B4) 205 E. Houston St. (Ludlow) 212/254-2246 Fax: 674-3270

F 7 / S 5 / A 4 / $10   Cash only   **TO/D**

This is where you go to get the salami presidents, celebrities, knowns and unknowns crave. Katz's has been filling the stomachs of the Lower East Side and the world (think orgasm scene in "When Harry Met Sally,") since 1888. "Great fatty food"—knishes, pastrami, kugel, cheesecake." "Service 10, I do it myself." Take a ticket, experience and enjoy.

SPEC: *Pastrami sandwich $6.90; Grilled frankfurters $1.70; Hot open faced sandwich plates (brisket, roast beef, or turkey) $7.95*

KHYBER PASS   LD   Afgani

(A4) 34 St. Marks Pl. (2nd & 3rd) 212/473-0989

F 6 / S 5 / A 4 / $17   MC V AE DIS   **TO/D**

Draped with middle-eastern rugs, tapestries, and antique Afghani objects, this romantically lit restaurant has tables where you can sit low to the ground and lean back comfortably, lounging languidly against throw cushions. A neighborhood favorite that also attracts out-of-towners, including celebrities like Warren Beatty and Susan Sarandon.

SPEC: *Shir-Chay traditional tea $3.75; Aushak (steamed scallion dumplings) $3.75; Kabobs $8.95-1$12.95; Telabee (traditional Afghan sweet) $2.50*

0	1	2	3	4	5	6	7	8	9	10
disappointing		fair		good		very good		excellent		perfect

KIEV   BLD   Russian

(A4) 117 2nd Ave. (7th) 212/674-4040

F 7 / S 6 / A 5 / $11   Cash only   **TO/D**

"Awful decor, great food," just about says it all. Choose anything on this vast 24-hour menu and you'll get fresh, hearty, home-cooked meals with an Eastern European touch. "Great people watching at 4 am." And the crowd reflects the neighborhood, which means you're likely to find a skinhead sitting alongside an up and coming artist.

SPEC: *Kielbasa & eggs $3.75; Kasha varnishkes & beef chunks $6.95; Kiev veal cutlet 11.50; Roasted 1/2 chicken $6.95*

L'UDO   LD   Continental

(A4) 432 Lafayette St. (at Astor) 212/388-0978 Fax: 388-1404

F 7 / S 7 / A 8 / $25   DIS   **TO**

Simulated 16th century frescoes and antique collections at the bar add to this restaurant's mystique. There is a cabaret during the winter months, and art exhibits in the garden during summer. Located directly across the street from the Public Theater, well-known playwrights and actors occasionally dine here. "Cool food," and there's "a great garden."

SPEC: *Goat cheese "feuillant" $7.50; Duck Maigret w/garlic $15.50; Fresh smoked water trout $14.50; Apple torte $6.50*

LA SPAGHETTERIA   LD   Mediterranean

(A4) 178 2nd Ave. (11th & 12th) 212/995-0900

F 7 / S 7 / A 7 / $24   MC V AE   **TO**

This dimly-lit, East Village oasis is a quiet neighborhood hangout for artists and musicians. With a relaxed but inviting lounge look, there's a touch of fun in the tiger-striped upholstered seats. "Beautiful, surprising, fascinating, always tasty. Reasonable prices and the food is good."

SPEC: *Swiss chard $4.95; Roasted chicken $10.95; Penne w/mushrooms $11.95; Chocolate almond torte $4.95*

LA STRADA 2   D   Italian

(B4) 78 E. 4th St. (2nd Ave.) 212/353-8026

F 6 / S 7 / A 7 / $22   MC V D AE DIS   **TO**

"La Strada" "the street," in Italian, serves sturdy Northern Italian favorites on a ramshackle albeit cozy East Village corner. The all-Italian staff, pasta made before your eyes, and options for indoor or outdoor dining make this bistro popular with locals and tourists. "Food is great, but the selection is limited."

SPEC: *Carpaccio $6.50; Vegetali marinati $5; Penne alla vodka $8; Bocconcini di vitello (veal) $12.50*

LANZA   LD   Italian

(A4) 168 1st Ave. (10th & 11th) 212/674-7014

F 6 / S 6 / A 5 / $22   MC V D AE   **TO/D**

A popular stop for neighborhood families looking for reliable Italian fare, including pasta and home-made mozzarella. The decor is old lace and woody, giving it a "homey," old Brooklyn Italian living room effect. The staff is helpful. And the garden in back is a pleasant spot to eat.

SPEC: *Mozzarella & peppers $5.50; Caesar salad $5.50; Spaghettini al Lanza $9.50; Petti di pollo all'Anice $10.50*

LIFE CAFE　　　　　　　BLD　　　　　　Mexican

(A5) 343 E. 10th St. (Ave B) 212/477-8791

F 5 / S 6 / A 6 / $15　　　MC V D

Quirky, eclectic and fun, or "pretentious"? We vote for the former. This landmark cafe/restaurant serving a mix of Cal-Mex and vegetarian food, was one of the first in this part of Alphabet City. A retrospective of the 40s, 50s and 60s, walls and tables are collaged with vintage issues of *Life* Magazine. Service can be "slow," but somehow here it's not such a bother. Just read your table.

SPEC: *Flash-fried calamari $4.95; Mega burrito $7.25; Life salad $6.50; Carrot cake $3.75; Mud cake $4*

LOUISIANA COMMUNITY BAR & GRILL　　D　　　Cajun

(B3) 622 Broadway (Bleecker & Houston) 212/460-9633

F 6 / S 5 / A 7 / $26　　　MC V D AE　　　　　　TO

You'll find a celebrative corner of New Orleans transplanted here. Wood-planked walls, signs and Mardi Gras decorations. The immense bar extends the length of what seems like a hallway. A popular post-6pm hangout where young office workers from both sides of Houston can let loose. "Loud crowd, but Harlem all-stars Saturdays is worth the noise." Try the traditional crawfish boil!

SPEC: *Cajun crawfish boil $9 per lb.; Red bean & rice, andouille sausage & cornbread $6; Crawfish etouffee w/rice $16; Chocolate dream cake $5*

LUCKY CHENG'S　　　　　LD　　　　　　　Asian

(B4) 24 1st Ave. (1st & 2nd) 212/473-0516 Fax: 473-0481

F 6 / S 6 / A 7 / $32　　　MC V D AE DIS

A beautiful interior, staffed by drag queens may be sufficient to keep you interested, but many find it "flabby, bland food and a tacky bridge and tunnel crowd no more fabulous than at the local mall." Others find it "great fun, if cross-dressing doesn't bother you," "dirty wild," and "exotic."

SPEC: *Spring rolls $4.75; Marinated shrimp $6.95; Grilled chicken in tamarind barbecue sauce w/mashed plantains $12.95;Lucky Cheng's paella $14.95*

MARION'S CONTINENTAL　　　LD　　　Continental

(B4) 354 Bowery (E. 4th & Great Jones) 212/475-7621

F 6 / S 8 / A 10 / $19　　　MC V　　　　　　　TO

One day it's "The Jersey Shore," the next "Back to School." Who knows what's next with this French/Italian restaurant with a "twist." These various themes affect the menu, although standards, like the potato turnip mashed potatoes, remain.

SPEC: *Spinach salad $5.50; Pate duck a l'orange $4.95; Grilled salmon $10.95; BBQ baby back ribs $10.50; Gateau du mort $4.50; Supreme dessert plate $10.50*

MEKKA　　　　　　　　　D　　　　　　Amer/Soul

(B5) 14 Ave. A (Houston) 212/475-8500

F 7 / S 7 / A 7 / $22　　　MC V D AE

A "jewel" in the "nearly rough" section of Alphabet City, this nouveau soul food and Caribbean stopover combines a hip East Village bar setting with some of the best jerked dishes in the city. Check out the backyard—reminiscent of a Bahamian dockside, with its bright blues and yellows, palm trees and, of course, the moon. Soon to be encased by sun-roofing in cold weather dining.

SPEC: *Soul fried strips $3.95; Corn meal dipped catfish $9.95; A very sassy grilled bird $10.95; Collards w/smoked turkey $2.95; Jerked fish of the day P/A*

0	1	2	3	4	5	6	7	8	9	10
disappointing		fair		good		very good		excellent		perfect

MIRACLE GRILL D Southwestern

(A4) 112 1st Ave. (6th & 7th) 212/254-2353

F 7 / S 6 / A 7 / $29 MC V AE **TO/D**

This Tex-Mex is like a pocket of Santa Fe in the heart of the city. The dimly-lit pueblo interior is fun, but the cute garden— "worth the price just to sit in,"— tucked between apartment buildings is a refreshing fill of greenery, ranging from peach trees to bamboo. "Superior medium-priced food," "with a healthy twist."

SPEC: *Quesadilla w/chiles, corn, zucchini, guacamole $8.50; Southwestern spring roll $6.95; Grilled portobello fajita $11.95; Ancho & black pepper crusted tuna $17.95*

MITALI LD Indian

(A4) 334 E. 6th St. (1st & 2nd Aves.) 212/533-2508

F 6 / S 6 / A 4 / $23 MC V AE **TO/D**

Mitali has survived for 20 years and with good reason. It meets the requirements of any good restaurant: "Always reliable." Good service; Good food; Good atmosphere; Good prices. You'll want for very little at this Indian classic, either east or west.

SPEC: *Indian hors d'oeuvres $5.95; Do-piaz curry $7.95; Seafood malai $15.25; Special mixed biriyani $9.25; Crabmeat pathia $16.95*

NoHo Star

NOHO STAR BLD American

(B3) 330 Lafayette St. (Bleecker) 212/925-0070 Fax: 226-6341

F 6 / S 6 / A 6 / $24 MC V D AE DIS **TO**

With a combination American and Classical Chinese cuisine, seemingly simple dishes manage to be accented in all the right places. Surrounded by 2 walls of windows, you can truly breathe while enjoying the generous portions. Patrons include local artists, business people and families. As one diner puts it, "consistent, convenient, fun."

SPEC: *Maryland crab cakes $8.50; Grilled breast of chicken w/lime & coriander $12.75; Roasted free range chicken w/grilled onions $13.25; Coffee cantata $5.75*

Top 10 $0-20
Inexpensive

O.G. D Asian

(A5) 507 E. 6th St. (Aves. A & B) 212/477-4649

F 7 / S 7 / A 5 / $20 MC V **TO**

Great example of how far you can stretch your dining $ if you're willing to trek to Alphabet City. Initials stand for "Oriental Grill." Innovative combos of Chinese, Japanese, Indonesian and Thai seasonings and cooking techniques make this an exciting place to eat. By 9:30, a predictably colorful cast of downtown characters starts to appear at the simply furnished and dimly lit restaurant, which can be a bit "noisy" when full.

SPEC: *Pu-pu platter P/A; Calamari salad w/miso vinaigrette $5.50; BBQ salmon $13.50*

OROLOGIO   D   Italian

(A5) 162 Ave. A (10th & 11th) 212/228-6900

F 7 / S 4 / A 5 / $19   Cash only   **TO**

Times they are a changin'. Nowhere is this more evident than at this charming Italian ristorante. There are clocks everywhere which, we shouldn't have to point out, accounts for the name. "Wonderful pasta," the prices are a "great value," and it's become a very popular spot for neighborhood denizens who nightly fill this rather cramped restaurant.

SPEC: *Pizzas $6.50-$7; Focaccia $6.50; Biancchi e neri $6.50; Farfalle al salmone $7.50; Marinated grill tuna $11.50*

ORSON'S   D   American

(A4) 175 2nd Ave. (11th & 12th) 212/475-1530 Fax: 475-4996

F 6 / S 5 / A 7 / $19   MC V AE DIS

An interesting mix of simple art deco with a touch of funky Southwest design against the background of an upscale diner. Specializing in martinis, this hip but sweet spot has candlelight and fluorescent, moon-blue lighting. If you're partial to wearing black, you'll fit right in. "Great pre-movie nosh, post-movie nightcaps."

SPEC: *Grilled portabello mushroom $6.25; Grilled seafood salad $7.25; Blackened chicken breast $11.25; Grilled pork chops w/garlic mashed potatoes $13.95*

PASSAGE TO INDIA   LD   Indian

(A4) 308 E. 6th St. (1st & 2nd) 212/529-5770

F 6 / S 6 / A 5 / $13   MC V D AE   **TO/D**

It's no secret that E. 6th is an Indian food junkie's paradise, and often you can't tell one restaurant from another. But a few stand out. This is one of them. The food is good and prices reasonable, though maybe a dollar or so higher than others. The Moghul design will remind you of the Taj Mahal. There's a clay oven where their famous tandoori dishes and nan bread are baked.

SPEC: *Tandoori $7.95-$10.95; Chicken Karahi $7.50; Mango lasei $2.25; Kheer vice custard $1.95*

PASSPORT   D   Southwestern

(A4) 79 St. Mark's Pl. (1st & 2nd) 212/979-2680

F 6 / S 6 / A 8 / $15   MC V D AE   **TO**

Santa Fe-styled with adobe booths by the bar. The lower level has a facade of a pink Catholic church made of wood and adobe that extends the length of the wall. Entering, you're greeted by an ornamental branched candlestick representing the tree of life. "Fun but romantic." Food is inexpensive and good.

SPEC: *Vegetarian escargot $3.50; Coconut & rum grilled shrimp $8.95; Sizzling fajitas $8.95; Chicken breast mole $8.95*

PHEBE'S PLACE   D   American

(B4) 361 Bowery (E.4th) 212/473-9008

F 4 / S 4 / A 2 / $15   MC V D AE DIS   **TO**

A hangout for out-of-work, hardly working, and hard working actors, artists, writers and neighborhood wannabes. The food is just okay—your basic burgers and the like, but the people are fun and interesting and the beer is about the cheapest in town. **Closed: Sunday**

SPEC: *Nachos grande $4.75; Sweet potato fries $3.25; Blackjack burger (chopped sirloin w/black peppercorns, flamed in Jack Daniels) $5.50*

0	1	2	3	4	5	6	7	8	9	10
disappointing		fair		good		very good		excellent		perfect

DONTE BURSE

Pisces

PISCES   D   Seafood

(A5) 95 Ave. A (6th) 212/260-6660 Fax: 260-6660

F 7 / S 7 / A 7 / $22   MC V D AE   **TO**

"Fish out of water, an East Village charmer." By serving fish and pasta with Mediterranean influences, under dim lighting this place draws an unusual array of diners. The fish is superbly prepared and smoked on the premises. Unusual brunch dishes include eggs with shrimp hash and tuna burgers. "A jewel on Ave. A."
SPEC: *Smoked bass $5.75; Steamed mussels $4.95; Tuna bresoala & smoked salmon carpaccio $7.50; Sautéed skate $9.95; Grilled tuna $14.50*

ROETTELE A.G.   LD   German

(A5) 126 East 7th St. (1st & Ave. A) 212/674-4140

F 7 / S 7 / A 7 / $22   MC V D AE DIS   **TO**

Who would have thought you could find a traditional German/Swiss restaurant in the very untraditional East Village? This "aromatic favorite" has 4 rooms that are right out of a story book, and the covered backyard garden boasts real Concord grapes. You can now celebrate Wigstock and Octoberfest in the same neighborhood. Life is good. **Closed: Sunday**
SPEC: *Dandelion salad $5; Vitello tonnato (cold sliced veal w/tuna-caper mayonnaise) $7.50; Sauerbraten $14.50; Emince duveau with Rosti $16*

ROSE OF INDIA RESTAURANT   LD   Indian

(A4) 308 E. 6th St. (1st & 2nd) 212/533-5011

F 6 / S 6 / A 6 / $11   Cash only   **TO**

A standout on "Curry Lane," not only for the food, but for the mind-bending, time-warped decor. It's Christmas every night at Rose of India, because the shoe-boxed shape room is heavily decorated with tinsel and Christmas lights, even in the dead of summer. Kinda makes you wanna bundle up and eat some hot, spicy food.
SPEC: *Shrimp poori $2.95; Chapati bread $1.75; Alu paratha (stuffed w/mashed and spice potatoes w/peas) $2.50; Tandoori mixed grill $7.95*

SAN LOCO   LD   Mexican

(A4) 129 2nd Ave. (7th & 8th) 212/260-7948

F 6 / S 4 / A 1 / $8   Cash only   **TO/D**

This tiny, storefront Mexican is well-known throughout the city for "items fresh—from scratch made in our own kitchen." Have it delivered (preferable perhaps, since the ambiance, including cowboy boots hanging from the ceiling, leaves plenty to be desired.) Or come in and browse the newsy bulletin board wall while you wait
SPEC: *Taco-locos $2.75-$3.25; Taco burgers $2.95; Burrito locos $5.95; Apple loco $2.05*

SAPPORO EAST   D   Japanese

(A4) 245 E. 10th St. (1st Ave.) 212/260-1330

F 8 / S 6 / A 5 / $15   MC V D AE   **TO**

Like a rural Japanese house, the interior has a no-frills quality, what with various specials taped haphazardly to the walls. Waiters dress in black: jeans and T-shirts with the restaurant's logo on the back. Casual and comfortable, the food is not only good, but a bargain. "Best 1/2 price in town."
SPEC: *Tempura $5.30; Box dinners $10-$10.50; Salmon teriyaki $9.50*

2ND AVENUE DELI   BLD   Deli

(A4) 156 2nd Ave. (10th) 212/677-0606 Fax: 477- 5327

F 7 / S 6 / A 5 / $12   AE   **TO/D**

The host of Yiddish Broadway in the heart of the East Village is world famous in more ways than one. "All things are relative" here, with "yummy pierogies" and "heavenly" pastrami. "Don't need ambiance with this food." Stop by and try the chopped liver, made fresh every day, because the 2nd Avenue Deli certainly ain't.
SPEC: *Knishes $2; Kasha varnishkes $3.50; Three decker sandwiches $9.75; Corned beef, pastrami, tongue, turkey & salami combo platter $12.50*

SIDEWALK   BLD   American

(A5) 94 Ave. A (6th St.) 212/473-7373 Fax: 982-5729

F 7 / S 5 / A 6 / $17   MC V D AE

If you're walking in the East Village and spot a line of vintage motorcycles parked at the curb, you're either in front of the Hell's Angel's headquarters or Sidewalk. Let's hope it's the latter. For some reason serious bikers frequent this "nothing special" hangout, which has become a popular neighborhood spot to eat and have a good time. And "outdoor seating is prime." The better to see those "hogs," we presume.
SPEC: *Spicy chicken wings $4.95; Vegetarian burger $4.95; Carne asada $7.95; Lemon chicken $7.95; Sugarless apple raisin pie $3.25*

SPORTSPAGE CAFE   D   American

(B4) 90 2nd Ave. (5th St.) 212/254-1562

F 3 / S 4 / A 2 / $22   MC V AE DIS

It doesn't get much dumpier than this, folks, and it ain't a bargain either. But inexplicably, on playoff nights fans spill onto the sidewalk. If you're in the East Village and you have to see the game, this must be the place. If you're in the East Village and you need to eat, this isn't.
SPEC: *Buffalo wings $7.95; Southern style wings $7.95; Burgers $6.95-$7.95; Combo barbecued ribs & chicken $14.95*

STINGY LULU'S   LD   American

(A5) 129 St. Mark's Pl. (Ave. A) 212/995-5191

F 2 / S 2 / A 6 / $13   Cash only   **TO/D**

A '50s diner with gaudy, garish accents. "Great decor, bad food and attitude," is how some diners see it. For us, the term "Miss thang" springs to mind. Pastas, burgers and "meat, fish and potatoes," with a Louisiana twang. The name alone may be worth the trip.
SPEC: *Turkish cigars (pan fried phyllo dough w/feta & parsley) $3.25; Marinated pork chops $8.25; Lulu's "FAB" meatloaf $7.50; Chocolate-espresso fudge cake $3*

0	1	2	3	4	5	6	7	8	9	10
disappointing		fair		good		very good		excellent		perfect

Telephone Bar & Grill

TELEPHONE BAR & GRILL LD British

(A4) 149 2nd Ave. (9th & 10th) 212/529-5000

F 6 / S 6 / A 7 / $20   MC V AE   **TO**

Three bright red antique English telephone booths with working phones, make up the facade of this spacious, atmospheric pub. We doubt there's any place else in the city serving fish and chips wrapped up inside The New York Times. "A twist on usually bland, English cuisine," and "the best veggie Shepherds pie in NY." Good outdoor seating a plus.

SPEC: *Salmon cakes $7; Stilton cheese fritters $6; Shepherd's pie $9 Fish & chips $9; "Rather spicy" roasted scrod $12*

TEMPLE BAR D American

(B3) 332 Lafayette St. (Houston & Bleecker) 212/925-4242

F 7 / S 7 / A 9 / $15   MC V D AE

"Atmosphere for days." "Very romantic and classy." An oasis of sophistication off hectic Houston street. "Pricey and secluded." All of this is true. Enjoy the anonymity of the room's inky blackness, while sipping the best martini in town.

SPEC: *Martinis $7; Caviar 1/2 oz $30; Caviar and smoked fish canapés $5; Smoked salmon w/corn pancakes & Tobiko caviar $9.50*

TERESA'S BLD Polish

(A4) 103 1st Ave. (6th & 7th) 212/228-0604

F 4 / S 4 / A 4 / $13   Cash only   **TO/D**

Not just your typical diner, though it may look like it. Mom's Polish cooking "really shines" here. The food is inexpensive and great. If you like potato pancakes, guess what? You're in luck.

SPEC: *Blintzes $3.95; Filet of salmon $9.95; ;Veal goulash $7.50; Duck, roasted & stuffed w/apples & prunes $7.50; Applecake $2*

THREE OF CUPS D Italian

(B4) 83 1st Ave. (5th) 212/388-0059

F 7 / S 6 / A 6 / $20   MC V AE   **TO**

The atmosphere is a little odd. Minimalistic medieval decor, including torches to provide light; a bar that could be a small cathedral; and oversized booths that make you feel like royalty. "The decor doesn't suggest Italy, but the food sure does." A wood-burning oven provides gourmet pizzas. After eating, saunter downstairs to the dark "lounge" to continue your evening incognito.

SPEC: *Pizzas $6.50-$15.50; Roasted garlic w/crostini $3; Classic spaghetti $6.75; Sicilian eggplant casserole $9*

TIME CAFE — BLD — American

(B3) 380 Lafayette St. (Great Jones & 4th) 212/533-7000

F 6 / S 6 / A 5 / $28   MC V AE   **TO/D**

Brunch is a fair of vanity and the busiest meal at Time Cafe. Jostle for space in the outdoor cafe with Russell Simmons and his support group of beauties, then sit back and enjoy the scene. Eco-friendly, even down to paper straws and organic foods on the menu. Some find it "overpriced and pretentious," and " too hip for its own good."
SPEC: *Hummus & chayote in a flour tortilla $4.75; Assorted spicy tapas $7.75; Broccoli frittata $12.50; Pizzas $9.75*

Toast

TOAST — D — Continental

(B3) 428 Lafayette St. (Astor Pl. & 4th) 212/473-1698

F 7 / S 7 / A 7 / $29   DIS   **TO**

Located in an 1831 landmark building, this "intimate, cozy" bar/restaurant serving multi-cultural cuisine, has a unique but elegant tropical feel. The walls, shellacked golden with a tint of red, were created by the owner himself. So were the oversized blades of the ceiling fans, and the bar itself. **Closed: Sunday**
SPEC: *Finger wontons $7; Taco loco for 2 $9; Grilled shrimp chipotle $16;*

TWO BOOTS — LD — Pizzeria

(A5) 36 Ave. A (2nd & 3rd) 212/505-5450

F 6 / S 5 / A 4 / $15   DIS   **TO/D**

Something different... A Cajun, Italian pizza joint. A '50's style soda shop. Checked tablecloths, various stylized boots, a great juke box and a lively, friendly atmosphere.
SPEC: *Creole popcorn $6.95; Pecan crusted catfish 8.95; Individual pizzas $5.50-$8.95; Pasta jambalaya $10.95*

WEST VILLAGE

AGGIE'S — BLD — American

(B3) 146 W. Houston (MacDougal) 212/673-8994

F 6 / S 5 / A 2 / $19   Cash only

If ambiance means anything, skip Aggie's. But if you're looking for good food, a hip crowd, and a "house" cat who'll rub up against your leg while you eat, this is the place. Personally, we don't mind a restaurant where instructions for the Heimlich maneuver are posted for all to see. Menu? Forget it. Check the blackboard behind the counter when you come in, then remember what you want when the waiter approaches. **Closed: Sunday dinner**
SPEC: *Meatloaf w/mashed potatoes $8.75; Salmon croquettes $9.75; Chicken caesar w/avocado $12.75; Key lime pie $4.25*

0	1	2	3	4	5	6	7	8	9	10
disappointing		fair		good		very good		excellent		perfect

Alison on Dominick

ALISON ON DOMINICK   D   French

(C2) 38 Dominick St. (Varick & Hudson) 212/721-7118

F 8 / S 8 / A 7 / $40   MC V D AE

Often declared the "most romantic restaurant downtown," Alison does not disappoint. Soft, flattering lighting, comfortable banquettes, high-backed chairs, and pretty people all add to the ambiance. "Always a great and fresh selection." But be prepared to pay for the refined atmosphere and service—prices are another feature which sets this stylish spot apart from other neighborhood restaurants.

SPEC: *Foie gras & roasted golden beet napoleon $17; Roast breast of squab $29; Muscovy Duck $27; Plum bread pudding $10; Chocolate Tart w/raspberry, creme fraiche & chocolate sorbets $10*

ANGLERS & WRITERS   BLD   Continental

(C2) 420 Hudson St. (Corner of St. Luke's Pl.) 212/675-0810

F 6 / S 6 / A 7 / $19   Cash only   TO

A celebration of the owner's love for angling, and the Village's love for writers. Books and tables resembling old desks share the room with fishing lures, fresh flowers and displays of mouth-watering desserts. A truly pretty and unusual spot for homemade chicken pot pie and grilled country ham. "Your mother's cooking—you wish." "Desserts knock your socks off!"

SPEC: *Hearty harvest soup w/chicken & vegetables $3.50; Lamb stew $12.50; Hot open-faced turkey sandwich $7.50; Angel food cake $4.25; Cherry or blackberry pie $4.25*

AREA CODE CAFE   BLD   Amer/Continental

(A2) 510 6th Ave. (13th) 212/924-3799

F 4 / S 4 / A 3 / $14   MC V   TO/D

An ice cream parlor meets diner in a phone booth that's low on atmosphere but offers creative variations on its dining themes. You can make free interstate calls on old-fashioned table-top phones while gnoshing on burgers from the all-day brunch menu. Dinner goes continental. "Charming staff, but not so for food.".

SPEC: *Grilled eggplant $5.95; Lots-A-Pasta $6.50; San Francisco stir-fry $7.50; Shakes and floats $3.95-$4.50*

ARTEPASTA   LD   Italian

(A2) 81 Greenwich Ave. (Bank & 7th Ave.) 212/229-0234

F 5 / S 6 / A 5 / $19   Cash only   TO/D

Upscale meets affordable. Interesting architectural decor and good food, reasonably priced. Somehow Artepasta manages to combine all these as well as being a great place for large parties or an intimate twosome. Go figure.

SPEC: *Carpaccio parmigiano $5.95; Spinach risotto $10.95; Red snapper $13.95; Key lime pie $3.95; Berry tiramisu $3.95*

ARTURO'S D Pizzeria

(B3) 106 W. Houston St. (LaGuardia & Thompson) 212/677-3820

F 6 / S 5 / A 6 / $24 MC V D AE **TO/D**

"Good food, festive, noisy." "Service and atmosphere don't matter—it's the pizza that counts and it's good." An excellent spot for celebrity sightings. Stevie Wonder's been known to wander in, sit down at the piano, and tinkle the ivories. And others, like Harvey Keitel, have been known to throw on an apron and serve a "coal oven" pizza or steak to hungry diners.

SPEC: *Coal oven pizzas $10-$16; Shrimp scampi $12.75; Saltimboca Raimond $12.25; Steak grilled in coal oven $14.50*

AU TROQUET D French

(A1) 328 W. 12th St. (Greenwich St.) 212/924-3413

F 7 / S 5 / A 6 / $31 MC V D AE

If Emma Bovary materialized in NYC in 1995, she'd surely feel most at home here. A quaint, French provincial restaurant, Au Troquet serves delicious home-style cooking a la Française. The atmosphere is complete with shirred lace curtains, small watercolors of streetscapes, Edith Piaf tunes crackling over the record player, and romantic lighting. "Solid, good for what it is. Heavy!"

SPEC: *Roasted quail w/port wine sauce & mushrooms $20; Creme brulee $7*

AUTOMATIC SLIMS D Cajun

(A1) 733 Washington St. (Bank & Bethune) 212/645-8660

F 5 / S 5 / A 6 / $19 Cash only

Was "Automatic Slim" a character in a grateful Dead song? We can't recall, but his food has as much soul as Jerry Garcia's voice and won't produce love handles. Plain bar decor and white brick walls, provide a "great place to hang out." Serves grilled Southern/Cajun cuisine with an emphasis on seafood and chicken. Unpretentious blues music, beer, and the ceiling fan complete the experience.

SPEC: *Yellow-tail tuna tacos w/salsa fresca (2) $5; Grilled chicken salad w/garden fresh vegetables $7; Shrimp Po'Boy $7.50; Slim's Own smoked baby back ribs $12*

BAR AND BOOKS D American

(A2) 636 Hudson St. (Horatio & Jane) 212/229-2642

See review on page 120.

BAR PITTI LD Italian

(B2) 268 6th Ave. (Houston & Bleecker) 212/982-3300

F 7 / S 6 / A 6 / $19 Cash only **TO**

Top 10 $0-20
Inexpensive

This very casual trattoria offers a bright and comfortable atmosphere. Its modest, albeit varied menu "does Northern Italian cuisines proud." Most come for the food and the social scene, so they don't seem to mind the slow service. Does the fact that they're "dog friendly on terrace" help?

SPEC: *Bean salad w/tuna & onions $5.50; Flat large noodle pasta w/smoked bacon $9.50; Torta della nonna $4.50*

Rosanna Scotto
TV news reporter

"When I think about great food and warm hospitality, naturally **Fresco**, my family's restaurant comes to mind. But as far as others are concerned, **Nobu** has put a wonderful spin on Japanese cooking. And it's always packed with a stylish crowd and some models."

0	1	2	3	4	5	6	7	8	9	10
disappointing		fair		good		very good		excellent		perfect

BAR SIX   LD   French

(B2) 502 6th Ave. (12th & 13th) 212/645-2439 Fax: 691-1392

F 6 / S 6 / A 6 / $24   MC V AE   **TO**

Staff motto is "no attitude," a welcome change. Brings in a unique crowd, "the suits meet the creatives," which might have something to do with offering late night cigars and micro-brewed beers. "Weird," pronounce some diners. We call the vibe "French-Moroccan indifference." Which explains why some "feel we're in Europe."

SPEC: *Harira (traditional Moroccan soup) $5.50; Moutabelle, hummus, white bean brandade w/pita bread $6.50; Monkfish bouillabaisse $16; Bisteeya (Moroccan chicken pie) $13.75*

BENNY'S BURRITO'S   LD   Mexican

(A2) 113 Greenwich Ave. (Jane) 212/727-0584 Fax: 242-3163

F 6 / S 5 / A 5 / $13   Cash only   **TO/D**

"Some of the best Mexican in town." A favorite for cheap, healthy, hearty Cal-Mex fare. "Blah atmosphere," but get a corner window for great street watching. Casual clientele, funky 70s kitsch decor and "huge" portions bring a lively crowd to both East and West Village locations.

SPEC: *Gazpacho $2; Grilled shrimp burrito $9.50; Vegetable burrito $6.25; Taco Dolores $5; Super enchilada $7.75*

The Black Sheep

BLACK SHEEP, THE   D   Amer/Continental

(A1) 344 W. 11th St. (Washington) 212/242-0010

F 7 / S 7 / A 7 / $29   MC V AE   **TO**

Named after the owner's black dog, this spot is both homey and "very romantic," "especially in winter." Diners may choose hearty French or Italian country dishes from the 5-course meal or regular a la carte format. And the recent addition of a piano, makes for an even nicer evening out.

SPEC: *Crudite aioli $5; Terrine of orange duck $8; Shoulder of pork $19; Crispy confit of duck leg $21; Double chocolate truffle cake $6*

BONDINI'S   LD   Italian

(A3) 62 W. 9th St. (5th & 6th) 212/777-0670

F 6 / S 6 / A 7 / $33   MC V D AE DIS   **TO/D**

In a dramatically lit, polished space, reminiscent of a vintage supper club, dine on consistently flavorful, satisfying and contemporary dishes in "this not well-known" ristorante. The owner's mother makes her valuable contributions: homemade parmesan, gnocchi and grappa. **Closed: Sunday**

SPEC: *Grilled calamari $8; Linguine w/clams, shrimps & calamari $16; Lobster risotto $24; Tangerine sorbet $6*

BURRITO LOCO
LD   **Mexican**

(B2) 166 W. 4th St. (6th & 7th) 212/675-1977

F 5 / S 5 / A 6 / $11   MC V D AE   **TO/D**

"Authentic Mexican" fare including the standards and some "unique dishes are offered here." Top this off with a festive environment and margarita parties daily, and you've got a real south of the border adventure, where a good time is had by all.

SPEC: *Ceviche $4.95; Quesadillas $5.95; Enchiladas verdes $9.95; Tamales rancheros $9.95; Burrito poblano $7.95*

BURRITOVILLE
LD   **Tex-Mex**

(A2) 148 W. 4th St. (6th & 7th) 212/674-7959 Fax: 475-9726

F 5 / S 5 / A 4 / $12   Cash only   **TO/D**

You can order it, but do you know how to eat it? Don't worry, the menu of this far-flung chain of reasonably priced, above average Tex-Mex restaurants, will instruct you, as well as giving you the legend of the mythical town of Burritoville. It may be full of beans, but all's forgiven after you take your first bite. And we're not the only ones who think so: "Great deal—cheap and super salsa."

SPEC: *Tijuana tacos $1.50-$3.50; Border burrito $3.95; Holy mole burrito $5.25; Mamacita's fajitas $8.95*

PETER MAUSS/ ESTO

C3

C 3
LD   **American**

(A3) 103 Waverly Pl. (MacDougal) 212/254-1200 Fax: 979-8373

F 6 / S 5 / A 5 / $25   MC V D AE   **TO**

Ever have a secret you just couldn't wait to tell everyone? Get the kitty litter, 'cause we're letting the cat out of the bag. C 3, connected to the landmark Washington Square Hotel, is "quaint, romantic, and delicious," with an innovative menu and a brownie of such merit it should be promoted to Scout. C 3 is both a finder and a keeper.

SPEC: *Apple & poached pear salad $5.50; Roasted chicken $11.95; Mom's meatloaf $9; Wild mushroom ravioli $11.75*

CACTUS CAFE
LD   **Tex-Mex**

1 W. 3rd St. (B'way) 212/674-5991

F 4 / S 4 / A 5 / $17   MC V AE   **TO/D**

Easy-going Tex-Mex in the left ventricle of NYU. Convenient for lower Broadway shoppers and browsers and those grabbing a bite before catching the show at the Bottom Line. Reasonably priced food that some call "mediocre," and two buck frozen margaritas at Happy Hour can't be beat for Friday night fun.

SPEC: *Chicken fingers $5.25; Chalupas $4.95; Cactus burrito $8.50; Enchiladas Suizas $9.95; Banana cream pie $3.50*

0	1	2	3	4	5	6	7	8	9	10
disappointing		fair		good		very good		excellent		perfect

Cafe de Bruxelles

CAFE DE BRUXELLES   LD   Continental

(A2) 118 Greenwich Ave. (8th Ave.)   *212/206-1830*

F 7 / S 6 / A 7 / $27   MC V AE   **TO**

This classy French-Belgian bistro is, surprisingly, best known for its french fries (served with mayo, of course), and its selection of Belgian specialty beers. Located in an historic landmark building, it boasts one of the few remaining "great" zinc bars. Subdued European lighting, along with a decor that includes lace curtains and dark green tablecloths. Some complain about "spotty" service, but even so, it makes for a very pleasurable dining experience.

SPEC: *Carbonade Flamande $15.50; Waterzoo do Poissons on Poulet (Belgian dish)$13.50 ($16.50 w/seafood)*

CAFE ESPAÑOL   LD   Spanish

(B3) 172 Bleecker St. (MacDougal & Sullivan) 212/505-0657

F 7 / S 6 / A 6 / $25   MC V D AE DIS   **TO/D**

This long-time Bleecker Street regular might look a little drab on the outside, but don't let that deter you. "It's been constantly good for the past 15 years." The Spanish/Mexican menu, including plentiful tapas and potent sangria and margaritas, has a faithful following, so they must be doing something right.

SPEC: *Octopus $5.75; Chalupas $4.50; Twin lobsters $17.95; Paella Valenciana $14.50; Flan $2.75*

CAFE LOUP   LD   French

(A2) 105 W. 13th St. (6th & 7th) 212/255-4746

F 7 / S 6 / A 7 / $29   MC V D AE DIS

"Wonderful! Wonderful! Wonderful!" An old Village standard serving reliable country French dishes. Popular for brunch or a more romantic meal. The staff is "lovely." The music is "jazzy," the room dark and atmospheric. Good for that special date.

SPEC: *Pommes frites $4.50; Smoked brook trout fillet $7; Cassoulet $18; Poulard roti a L'estragon $14.50*

CAFFE PANE E CIOCCOLATO   BLD   Italian

(A3) 10 Waverly Pl. (Mercer) 212/473-3944

F 6 / S 6 / A 10 / $18   Cash only   **TO**

Sometimes you feel like you just want to stop the world and get off. But instead of doing that, simply stop by this charming cafe and they'll take care of you. They'll feed you (very reasonably), and provide a peaceful, satisfying atmosphere while they're at it. A great spot in the Village just to "hang out."

SPEC: *Focaccia $5.50-$6; Osso buco $9.75; Antipasto freddo sandwich $6; Pecan tart w/cream $3.50; Kahlua mocha mousse pie 3.50*

CAFFE REGGIO — BLD — Italian

(B3) 119 MacDougal St. (W. 3rd) 212/475-9557

F 5 / S 4 / A 6 / $12   Cash only

Way, way, way before the "great coffee craze," there was Caffe Reggio which, since 1927, has been supplying the "numerous perks" of coffee houses. Art—paintings, sculptures, stained glass, antiques—that is packed into this truly European style cafe "make you feel like you're in Italy." A great spot to linger over an espresso, and catch up on the news of the day.

SPEC: *Reggio's focaccia $3.50; Manicotta alla Romana $3.50; Ravioli alla vodka $4.95; Pastries from $2.50-$3.50*

CALIENTE CAB CO. — LD — Mexican

(A3) 61 7th Ave. (Bleecker) 212/243-8517
(B2) 21 Waverly Pl. (B'way & Univ. Pl.) 212/529-1500

F 4 / S 6 / A 6 / $19   MC V   **TO**

Party down, dudes! Mexican style. Big portions of Tex-Mex cuisine are the order of the day, but the focus here is really on fun. The potent flavor-varied margaritas take care of that. "Shooter girls" cruise the restaurant with shot glasses and tequila in their holsters, looking for takers—and they don't have to look far. D.J.s and big screen TVs, also add to the festive atmosphere.

SPEC: *Buffalo chips $3.50; Mission burrito $8.95; Enchiladas La Banderas $11.95*

Caribe

CARIBE — LD — Caribbean

(B1) 117 Perry St. (Greenwich & Hudson) 212/255-9191

F 6 / S 5 / A 5 / $17   MC V   **TO**

Hot and spicy music, hot and spicy people. Caribe offers the "best" in West Indian, Caribbean and Spanish cuisine, as well as bringing to life the fun-loving, good-natured characteristics of the areas. The "dark room with lots of plants" makes you feel like you're in the the jungle. The prices are right. Come, to the Caribbean.

SPEC: *Seviche, Peruvian style $3.95; Conch salad $3.95; Salt fish (cod) $8.95; Frog legs $7.95; Fried bananas & rum $3.95*

CEDAR TAVERN — LD — American

(A3) 82 University Pl. (11th & 12th) 212/243-9355

F 5 / S 6 / A 7 / $19   MC V D AE DIS   **TO**

If it was good enough for Jackson Pollock and the Beat poets, it's good enough for us. The "spectacular" hand-carved ornate cherry-wood bar is over 130 years old, only one little detail that entrances us enough to make us want to stick around, even if the food is only average. Still, the burger rates high with the "perfect crowd." You can cut the history and the atmosphere with a knife, but if you crave a breath of fresh air, take yourself up to the roof garden.

SPEC: *Escargots $5.25; "Thriller" chicken wings $5.50; Roast prime ribs of beef $13.50; Breast of chicken sautéed w/garlic & herbs $9.50*

0	1	2	3	4	5	6	7	8	9	10
disappointing		fair		good		very good		excellent		perfect

CENT' ANNI RESTAURANT — LD — Italian

(B2) 50 Carmine St. (6th & 7th) 212/989-9494

F 7 / S 7 / A 6 / $28   MC V AE

Freshly imported ingredients form a diverse and authentically Florentine menu. And, if you're stuck for choices, "the owner will order for you." A quiet, quaint atmosphere permeates this West Village storefront. Elegant impressionistic paintings and dated photographs add to the intimate setting.

SPEC: *Insalata di pesce $9; Capellin con aragosta $16; Rabbit w/white wine, onions, carrots & tomatoes $15; Porterhouse for 2 $45*

CHARLIE MOM — LD — Chinese

(A2) 464 6th Ave. (11th & 12th) 212/807-8585 Fax: 807-8099
(B2) 47-49 7th Ave. S. (Bleecker & Morton) 212/255-2848

F 4 / S 8 / A 3 / $16   MC V AE   **TO/D**

"Unsmiling waiters, mediocre food," or "good neighborhood place?" Take your choice. The menu is huge—offering Szechuan, Hunan and Cantonese specialties. And at least one dish "the soft shell crabs in season," receives high praise.

SPEC: *Crab claws stuffed w/shrimp $4.75; Sautéed baby bok choy $6.95; Steak kew w/lobster sauce $11.95; Almond suan-pien $9.95*

Chez Jacqueline

CHEZ JACQUELINE — D — French

(B2) 72 MacDougal St. (Houston) 212/505-0727

F 7 / S 7 / A 7 / $29   MC V AE

If you can't spend a year in Provence, spend an evening in this homey, attractive restaurant. It's a genuine French country experience and, thankfully, you won't need your passport. "Friendly, relaxed, consistent," "a fabulous find." Warm weather permits sidewalk dining. During the week no lunch, but they do serve brunch on the weekend.

SPEC: *Fish soup $6.50; Escargots au pastis $7.50; Seafood casserole $19.50; Veal kidneys $14.50*

CHEZ MA TANTE CAFE — D — French

(A2) 189 West 10th St. 212/620-0223 Fax 212/242-4127

F 6 / S 6 / A 4 / $22   MC V D AE DIS   **TO**

This bistro serves a variety of grilled meat specialties, French soups and a prix-fixe brunch. Though the restaurant itself is not highly atmospheric, its location on a bustling corner, tables set close together, and summers when the doors open to the outside, transforms it into an intimate night spot.

SPEC: *Escargots de Bourgogne $5.95; Canard aux Cerises $14.95; Poulet ma tante $13.95; Le Roti de veau aux Asperges $17.95; Profiterole aux deux chocolats $5.95; Tarte tain $5.95*

CHUMLEY'S   D   American

(B2) 86 Bedford St. (Barrow) 212/675-4449

F 5 / S 5 / A 6 / $21   Cash only   **TO**

If you're looking for a sign, forget it. In existence since 1923, Chumley's has somehow survived an inconspicuous, easy-to-miss location. It "maintains its atmosphere at all costs," making it a "great hangout." But some think "they haven't cleaned it since Prohibition." The food may be only adequate, but you haven't really experienced New York unless you visit.

SPEC: *Spicy wings $6; Caesar salad $6; Free range chicken $12;Roasted duck $13; Burger w/fries $7.50*

CORNELIA STREET CAFE   BLD   Mediterranean

(B2) 29 Cornelia St. (West 4th) 212/989-9319

F 6 / S 6 / A 6 / $25   MC V D AE

This quintessential bistro/cafe combines a European feel with an artistic twist—gourmet dishes served on beautiful hand-painted tables. "Relaxed, friendly, no hype," with a highlight being a "romantic brunch." At night, in the cabaret downstairs, you might find a poetry reading or an experimental jazz performance. Go for dinner, stay for the show.

SPEC: *All day breakfast special $5.50; Grilled eggplant salad $6; Prince Edward Island mussels $7.50; Grilled black angus burger $9; Double rib pork chop $15*

CORNER BISTRO   LD   American

(A2) 331 W. 4th St. (Jane St. & 8th Ave.) 212/241-9502

F 7 / S 5 / A 6 / $13   Cash only   **TO**

In this landmark Village saloon you can cut the history with a knife... but the Bistro burger is just way too big for that. Voted "one of the best burgers in the city," it might "take forever to get one. But the beer and Smokin' Jaxx on the jukebox make up for it." A great place for making new friends.

SPEC: *Hamburger $3.75; Chili $3.75; Breast of chicken sandwich $4.25*

COTTONWOOD CAFE   LD   Southern

(A2) 415 Bleecker St. (11th & Bank) 212/924-6271

F 5 / S 4 / A 5 / $17   MC V D   **TO**

Looking for Texas flair? Look no further. Big movie posters of obscure westerns line the walls. Giant cacti fill the front windows. The portions are Texas-size, and the wait staff have smiles almost as big as the Lone Star state itself. Live music nightly with a BIG sound. Why aren't we surprised?

SPEC: *Fried stuffed jalapeños $5.50; Catfish fingers $5.50; BBQ combo (ribs & chicken) $12.75; Grilled BBQ pork chops $9.75*

COWGIRL HALL OF FAME   LD   Tex-Mex

(A1) 519 Hudson St. (West 10th) 212/633-1133   Fax: 633-1892

F 6 / S 6 / A 6 / $22   AE   **TO**

The staff here uses "Honey," more often as an endearment than as a condiment. It's as delightfully country as you can 'git' in The Big Apple. Authentic cowgirl artifacts, a country general store and "fine chuckwagon cuisine," like Frito pie (a Frito bag split open and covered with chili), that'll make you slap yer grandma. "Great place for kids," though some find it a little "hokey" for their tastes.

SPEC: *Frito pie $4.25; Chicken fried chicken $9.95; Smoked spare ribs $11.95; BBQ beef on a bun $7.95; Mashed potatoes $1.65; Ice cream baked potato $4.25*

0	1	2	3	4	5	6	7	8	9	10
disappointing		fair		good		very good		excellent		perfect

CUCINA DELLA FONTANA **LD** Italian

(B2) 368 Bleecker St. (Charles St.) 212/242-0636

F 4 / S 4 / A 6 / $17 MC V **TO**

Dining here is like eating in an "enclosed winter garden." Wrought iron furniture, foliage and a working fountain all help create this effect. The food is "inexpensive and good," Northern Italian fare. Downstairs there's a room offering nightly cabaret, adding a quirky twist to this simple elegance.

SPEC: *Baked stuffed clams $5.95; Stuffed mushroom caps $4.95; Chicken scarpariello $8.95; Brook trout $9.95*

CUCINA STAGIONALE **LD** Italian

(B2) 275 Bleecker St. (6th & 7th) 212/924-2707

F 7 / S 6 / A 6 / $15 Cash only **TO**

"An Italian mother's dining room—you're at home here." "Closer quarters you won't find," but the "lovely, delightful and wonderful food," more than makes up for it. Though the regular menu offers a wide choice of possibilities, we suggest going with the daily specials. If you prefer wine with your meal, you'll have to bring it yourself.

SPEC: *Caesar salad $4.95; Seafood antipasto $6.95; Brook trout $9.95; Shrimp marinara $9.95*

DA SILVANO **LD** Italian

(B2) 260 6th Ave. (Houston & Bleecker) 212/982-0090

F 7 / S 6 / A 6 / $27 MC V AE

The staff here speaks in hushed tones about their "quality clientele," including editors, models and actors. But a colorful display of their best antipasti suggests their true pride lies in the kitchen's "real Tuscan" cuisine creations. The large, comfortable outdoor cafe is situated perfectly for those who can't decide on dinner in SoHo or the West Village.

SPEC: *Grilled sausage w/broccoli rabe $9.50; Panzanella $6.50; Ossobuco alla Milanese $19.50; Ravioli bella Firenze $12.50*

DERBY, THE **D** American

(B2) 109 MacDougal St. (Minetta Lane) 212/475-0520

F 6 / S 7 / A 6 / $29 MC V AE **TO**

Steak and seafood is cooked to your specifications on a charcoal grill in the middle of this cozy "old standby." Since 1917, a family owned and operated grocery store. Today you can still find the same tile floor, tin ceilings and family who started it all.

SPEC: *French onion soup $4; Chopped chicken livers $4; Beef tips over homemade noodles $10.95; Double steak (for two)*

DIX ET SEPT **D** French

(A2) 181 W. 10th St. (7th Ave. S.) 212/645-8023

F 7 / S 6 / A 7 / $31 MC V D AE **TO**

This duplex Parisian bistro is charming, casual and extremely pleasant to dine in. "It's like being in Paris, but with very nice waiters." Photos taken by the 1920s photographer, Brasaie, hang on the wall, alongside new work from artists Fran Slade and Colin Ruffell. The new art is for sale, the old is not.

SPEC: *Onion soup $6; Coquille St. Jacques niçoise $18; Bouillabaisse $23; Cous cous de mer $19.50; Creme brulee $6*

DOJO   LD   Japanese

(B3) 14 W. 4th St.   (Mercer B'way)   212/505-8934

F 4 / S 6 / A 3 / $13   Cash only   TO

The decor and the menu combinations may be a bit confusing, but this Japanese-American restaurant is well known in the Washington Square area as a place to get "cheap, but delicious and healthy" eats. Some find it "dirty," but the reaction of most is, "What a surprise such a dump could have such great food."
SPEC: *Soy burgers $1.95-$2.95; Chicken or beef curry $5.95; Shrimp or scallop curry $6.25; Lemon meringue pie $3.25*

E.J.'S LUNCHEONETTE   BLD   Diner

(A2) 432 6th Ave.   (9th & 10th)   212/473-5555

See review on page 228.

EDDIE'S   LD   American

(A3) 14 Waverly Pl.   (Mercer & Washington Sq.)   212/420-0919

F 5 / S 6 / A 5 / $12   Cash only   TO

An odd mix of American, Oriental, Mexican and health food in "large portions" is on the menu in this neighborhood pub. "A lot of food, good and cheap." But just in case you're not quite filled up, amble over to the bar where you can munch on free popcorn made before your eyes. **Closed: Sunday**
SPEC: *Tofu salad $3.85; Chili $5.05; California burritos $3.90-$5.70; Tuna steak burgers $4-$5.95; Fried tofu fajitas $5.30; Carrot cake $2*

EL CHARRO ESPANOL   LD   Spanish

(A2) 4 Charles St.   (7th & Greenwich)   212/242-9547

F 6 / S 7 / A 6 / $29   MC V AE DIS   TO

This dark, romantic Mediterranean spot, a Village institution for 70 years, serves a variety of popular Spanish dishes. The portions are so large families could live for days off a single serving of paella.
SPEC: *Nachos supreme $6; Fajitas $15.75; Chicken mole poblano $12.50; Lamb chops w/onion & red peppers $18.75; Pork chops $12.50*

EL FARO   LD   Spanish

(A1) 823 Greenwich St.   (Horatio)   212/929-8210   Fax: 929-8295

F 7 / S 6 / A 5 / $31   MC V D AE DIS   TO

Ample and delicious portions of authentic, "consistently good," Spanish cuisine. Couples return after 25 years to the same red booth they shared on their first date to find the food, unpretentious decor, and even the waiter, virtually unchanged. Definite good vibes here.
SPEC: *Gazpacho $3.25; Breast of chicken w/bechamel cream $16; Mariscada w/green sauce $17; Natilla (vanilla custard) $3.75; Guave w/cream cheese $3.75*

ELEPHANT & CASTLE   BLD   American

(A2) 68 Greenwich St.   (7th Ave. S. & W. 11th)   212/243-1400

F 6 / S 6 / A 5 / $17   MC V AE   TO

Downtown New Yorkers know E&C as a consistently good spot for breakfast, lunch or dinner. "The price is right, and so's the food." "Great burgers and breakfast." The atmosphere is "comfortable," and there's almost always "service with a smile."
SPEC: *Elephantburger $7.75; Provencale omelette, zucchini, tomato, onions, pesto & parmesan $7; Grand Marnier dessert crepe $5.25*

0	1	2	3	4	5	6	7	8	9	10
disappointing		fair		good		very good		excellent		perfect

FANNIE'S OYSTER BAR   D   Cajun

(A1) 765 Washington St. (W. 12th & Bethune)   212/255-5101

F 7 / S 7 / A 7 / $24   Cash only   **TO**

Dark, eclectic and homey, especially if you've got a yearning for the Big Easy. Solid Louisiana cooking with a hip, yet welcoming atmosphere. Live music downstairs filters up nicely through the restaurant, into the dining room. Fresh flowers are a nice touch, as is the relaxed and "laid back" staff. You'll be back.

SPEC: *Drinks: Dixie Voodoo $4.50; Femme Creole $5; Fannie's Lemonade $6*

FLORENT   BLD   French

(A1) 69 Gansvoort St. (Wash. & Greenwich)   212/989-5779

F 6 / S 6 / A 6 / $25   Cash only   **TO**

This 24-hour, "fun and funky" retro diner lurking in the smelly meat packing district is actually a "nice French restaurant." No kidding. The crowd is "downtown cool," diverse, especially after the witching hour, and the food is reliable—though nothing extraordinary—around the clock.

FLYING BURRITO BROTHERS   LD   Mexican

(B2) 165 W. 4th St. (6th & 7th)   212/691-3663

F 6 / S 8 / A 6 / $16   Cash only   **TO/D**

Many a flea market was visited to decorate this healthy Cal-Mex restaurant offering pleasure to the palate as well as to the eye. A rambunctious display of '50s lamps, airplanes and a black velvet portrait of Elvis accompany a defiant crowd. Try one too many of the 24 tequilas available and the burritos may not be the only things flying.

SPEC: *Master quesadilla $5.95; Flying burrito $5.95; Flying fajitas $8.50; Vegetable special $5.95; Mother's chocolate mousse $3.75*

FRENCH ROAST   BLD   French

(A2) 458 6th Ave. (11th)   212/533-2233

F 6 / S 4 / A 6 / $24   AE   **TO**

Trying to figure out a cool place to go that's still open at 2am? French Roast a 24 hour full service Parisian cafe, might be the place. Breakfast, lunch, dinner, late night snack... it's all here and with that French feel minus the "attitude." Order your meal, and stay as long as you like. But keep in mind the "service can be so unaccommodating," you might think you're "in Paris."

SPEC: *French onion soup $4.50; Duck mousse pate $4.75; Roasted herb chicken $8.75; Steak frites $12.75; Chocolate deca-dense cake $4.95*

FRESCH   D   Italian

(B1) 143 Perry St. (Greenwich & Washington)   212/924-0546

F 5 / S 6 / A 5 / $23   AE   **TO**

Located on the fringe of the West Village, Fresch serves fresh grilled fish and pasta to smokers and non-smokers alike. It's decidedly "low key" and the space is decorated with a rotating exhibit of work from local artists, but otherwise is nondescript. If the weather allows, sit outside and enjoy the neighborhood instead.

SPEC: *Caesar salad $5.95; Seared brook trout $12.95; Spinach parpadelle $11.95; Tiramisu $4.95; Chocolate mousse $4.95*

FUDDRUCKERS   LD   American

(B2) 87 7th Ave. So. (Bleecker & Christopher) 212/255-9643
See review on page 185.

GOTHAM BAR & GRILL   LD   American

(A3) 12 East 12th St. (5th & University) 212/620-4020

F 8 / S 7 / A 8 / $50   MC V D AE

Muted elegance and unintrusive luxury. This sophisticated atmospheric restaurant is sure to draw you in. You know you're in a top restaurant without having to be hit over the head. The wine list is good enough to have won the "Wine Spectator Award of Excellence." Diners applaud the "creative, imaginative food," as "good as 3 stars in Paris," and marvel at the "tall towers of food that provide humor and a good bargain." Others feel "cuisine is not as good as people say."
SPEC: *Hot smoked salmon salad $14; Duck & foie gras terrine $14.50; Sauteed wild striped bass $17; Grilled lamb sausage $15.50*

GRANGE HALL, THE   LD   American

(B2) 50 Commerce St. (Barrow) 212/924-5246 Fax: 255-2117

F 7 / S 6 / A 7 / $29   AE   **TO**

With a huge W.P.A. inspired mural, mahogany details, and truly hip downtown crowd, believe it or not, this is a place your midwestern mother would love. Housed in a 1930s speakeasy, they serve "wonderful homestyle" American classics with '90s flair, and healthy preparation. The service is relaxed and gracious.
SPEC: *Yam fried potatoes $3.75; Half chicken $11.75; Cranberry glazed pork chops $12.75; Wild rice pudding $5*

GRAZIELLA RISTORANTE   D   Italian

(A2) 41 Greenwich Ave. (Charles & Perry) 212/243-9650

F 6 / S 6 / A 4 / $20   MC V AE   **TO**

A friendly, reasonably priced neighborhood find —"Great value, great food and service." A real family affair. Graziella, the owner's sister, makes all the pasta fresh daily, while her two brothers whip up meals that would be at home at a far more expensive restaurant. Even the waiter and waitress, originally from Chile, are brother and sister. No lunch, but brunch on weekends.
SPEC: *Panzanella $3.75; Gamberetti E Fagioli (sauté shrimp and white bean salad) $5.25; Tagliarini Contadina $7.95*

GROVE   D   American

(A2) 314 Bleecker St. (Grove) 212/675-9463

F 5 / S 5 / A 6 / $21   MC V D AE

"Three reasons to go: the garden, the garden, the garden." For a romantic fair weather feast, don't miss that garden, which puts the grove back into Grove street. In cold weather, the dining room fills up fast. So reservations are a must. The menu is understated, but proud, like any homestyle American with a French twist should be.
SPEC: *Rabbit terrine $6; Fried calamari $6; Sautéed breast of chicken $12; Hangar steak $14*

GUS' PLACE   LD   Greek

(A2) 149 Waverly Pl. (6th & Christopher) 212/645-8511

F 7 / S 7 / A 7 / $24   MC V D AE DIS

The charming, light decor is as inviting as a Grecian breeze off the Mediterranean. Feels more expensive than it is and Saturday night provides live Greek music and dancing. If you're dining and suddenly a wedding party shows up, relax. It's just the cast and audience of "Tony & Tina's Wedding," which uses Gus' as their "reception" hall.
SPEC: *Appetizer plate w/fish, lamb brochette, chicken liver $13; Marinated seafood $11; Warm grilled tuna salad $18*

0	1	2	3	4	5	6	7	8	9	10
disappointing		fair		good		very good		excellent		perfect

85

HARRY'S BURRITO JUNCTION   LD   Mexican

(B3) 230 Thompson St.   (West 4th & Bleecker)   212/260-5588
See review on page 230.

HOME   BLD   American

(B2) 20 Cornelia St. (Bleecker & West 4th) 212/243-9579
F 7 / S 7 / A 7 / $29   AE

Small as it is, Home has won blue ribbons all over the "county" for
everything from their pork chops to apple crumb pie. "Casual
atmosphere is a blessing in an often too pretentious restaurant city."
Quaint, friendly and romantic, grab a seat in the garden and plan to
stay awhile. In this case at least, there's ONE place like home.
SPEC: *Roasted chicken $14; Potato & sardine cake $8; Oyster Po boy
on zito bread $8; Blue cheese fondue $7*

JANE STREET SEAFOOD   D   Seafood

(A2) 31 8th Ave. (Jane) 212/242-0003
F 6 / S 6 / A 6 / $34   MC V D AE DIS   **TO**

For 15 years Kevin McCallion has been serving up honest, wholesome seafood in this landmark building. It "deserves its wondrous
reputation." "It's like a vacation at Martha's Vineyard." Stroll through
the doors and be transported to a comfortable New England seafood
shack. Slap on a bib while you're at it and have some terrific lobster.
SPEC: *Clams oreganato $7.25; Crispy rock shrimp $7.75; Sole
Portuguese $17.95; Strawberry rhubarb pie $3.95*

JOHN'S PIZZERIA   LD   Pizzeria

(B2) 278 Bleecker St. (6th & 7th) 212/243-1680
F 7 / S 5 / A 5 / $15   Cash only

"When the moon hits your eye..."John's has been named New York
City's best brick-oven pizza more times than...not. The line to get in
can be long and the service sometimes "stinks." But it's worth the
wait if you have a craving. Don't be shy, chat with a stranger. Then,
when you make your lunch date with them, split the calzone for a
pleasant surprise.
SPEC: *Margherita pizza $8.50 (sm); Pizza bianca (ricotta & moz-
zarella) $9.50 (sm); Additional toppings $1-$2.50*

KNICKERBOCKER BAR & GRILL   LD   American

(A3) 33 University Pl. (9th) 212/228-8490 Fax: 254-2381
F 5 / S 6 / A 6 / $28   MC V D AE DIS

What a New York steak house ought to be. Handsome, cozy, and
reasonably priced. They offer live jazz (Harry Connick, Jr. got his
start here), which rivals a concert series. Lunch and Sunday
brunch are a terrific deal. But one diner warns, "Great bar and
music: AVOID EATING."
SPEC: *Caviar pie $6.50; Grilled quail $7.50; T-Bone steak $23.75;
Roasted boneless chicken $13.75; Chocolate espresso cake $5.75*

LA BOHEME   D   French

(B3) 24 Minetta Lane (W. 3rd & Bleecker)   212/473-6447
F 7 / S 7 / A 7 / $31   AE

This friendly yet understated French bistro "is never a disappoint-
ment." It offers a combination of outstanding Provencal cuisine as
well as a surprising array of delicate and well-prepared pizzas. It's
a tender respite from the jarrings of urban life and....ssshhhh, the
prices are really reasonable. **Closed: Monday**
SPEC: *Pizzas $12-$13; Breast of chicken $15.75; Lambshank
w/couscous, spinach & rosemary sauce $16; Striped bass $16.50*

LA DOLCE VITA   LD   Italian

(A3) 54 W. 13th St.   212/807-0580

See review on page 51.

LA FOCACCIA   D   Italian

(A1) 51 Bank St. (W. 4th) 212/675-3754

F 7 / S 6 / A 7 / $27   MC V   **TO**

Tight quarters are made to feel open and airy due to the tasteful decor in this "beautiful space." There's a brick oven that doubles as a fireplace in winter, and the blue and white tiles on the tables, and the red brick tiled floors, give La Focaccia a kitcheny feel.
SPEC: *Cheese pie $10; Gnocchi $11.50; Grilled shrimps & calamari $15; Tagliata (sliced sirloin steak) $17.50*

LA PENTOLA PIZZA   LD   Italian

(A2) 133 W. 13th St. (6th & 7th) 212/741-3663

F 5 / S 5 / A 5 / $20   MC V D AE DIS

This "Crazy Sauce Pot" is the "new deal" at the formerly "New Deal" restaurant. A little like your better mall restaurants, with cartoon tomatoes helping create a fun family motif. There's a spacious garden and working fireplace for the more sophisticated crowd.
SPEC: *Clams possillipo $6.95; Chicken savoy $11.95; Shrimp Monaco $15.95; Chocolate amaretto cheesecake $4.50*

LA RIPAILLE   D   French

(A1) 605 Hudson St. (W. 12th & Bethune) 212/255-4406

F 7 / S 6 / A 7 / $28   MC V AE

Many restaurants position themselves as authentic French bistros. This one delivers. Outstanding cuisine in an unpretentious atmosphere. Where else can you dine on broccoli mousse under a 17th century tapestry with Madonna at the next table...? **Closed: Sunday**
SPEC: *Broccoli mousse $6; Cassollete of snails $7; Duck breast in apple cider & green apple sauce $18*

LE ZOO   D   French

(A2) 314 W. 11th St. (Greenwich) 212/620-0393

F 7 / S 7 / A 6 / $24   MC V AE

On most nights the line to get into this trendy, new hot spot spills out onto the street. The restaurant is cramped and "needs more room and more windows." But the food...ah, mais oui... The chef, Luc Dendievel, trained at Paris' famed Lucas Carton, creates haute cuisine at tres reasonable prices, while the staff ingeniously maintains the fine line between civility and chaos. **Closed: Monday**
SPEC: *Crispy sweetbread salad $7.50; Roasted monkfish $12.50; Almond blancmanger $4; Chocolate marquise w/pistachio sauce $4*

LES DEUX GAMINS   BLD   French

(A2) 170 Waverly Pl. (Grove) 212/807-7047 Fax: 627-9087

F 7 / S 6 / A 7 / $30   AE   **TO**

If you can't afford to fly to Paris, take the 7th Ave. subway to Christopher and have un petit dejeuner, dejeuner, ou diner here. The atmosphere is relaxed, the wait staff "friendly" and, at least in summer, scantily clad, and the food satisfying. Take a book, gaze out the window over the flowerbox, and let yourself drift off into a reverie about Hugues and that crazy night at Les Bains-Douche.
SPEC: *Frisee, bacon, poached egg, tomato $9; Onion soup $5; Mertuez frites $12.50; Hangar steak w/shallots $16*

0	1	2	3	4	5	6	7	8	9	10
disappointing		fair		good		very good		excellent		perfect

LIFE CAFE   D   Mexican

(A2) 1 Sheridan Sq. 212/929-7344
See review on page 67.

LION'S HEAD PUB, THE   D   American

(A2) 59 Christopher St. (7th Ave. S.) 212/929-0670

F 6 / S 7 / A 7 / $24   MC V D AE DIS   **TO**

This legendary literary haunt "with an engaging Bohemian atmosphere," has the requisite great burger, Shepherd's pie and tepid stout. But old lions can learn new tricks: the venison specials are worth writing home about. And please try the Prince Edward Island mussels.
SPEC: *French onion soup gratinee $4.50; Duck confit salad $7.95; Bangers & mash $8.95; Shepherd's pie $10.75*

MAGIC CARPET, THE   LD   Middle Eastern

(B2) 54 Carmine St. (Bedford & Bleecker) 212/627-9019

F 5 / S 5 / A 5 / $18   MC V D AE DIS   **TO/D**

With its salad bar and dessert rack, this is what a Moroccan diner might look like. The portions are generous, the ingredients are healthy, and the service "kind." Try the creamy humus, tender lamb kebobs and the cous cous, which, we're told, people come from as far away as L.I. to sample.
SPEC: *Falafel $3.95; Cous cous $9.75; Ouzi $9.50-$10.50; Baloza (orange and milk parafait pudding) $3.50*

MAPPAMONDO (DUE)   LD   Italian

(A1) 581 Hudson St. (Bank) 212/675-7474

F 6 / S 6 / A 5 / $20   Cash only   **TO/D**

"Good, cheap eats," consistent service and "decor"—which means lots of globes and maps, naturally. Simple and delicious, and slightly roomier than Mappamondo Uno, just down the street.
SPEC: *Sauté shrimp & white bean salad $5.50; Striped bass filet $11; Farfalle al Salmon $7.50*

MAPPAMONDO (UNO)   LD   Italian

(A1) 11 Abingdon Square (8th Ave.) 212/675-3100
See review above.

MARUMI   LD   Japanese

(B3) 546 LaGuardia (Bleecker & W. 3rd) 212/979-7055

F 5 / S 6 / A 6 / $20   MC V AE   **TO**

Meaning "round" and signifying harmony, this tiny Japanese restaurant in the heart of the NYU campus isn't a secret any longer. They do a beehive of a lunch business due to their quick service and reasonable prices. The same can be said for dinner, but at a slower pace. **Closed: Sunday**
SPEC: *Shrimp tempura roll $5; Avocado & tuna salad $6.50; Teriyaki $8.75; Eel kabayaki $9.50*

MARYLOU'S   D   Continental

(A3) 21 W. 9th St. (University and 6th) 212/533-0012

F 7 / S 8 / A 8 / $29   MC V D AE DIS

This classy, understated restaurant has 4 rooms with fireplaces. Unfortunately, there's "no scenery or view," but diners agree Marylou's "can't have it all." What this celebrity favorite does have is a "friendly, comfortable atmosphere, "extensive specials, a healthy menu and the hospitality of the Baratta family, who own it.
SPEC: *Pasta fagiola $5.95; Mussels ariniece $6.95; Grilled swordfish steak $19.95; Roast port w/apples & calvados sauce $17.95*

MARYS RESTAURANT　　D　　American

(B2) 42 Bedford St. (Leroy) 212/741-3387

F 6 / S 6 / A 5 / $25　　AE　　**TO**

The decor is faded elegance, and the casual, convivial atmosphere has been described as a downtown Lutece. This "hidden treasure" has been a restaurant since 1909. Food and service are great, but go there for the "Cosmopolitan" and "campy" feel...really.

SPEC: *Steamed mussels Madrilene $6.50; Roasted pork loin w/shallot-sage jus $12.95; Chocolate raspberry tarte $5.50; Creme brulee $5.50*

MCBELL'S　　LD　　Continental

(B2) 359 6th Ave. (W. 4th & Washington Pl.) 212/675-6260

F 6 / S 7 / A 6 / $20　　Cash only　　**TO/D**

McDonalds and Taco Bell merged? Not quite. Formerly an old sailor's bar and the original Jack & Charlie's "21" Club, McBell's has been around since 1963—sufficient time to take on a few personalities. Enjoy quiet conversation in the back dining room (voted most romantic in '92) with skylight, teardrop lamps and brick walls. Or try the traditional pub dining front and center.

SPEC: *Hamburgers $6.50; Shrimp-avocado salad $11.25; Chicken pot pie $11.75; Steak & kidney pie $11.75*

MI COCINA RESTAURANT　　D　　Mexican

(A1) 57 Jane St. (Hudson) 212/627-8273 Fax: 212/627-0174

F 7 / S 5 / A 6 / $20　　MC V D AE

Kick-ya-in-the-pants "fabulous nouveau" Mexican cuisine is always available at this sometimes noisy restaurant. The decor is rather bland, but the regional specials are definitely not. Try something hot..g'head.

SPEC: *Enchilada de mole poblano $13.95; Carne asada a la tampiquena $16.95; Pechuga con rajas a la crema $13.95*

MINETTA TAVERN　　LD　　Italian

(B3) 113 MacDougal St. (Minetta Lane & Bleecker) 212/475-3850

F 5 / S 6 / A 6 / $25　　MC V D AE DIS

Since 1937, this downtown landmark has been a caricature gallery for the immortal and mortal of Greenwich Village. A slice of history in every nook and cranny. Minetta is rather informal, but their prices aren't. Though not through the roof, they might surprise you. Village charm doesn't always come cheap.

SPEC: *Sautéed shrimp, cannellini beans $7; Almond-fried calamari $7; Gorgonzola filled agnolotti w/walnut sauce $11; Grilled veal chop $19.50*

MITALI WEST　　LD　　Indian

(B2) 296 Bleecker St. (7th Ave. S.) 212/989-1367
See review on page 68.

MOUSTACHE　　LD　　Middle Eastern

(B2) 90 Bedford St. (Barrow & Grove) 212/229-2200 Fax: 647-9898

F 7 / S 6 / A 6 / $20　　Cash only　　**TO/D**

Top 10 $0-20

Inexpensive

Highly civilized but really small, this is a self-proclaimed "slow food establishment." Quick (but not hasty) and great (no, not just good) Middle-Eastern food. You can trust this lively place for fantastic falafel, fresh baked pita and...are you ready?... "yummy" pitza (try it). **Closed: Monday**

SPEC: *Falafel $4.50; Chicken pitza $9; Ouzi $12; Basboussa (Egyptian cake) $2; Loomi (middle-eastern citrus drink) $1.50*

0	1	2	3	4	5	6	7	8	9	10
disappointing		fair		good		very good		excellent		perfect

NADINE'S   LD   American

(A1) 99 Bank St. (Greenwich St.) 212/924-3165

F 7 / S 7 / A 7 / $27   MC V D AE   **TO**

Nadine's has been called "the living room of the Village." The
large dining room looks romantic, but quiet conversation can be
difficult on busy nights. "More fun and friendly than purely good,"
the cuisine is American eclectic, with a nod to our great
Southland.
SPEC: *Black bean pancakes $6.50; Sesame crusted yellowfin tuna on
wasabi mashed potato in soy & papaya glaze $17*

9 Jones Street

9 JONES STREET   D   American

(B2) 9 Jones St. (Bleecker & W. 4th) 212/989-1220

F 7 / S 7 / A 7 / $31   MC V D AE DIS   **TO**

"Formerly my secret, now everyone knows," sadly proclaims one
diner. Well, not quite everyone, but now... Live jazz on Mondays.
Wine tastings on Tuesdays. Sunday brunch that tickles your taste
buds at a reasonable price. Combine all this with a bright, warm
atmosphere and sincere service and you've got a restaurant that
seems to really care about its customers.
SPEC: *Jones Caesar $6.75; Salmon tartare $8.75; Newport Steak
$19.75; Chicken w/cavattelli, escarole & roasted tomato sauce
$15.75*

NINE MUSES CAFE   LD   Greek

(A1) 569 Hudson St. (W.11th) 212/671-0009

F 6 / S 4 / A 5 / $26   MC V D AE DIS   **TO**

A lovely, airy neighborhood hang-out that specializes in seafood.
Let the owner, Nick, guide you through the menu and tell tales
about how he learned to cook years ago in Greece. He loves food
and is happy to explain preparations to patrons. Try for a table near
the window for a great view of the neighborhood.
SPEC: *Shrimp saganaki $8.95; Souvlakia $5.25; Grilled swordfish
$5.95; Striped bass $13.95; Lamb kebab $13.95; Galaktobouriko
$3.25*

OLIVE TREE CAFE   LD   Middle Eastern

(B3) 117 MacDougal St. (W. 3rd & Bleecker) 212/254-3480

F 5 / S 5 / A 5 / $18   MC V AE   **TO**

A restaurant for the seriously broke. The good, cheap food makes
up for "the dopey service." If you have nothing else to do, you can
sit for hours watching Chaplin movies replayed on the big screen,
or playing tic-tac-toe on the slate table-tops.
SPEC: *Borscht $3.95; Schwarma (lamb flank marinated & barbe-
cued, w/rice and vegetables) $8.50; Babaganush $2.95*

One If By Land, Two if By Sea

| **ONE IF BY LAND, TWO IF BY SEA** | **D** | **American** |

Top **10** $36-55

Expensive

(B2) 17 Barrow St. (7th Ave. & W. 4th) 212/228-0822

F 9 / S 8 / A 9 / $54　　MC V D AE

A proven 23 year tradition of excellence accompanies the reputation of this lovely restaurant. It's located in 18th century carriage house once owned by Aaron Burr. Four working fireplaces, graciously appointed dining rooms, fresh flowers—nothing is overlooked including a "great piano player." The cuisine is heavenly and...psst...after midnight the drink prices at the bar make it an affordable treat.
SPEC: *Warm lobster medallions $15; Salmon fillet w/crispy skin, black truffle potato pureé $30; Beef Wellington $35; Bittersweet chocolate mousse torte $7.50*

| **ORBIT** | **D** | **Continental** |

(B2) 46 Bedford St. (7th Ave. So.) 212/463-8717

F 7 / S 7 / A 7 / $28　　MC V AE

Eclectic, lively and fun, with a brilliant (and operational) mosaic fronted fireplace. A mahogany bar overlooks the narrow table space which is cozy in winter and downright airy in summer. Spanish-American-Italian cuisine—okay, so they're indecisive. The clientele is as diverse as the menu. There's "a bustling bar scene," and it's "gay-friendly."
SPEC: *Fried green plantains $5.95; Paella Valenciana $14.95; Orbit burger $8.95; Pasta putanesca $12.95; Flaming queen (bread pudding)*

| **OSSO BUCO** | **LD** | **Italian** |

(A3) 88 University Pl. (11th & 12th) 212/645-4525

F 6 / S 6 / A 5 / $25　　MC V D AE DIS　　**TO/D**

The upscale decoration reflects a modern yet classy establishment. But don't let its looks fool you. This is a family-style restaurant, with tables that seat up to 10 and food platters that serve several. The food is standard Italian fare, but some echo the comment: "Chef Boyardee could do better."
SPEC: *Vongole al forno (baked clams) $9.25; Fried calamari $15.25; Osso buco $22; Veal cutlet parmigiana $16.50*

| **PARIS COMMUNE, THE** | **LD** | **French** |

(B2) 411 Bleecker St. (Bank & W.11th) 212/929-0509 Fax: 989-4489

F 6 / S 6 / A 6 / $24　　MC V D DIS

Commonly known as "the brunch place" in the Village, The Paris Commune, gay owned and operated since WWII, boasts a mixed crowd in an intimate setting. Cuddle up to the fireplace with a new flame in this old New York hot spot, equipped with brick walls and wooden floors. And when in Paris order, what else? French toast, a favorite.
SPEC: *Onion soup $4; Homemade pate (pork & veal) $4.50; Chicken Basque style $12; Grilled leg of lamb w/onion marmalade $16; Chocolate ganache $5; Fruit tart $5*

0	1	2	3	4	5	6	7	8	9	10
disappointing		fair		good		very good		excellent		perfect

PINK TEA CUP, THE · BLD · Southern

(B2) 42 Grove St. (Bedford & Bleecker) 212/807-6755

F 6 / S 6 / A 6 / $17 · Cash only · **TO**

The smell of fresh fried chicken, apple dumplings, or Big Bad John barbecue sandwiches wafting down tree-lined Grove street originates from this kitchen. The biscuits—and the Southern luncheonette itself—are warm and fresh. Known for reliable home-baked food and "kooky fun." Bring your own booze, appetite, and possibly Alka Seltzer, but you won't break the bank for the meal.

SPEC: *Fried chicken $10.95; Ham hocks $10.50; Beef tips over rice $11.50; Chicken-n-dumplings $13.50; Sweet potato pie $1.95*

PITA GRILL, THE · LD · Mediterranean

(B2) 140 W. 4th St. (6th) 212/533-9700

F 6 / S 6 / A 4 / $8 · Cash only · **TO/D**

The sun of the Mediterranean shines inside and out of this small, modern restaurant serving healthy, low-fat, low-salt fare. The service is quick and good. The food is downright inexpensive. The clientele are "repeat offenders" and very vocal about it. Need we say more?

SPEC: *Tabouleh $4.50; Falafel platter $3.25; Chicken gyro platter $6.50; Shish kebab platter $6.50; Baklava $1.50*

PO · LD · Italian

(B2) 31 Cornelia St. (Bleecker & W. 4th) 212/645-2189

F 8 / S 7 / A 7 / $24 · AE

One of the ways you can tell if a restaurant is any good is by who eats there and in this case, we're impressed. Many diners are other restaurant owners who obviously appreciate the fine modern Italian cuisine, good service and unpretentious setting. But more than one diner pleads, "Shh, please keep this a secret."
Closed: Monday

SPEC: *Steamed clams $8; White bean ravioli $10; Grilled guinea hen $13; Terrine of dark chocolate, amaretti & vin santo $4*

POPPOLINI'S · LD · Italian

(A3) 16 Waverly Pl. (Wash. Sq. Park) 212/475-1722

F 7 / S 6 / A 6 / $16 · V AE · **TO/D**

This Mom and Pop-polini's owned restaurant is happy to oblige if you want something special, what with over 197 mix and match combinations of pasta. But chances are, after being in business for 10 years, they've thought of them all.

SPEC: *"Poppolini" (thin noodle crepe stuffed w/sautéed ground beef, parmesan, mozzarella, & ricotta cheese) $8.50; Peanut butter fudge pie $3.50*

PROVENCE · LD · Mediterranean

(B3) 38 MacDougal St. (Houston & Prince) 212/475-7500

F 7 / S 6 / A 7 / $38 · AE

Bastille Day is a huge event here, as it should be for this authentic French restaurant named for the region of southeast France on the Mediterranean. A favorite of Francophiles, neighborhood diners, and various celebrities, the restaurant is decorated like a country home and the food reflects these rural values. "Some find the service "hostile," and the food "over-hyped." But others find it "delicious."

RED LION, THE   LD   American

(B3) 151 Bleecker St. (Thompson) 212/473-9560

F 2 / S 4 / A 4 / $18   Cash only

With 5 TVs and 2 lounge areas, this Bleecker Street standard is well-known for its live music and sports scene. Expect basic bar fare, with pasta and steak additions. The lighting? What there is of it is low, low, low—so if you're on the lam, but want to catch the game on the tube, this is the place.
SPEC: *BBQ wings $5.95; Fried calamari $7.95; Burger $6.95; T-bone steak $12.95; Caesar salad w/grilled chicken $9.95*

RIO MAR   LD   Spanish

(A1) 1 9th Ave. (W. 12th) 212/243-9015

F 6 / S 7 / A 6 / $24   AE

"Tough to find, tough to forget." Two floors of authenticity with genuine flamenco music from guitar playing dudes leaves yuppies stuffed with paella and rolling their Rs. There's no doubt as to why Spanish is one of the romance languages. "A divey, lively goof." It's no bull.
SPEC: *Pulpo a la Gallega (octopus) $7.25; Pollo Rio-Mar $9.50; Paella de la casa $13.50; Flan caramel custard $2.75*

ROSE CAFE & BAR   LD   American

(A3) 24 5th Ave. (9th) 212/260-4118

F 6 / S 6 / A 7 / $24   MC V D AE DIS   **TO**

Don't be intimidated by its glassed in exterior. Rose Cafe is welcoming and reasonable. "Everyone is very polite and nice to older people. This is where I take my grandmother." Sit at the window and watch lower Fifth Avenue float by. Or sit in the dining room and look for the roses on the walls (hint: think Pete Rose, Rose Kennedy, etc.)
SPEC: *Butternut squash soup $3.95; Grilled chicken paillard $12.95; Flourless chocolate cake $4.75; Chocolate bread pudding $4.75*

RUBYFRUIT BAR & GRILL   D   American

(B2) 531 Hudson St. (Charles & 10th) 212/929-3343

F 4 / S 4 / A 6 / $22   MC V D AE   **TO/D**

With thrift store gothic decor, this relatively new West Village cubbyhole is awash in romantic ambiance. The upstairs bar is a cozy regular hotspot for women. The cuisine is an average mix of American, Italian and seafood, but reasonably priced.
SPEC: *Blackened shrimp over tossed greens $7.95; Sizzling burger in garlic herb sauce $4.95*

SAZARAC HOUSE, THE   LD   American

(B2) 533 Hudson St. (Charles & W. 10th) 212/989-0313

F 6 / S 8 / A 7 / $23   MC V D AE   **TO**

The "Saz" is one of those old Village finds, "a dependable neighborhood spot offering a taste of New Orleans with the flavor of Old New York." It's housed in an 18th century landmark building that you might miss unless you step back and look. The cuisine reaches way down south for its influence, and comes up smellin' like a rose. Please try the Key lime pie—for us.
SPEC: *Cajun popcorn shrimp $7.95; Grilled portobello mushrooms $6.95; Louisiana crab cakes $15.95; Buttermilk batter chicken $11.95; Key lime pie $5.25*

0	1	2	3	4	5	6	7	8	9	10
disappointing		fair		good		very good		excellent		perfect

SEVILLA RESTAURANT & BAR   LD   Spanish

(A2) 62 Charles St.   (Corner of 4th) 212/929-3189

F 7 / S 7 / A 7 / $27   MC V D AE

A surprisingly old-fashioned restaurant. Red-jacketed waiters hurry through the darkened room carrying steaming plates of paella. Some look like they've been working here since the place opened in 1941. If you're looking for authentic cuisine, this is where you'll find it. One of the few complaints: "Chef is salt-happy."

SPEC: *Mushroom stuffed w/crab meat $6.75; Paella a la Marinera $18.25; Caramel custard $3.30; Guava w/cream cheese $3.30*

DONTE BURSE

Tanti Baci Caffe

TANTI BACI CAFFE   LD   Italian

Top 10 $0-20
Inexpensive

(A2) 163 W. 10th St. (7th Ave.) 212/647-9651

F 7 / S 7 / A 6 / $14   MC V AE   **TO/D**

Hard to find, but this "flower in the Village," is worth the search. "Price, quality and atmosphere can't be beat." Although alcohol isn't served, you can BYOB or have it delivered from a liquor shop around the corner.

SPEC: *Insalata caprese $4.75; Fettucine all'uo vo $6.50; Gnocchi di patate $6.50; Wild raspberry torte $3.75; Chocolate torte $3.75*

TARTINE   BLD   French

(A2) 253 W. 11th St. (W. 4th) 212/229-2611

F 6 / S 4 / A 5 / $20   Cash only

This "perfect" little patisserie and cafe on the most perfect corner in the West Village offers reasonable meals and a great outdoor cafe. All pastry and desserts are made on the premises, which can be enjoyed inside or outside. Folks rave about the "wonderful brunch," though some say dinner entrees can be "uneven.".

SPEC: *French onion soup $3.75; Grilled saucisson $6.50; Beef mignonette aux poivres $9.25; Grilled salmon $9.75*

TEA & SYMPATHY   LD   British

(A2) 108 Greenwich Ave. (12th & 13th) 212/807-8329 Fax: 727-1490

F 6 / S 6 / A 6 / $21   **TO**

"Escape to rural England," by visiting this absolutely fabulous spot where the likes of Johnny Rotten and a bloody 95-year-old can be found rubbing elbows. As a hangout for prominent Brits, none of whom are likely to be short or stout, it offers "authentic" traditional British food, well-conditioned waitresses, and proper tea.

SPEC: *Welsh rarebit $5.75; Shepherd's pie $10.95; Bangers $10.25; Tweed kettle pie (salmon & cod in parsley sauce w/potato topping) $10.95; Apple crumb pudding $3.95*

TORTILLA FLATS   LD   Mexican

(A1) 767 Washington St. (W. 12th) 212/243-1053 Fax: 627-1251

F 6 / S 6 / A 7 / $19   AE   **TO/D**

"A hip place to kick back and relax, where the only thing flat are the tortillas." The atmosphere is a carnival "cavalcade of fun." Try dodging the M.C. guy in the leisure suit, order up a fabulous margarita, and toast to the Ernest Borgnine shrine. Wednesday is Vegas Night; Monday and Tuesday, Big Prize Bingo; late night Happy Hour, 1am-4am. The food is good, the service is caught up in the fun. Wait! Was that Elvis who just won the egg toss?

SPEC: *Guacamole $5.50; Quesadilla grande $7.25; "La Bomba" Burrito Grande $8.95; Fajitas $11.95-$12.95; Margaritas $5-$7*

TRATTORIA PESCE PASTA   LD   Italian

(B2) 262 Bleecker St. (Cornelia) 212/645-2993

F 6 / S 8 / A 6 / $20   MC V AE   **TO**

A small space, but surprisingly roomy enough even with a packed house—which is the norm. The exposed brick nicely complements the classic Italian prints in gilded frames. For 5 or more, reservations are accepted. The wine list is extensive, as is the menu.

SPEC: *Antipasto della casa $4.50; Caesar salad $3.75; Fettuccine amatriciana $9.95; Chicken romana $10.25*

TRE EST   LD   Italian

(B2) 64 Carmine St. (Bedford & 7th Ave.) 212/255-6294

F 7 / S 7 / A 6 / $30   MC V D AE

A standout in large part because owner Ante Grgas does everything in his power to make it so. He considers diners family, which is fine with us. The decor makes it feel like you're in the midst of a garden, and there's an atrium for smokers. The food is exemplary and if you ask Ante for recommendations be prepared to take a fascinating culinary journey through the menu.

SPEC: *Portobello alla griglia $9; Pepperoni arrostiti caldi $8; Pappardelle w/wild pheasant sauce $13; Calamari con inchiostro $14*

TUTTA PASTA   LD   Italian

(B2) 26 Carmine St. (Bleecker & Bedford) 212/463-9653
(B3) 504 LaGuardia Pl. (Bleecker & Houston) 212/420-0652

F 6 / S 7 / A 4 / $17   MC V AE DIS   **TO/D**

Besides keeping many Manhattan restaurants stocked with home-made pasta, they keep the public stocked as well, with "cheap and good Italian food." Though some suspect "portions have been cut in half." If you're sick of cooking and want to get out for a nice, quick Italian meal, reasonably priced, stop by one of their 5 locations around town.

SPEC: *Fried zucchini $4.50; Panzarotti pizza $6.95; Filetti dipomodori $7.25; Chicken scarpariello $11.45*

TWO BOOTS   LD   Pizzeria

(A2) 75 Greenwich Ave. 212/633-9096

(B3) 74 Bleecker St. (B'way) 212/777-1033

See review on page 73.

0	1	2	3	4	5	6	7	8	9	10
disappointing		fair		good		very good		excellent		perfect

UNIVERSAL GRILL   LD   American

(B2) 44 Bedford St. (7th & Carmine) 212/989-5621

F 6 / S 5 / A 5 / $23   AE   **TO**

A romping must for birthdays and any other occasion. Despite
elbow bumping in the small space, Universal has terrific food
and energy that won't quit. Funky and kitschy. Loosen up, meals
are supposed to be fun. And leave the suit at home.
SPEC: *Yellow lentil soup w/smoked ham $3.50; Caesar salad $3.95;
Chicken fried steak $7.95; Chicken pot pie $7.95*

Top 10 $21-35
Moderate

VILLA MOSCONI   LD   Italian

(B3) 69 MacDougal St. (Bleecker & Houston) 212/637-0390

F 8 / S 6 / A 5 / $28   MC V D AE DIS

Have a sense of humor about the oil paintings, and enjoy the homemade pasta, fresh fish and relative obscurity of this cozy Village
restaurant. It must be good, otherwise how to explain folks from
Brooklyn and New Jersey bringing their mammas here to dine.
"Worth the trip for the zuppa di pesce!"
SPEC: *Antipasto Speciale $7.75; Zupa di pesche $15.50; Gnocchialla
pesto $12.50 ; Zabaglione a la Mosconi $4.25; Pears alla Mosconi
$4.25*

JOHN ESPINOSA

Village Atelier

VILLAGE ATELIER   LD   American

(A3) 436 Hudson St. (Morton St.) 212/989-1363

F 7 / S 7 / A 8 / $29   V AE

Entering this restaurant is like walking into a French farmhouse,
"or eating in an antique shop." It's made romantic with candle-light
and flowers arranged in mismatched vases and teapots. Though
they don't appear on the menu, don't pass up the fresh fruit pies or
cobblers prepared by owner Craig Bero's mother, Charlotte.
Closed: Sunday
SPEC: *Roast garlic $6; Feuillete of asparagus $8.50; Herb roast
chicken $15; Sautéed duck breast $17*

VINCE & LINDA AT ONE FIFTH   LD   American

(A3) 1 5th Ave. (8th) 212/979-1515 Fax: 979-1699

F 6 / S 6 / A 3 / $31   MC V D AE DIS

Old standards played on the piano, a landmark setting that evokes
memories for every local who ventures in, and a chef/author who's
written a successful mystery. What more could you ask? How about
well-prepared American bistro-style food, and a view from the back
of the historic Washington mews?
SPEC: *Jumbo lump crabmeat $10.95; Wild mushroom & truffle ravioli
$9; American bouillabaisse $21; Grilled swordfish $18.95; Fallen
chocolate soufflé $6*

Vittorio

VITTORIO D Italian

(B2) 308 Bleecker St. (7th Ave. S.) 212/463-0730

F 8 / S 9 / A 9 / $25   MC V AE DIS   **TO**

Spacious garden seating; pasta, breads and desserts made on the premises; separate rooms for smokers and non-smokers; tasteful decor; monthly changes in the menu covering every region of Italy. Whether you're wearing an Armani suit or Levis, the staff makes you feel at home. "Try the pasta wheel."

SPEC: *Sautéed spinach & stuffed mushrooms $7; Toscana veal chop $20; Sicilian swordfish steak $19; Romagna game cornish hen $17.50*

WHITE HORSE TAVERN LD American

(A1) 567 Hudson (W. 11th and Perry) 212/989-3956

F 4 / S 4 / A 5 / $11   Cash only

Once a popular literary hang-out, this American pub—heavy on the spirits, light on the food— has maintained its legendary lure and then some. The dichotomy of contemporary and antiquity is apparent when you (and the horse you rode in on)pass the hanging memorabilia, approach the 116-year old wood bar and order the signature White Horse ale and a 9 oz. burger. You think, "some things never change," and hope history is the only thing that'll repeat itself.

SPEC: *9 oz. burger $4.25; Buffalo wings $3.75; Chicken cutlet sandwich w/bacon, Swiss, french fries $5.95*

WOODY'S RESTAURANT & BAR LD American

(A2) 140 7th Ave. S. (10th & Charles) 212/242-1200

F 7 / S 7 / A 6 / $18   MC V D AE   **TO**

A comfortable spot for couples, the Christopher Street crowd, and anyone who wants a broad menu with moderate prices. The funky bar—an oak monstrosity more than a century old—produces fine drinks. The kitchen does everything from burgers to vegetarian salads.

SPEC: *Duck & pine nut dumplings $4.95; Woody's Grecian salad $9.95; Tuna nicoise $10.95; Grilled steak tacos $9.95*

YE WAVERLY INN LD American

(A1) 16 Bank St. (Waverly Pl.) 212/929-4378

F 6 / S 6 / A 8 / $24   MC V D AE DIS

This 1844 carriage house comes complete with 3 fireplaces, wooden booths, and a converted garden. With hearty chicken pies and peasant meatloaf on the menu, the weary traveler will find comfort, charm and history here, even if it means only crossing 6th Avenue. But some warn: "After the quaintness wears off, forget it."

SPEC: *Baked brie en croute $7; Shrimp country Dijonaise $7.75; Chicken pot pie $12.75; Baked peasant meatloaf $11.25*

0	1	2	3	4	5	6	7	8	9	10
disappointing	fair			good		very good		excellent		perfect

ZINNO   LD   Italian

(A2) 126 W. 13th St. (6th & 7th) 212/924-5182

F 7 / S 7 / A 7 / $32   MC V D AE

This jazz spot for the 30-something crowd serves northern Italian classic cuisine set to music. Pasta is served for one or family style. Some maintain that recently, "the food has slipped," while others insist that it's still "reliable."

SPEC: *Stuffed eggplant $6.95; Osso buco $16.95; Chicken alla Giuseppe (rolled chicken breast stuffed w/eggplant, prosciutto & fontina cheese) $15.95*

EAST 14TH–42ND STREET

ABBEY TAVERN   LD   Irish-American

(E11) 354 3rd Ave. (26th) 212/532-1978

F 5 / S 5 / A 6 / $22   MC V D AE   **TO**

Once your eyes adjust to the dim lighting, you'll notice the Tiffany-style, stained glass lighting fixtures and windows, and antiques lining the walls. Offerings include "good Guinness and burgers," Try the Shepherd's pie, then join the folks at the bar for some interesting conversation.

SPEC: *Baked stuffed clams $4.50; Shepherd's pie $8.50; Chicken pot pie $8.50; Dublin mixed grill $11.75; San Francisco carrot cake $3*

ABBY   LD   Amer/Continental

(E10) 254 5th Ave. (28th & 29th) 212/725-2922

F 5 / S 5 / A 6 / $19   MC V D AE

Unfortunately, "unspoiled gem," "an oasis on 5th Ave. desert," doesn't have an ideal location. But they do a good business lunch, have nice outdoor tables, attractive contemporary decor (with a rotating art exhibit), and nice staff. Would thrive farther downtown, but the belle of the ball where it is. **Closed: Saturday and Sunday**

SPEC: *Tajine of baby calamari $7; Black squid ink linguine w/shrimp $12; Seafood couscous $14; Dark chocolate Armagnac cake $6*

ADIRONDACK GRILL   BLD   American

(C11) 120 E. 39th St. (Lex. & Park) 212/686-1600 Fax: 779-7822

F 6 / S 6 / A 6 / $28   MC V D AE

For those smokers (and cigar lovers) who want a welcoming place where you won't be treated like a 2nd-class citizen, this "quaint, cozy" Adirondack scene is for you. Dimly lit, this hotel-owned grill has remained a secret—and with good reason. The plaque outside still belongs to the previous restaurant, which no longer exists.

SPEC: *Oriental seared shrimp salad $8.50; Pan-seared tuna fillet sandwich $13.50; Shrimp and scallops tomato penne $17.50; Chocolate mousse cake $6*

ALBUQUERQUE EATS   LD   Southwestern

(E11) 375 3rd Ave. (27th) 212/683-6580

F 6 / S 6 / A 6 / $25   MC V AE

Kick the dust off your boots and have a margarita. The atmosphere is "hip, relaxed." Yes, the buffalo over the bar is real (stuffed). Take a dip in the water tower (just kiddin'). You're encouraged to draw on the tables. But when the sun goes down, it's loud. After dinner, mosey next door to the Rodeo Bar, where there's usually some hot country & western or blues.

SPEC: *White corn chowder $3.95; Fajitas $9.95-$11.95; Grilled chicken breast $10.95; Kahlua nut brownie $3.95*

ALVA   LD   American

(E10) 36 E. 22nd St. (Park Ave. S. & B'way) 212/228-4399

F 7 / S 6 / A 6 / $29   MC V D AE

A dark cafe named after, you guessed it, Thomas Alva Edison. Ironically gloomy for a place with a light bulb theme, it conjures up thoughts of the industrial revolution. To some the "food seems like an experiment that didn't work." While others call it "the best new-comer—fabulous food."

SPEC: *Duck & smoked chicken terrine $7; Braised veal stew $16; Double-garlic roast chicken $17; Pineapple upside down cake $6*

AMERICA   LD   American

(F10) 9 E. 18th St. (5th & B'way) 212/505-2110 Fax: 353-3920

F 5 / S 5 / A 5 / $21   MC V D AE   **TO**

You may be in America, but with a capacity of 400 in the huge dining room, and the decibel count sky-high, you might as well be on Ellis Island. "A baby can cry here and no one would hear it." "Enormous menu choices." "Great for kids and crowds." And many "love the location of the bar overlooking the diners."

SPEC: *San Francisco poached shrimp $7.95; Kennebunkport, Maine raviolis filled w/lobster $7.95 Puget Sound sea scallops & Gulf shrimp $18.95; Boston baked banana fruit tart $4.50*

AN AMERICAN PLACE   LD   American

(D11) 2 Park Ave. (32nd) 212/684-2122

F 7 / S 7 / A 7 / $45   MC V D AE

With high-vaulted ceilings, well-spaced tables and contemporary elegance, it's easy to understand why Larry Forgione's gastronomical delight is the place where American cuisine was created. Dining is civilized and "food is beautifully presented." Though some find it "over-rated." The wine list is extensive.

SPEC: *Gorgonzola potato pancake $8.50; Peanut barbecued duck spring roll $8.50; Roast boneless quails $24; Cedar planked Atlantic salmon $27*

BACK PORCH   LD   Southwestern

(D11) 488 3rd Ave. (33rd) 212/685-3828 Fax: 725-9210

F 4 / S 5 / A 5 / $17   MC V D AE DIS   **TO**

After a hard day at the office, you may be tempted to stop here for a casual dinner or loosen up with a frosty margarita at the bar. But many say "it's not worth the time," because of "poor food," and "slow service." There is, however, outdoor seating to make up for what the food lacks.

SPEC: *Chili con carne $5.25; Popcorn shrimp $5.95; Pizza Mexicana-$7.95; Quesadilla w/corn & zucchini $6.95; Apple crumb pie $4.25*

BAMIYAN   LD   Afghani

(E11) 358 3rd Ave. (26th) 212/481-3232

F 6 / S 5 / A 6 / $19   MC V D AE   **TO/D**

Named after the Afghanistan site where 2 giant Buddhas were carved from limestone between the 2nd and 3rd centuries. Sitting on cushions at floor tables (regular tables are also available), eating "delicious" kabobs, or other authentic Afghani cuisine, you can ponder this historical oddity. **Closed: Monday**

SPEC: *Steamed scallion dumplings $3.75; Sautéed eggplant slices $3.75; Traditional Afghani dinner for 2 $44; Diced filet mignon $11.95; Jelabee (traditional Afghan sweet) $2.95*

0	1	2	3	4	5	6	7	8	9	10
disappointing		fair		good		very good		excellent		perfect

DONTE BURSE

Bistango

BISTANGO LD Italian

(E11) 415 3rd Ave. (29th) 212/725-8484

F 5 / S 5 / A 5 / $20 MC V D AE **TO/D**

This new Murray Hill Italian bistro emphasizes northern regional favorites, and draws diners from the neighborhood. The atmosphere is clean, albeit a bit "antiseptic." But sidewalk dining and friendly service enliven the experience.

SPEC: *Sautéed baby artichokes $4.95 Rigatoni alla Siciliana $9.95; Farfalle salmonate $10.95; Linguine fra diavolo $12.95; Creme brulee $3.95*

BOBBY O'S CITY BITES LD American

(C11) 560 3rd Ave. (37th & 38th) 212/681-0400

F 4 / S 5 / A 5 / $20 MC V D AE **TO**

A mid-town trendy scene. Blown-up B & W photos adorn the walls, each a mouth pose of someone snarfing down or flirting with their food. Owned by Bobby Ochs (Mulholland Drive), it relies on pretty much the same food formula—comfort eating. Comments include "bridge and tunnel people," "terrible, a waste of time," "tourist trap," "SWJF 30s seeks..." to "Unbeatable scene for NYC watchers." "Fun for kids—menu is juvenile and they can scream."

SPEC: *Carolyn's chili 6.25; Shoestring fried zucchini $5.75; Roasted chicken $9.75; Sam's meatloaf $9.50; Garlic mashed potatoes $2.50*

BOLO LD Spanish

(E10) 23 E. 22nd St. (Park Ave. S. & B'way) 212/228-2200

F 7 / S 7 / A 7 / $38 MC V D AE DIS

Another Bobby Flay creation. Contemporary Spanish cuisine and bright, graphic decor reminiscent of Rio tie this sister to the Mesa Grill together. "Trendy and interesting menu." And "wonderful birthday place." Be sure to make a reservation, as it's as popular as carnivale.

SPEC: *White bean & roasted onion soup $6.50; Warm octopus & chickpea salad $10.75; Red snapper $23.50; Roasted lamb shank $24*

BREW'S LD American

(D11) 156 E. 34th St. (Lex. & 3rd) 212/889-3369

F 7 / S 8 / A 8 / $22 MC V D AE **TO**

New York's incarnation of "Cheers", the pub where everybody knows your name is called by some the "coolest place in town." We don't know about that, but Kieran and Jennifer Brew are the ideal restaurateurs—gregarious and easy-going with a good sense of what people like. There's an astounding variety of foreign and domestic beers. Try the food, too—it's surprisingly good. Upstairs, there's a club with live music.

SPEC: *BBQ baby back ribs $6.95; Grilled chicken breast $6.95; Penne w/smoked salmon $12.95; Seafood pot pie $12.95*

Brew's

BYBLOS LD Middle Eastern

(C11) 200 E. 39th St. (2nd & 3rd) 212/687-0808 Fax: 687-0808

F 7 / S 7 / A 6 / $22 MC V D AE DIS **TO/D**

Named for an ancient city in Lebanon. A wall is scenically painted to create the illusion that you're within a building looking out at the beachy oceanside and the magnificent architecture beyond. The food might transplant you there. "Solid middle-eastern food." Good, but small portions."

SPEC: *Falafel $3.75; Homous $3.50; Broiled shish taouk $14.95; Stuffed grape leaves $8.75; Baklava $3; Halaawa $2.95*

C.T. LD French

(E11) 111 E. 22nd St. (Park Ave. S. & Lex) 212/995-8500

F 7 / S 7 / A 7 / $42 MC V D AE DIS

"Wow! French with tropical twists." Named for the initials of chef/owner, Claude Troisgros, this whimsical, contemporary place instills the desire to eat well. The decor is smoke blue with deep coral colors, not to mention Dr. Suess-style banisters and a downstairs gallery, all of which makes this a fine addition to the Gramercy Park eating scene. "When your father, who taught you, is one of the best chefs in France, how bad can it be?" But several diners complain about "snooty attitude of wait staff." **Closed: Saturday lunch. Sunday**

SPEC: *Watercress mousse $12; Lobster w/fresh vegetables $14; Rack of lamb, angel hair pasta $27; Strawberry Napoleon w/ice cream $12*

CAFE BEULAH D Creole

(F10) 39 E. 19th St. (B'way & Park Ave. S.) 212/777-9700

F 8 / S 6 / A 7 / $33 MC V D AE

Beulah's no Bayou Mammy. Her cafe serves upscale, down-home food, emphasizing game, fish and chicken prepared in Southern and Creole styles. The restaurant adds an extra ingredient—style—to the often uneven results that come out of most soul kitchens. Most rave about the "excellent southern food," but some deplore "sloppy service" and "portions that are too small."

SPEC: *Okra & barbecue shrimp plate $9; Deviled crab cakes $10; Alexander's gumbo plate $23; Free range duck w/barbecue sauce $20*

CAFE JOURNAL BL French

(E10) 47 E. 29th St. (Pk. Ave S & Mad) 212/447-1822 Fax: 447-1824

F 6 / S 7 / A 6 / $9 MC V AE **TO/D**

"Very French." A breakfast and lunch spot, serving fresh breads, sandwiches, quiches, tarts, eclairs and cakes. The menu changes each day, so watch the large blackboard for daily specials. Service is on the slow side, so just relax and enjoy. **Closed: Sunday**

SPEC: *Croissant au beurre $1.35; Ratatouille Provençale $3.50; Val D'Aoste $7.25; Parisian sandwich (ham, Swiss cheese) $5.95*

0	1	2	3	4	5	6	7	8	9	10
disappointing		fair		good		very good		excellent		perfect

CAMPAGNA   LD   Italian

(F10) 24 E. 21st St. (Park Ave. S. & B'way) 212/460-0900

F 7 / S 8 / A 6 / $37   MC V D AE

A cheerful, warm spot perfect for a rainy day... or any day you long for the Italian countryside. Almost makes you wish they could serve your meal while you relax under an olive tree. "Even better than the previews, but where's all the attitude? What a pleasant surprise." "Nine out of ten dishes are knockouts." "Bravissimo!"
Closed: Sunday lunch

SPEC: *Assorted antipasti $9.50; Seafood stew on bruschetta $12; Grigliata ai frutti di mare $24; Breast of guinea hen $26*

CANASTEL'S   LD   Italian

(F11) 233 Park Ave. S. (19th) 212/677-9622

F 5 / S 5 / A 6 / $27   MC V D AE

Ten years and still going strong, this Park Ave. S. pioneer has a "nice space, but frightening looking crowd hangout." Yes, somehow its atmosphere makes one nostalgic for the Reagan Era. Maybe it's all those beautiful people still on the make? Many feel food has "gone downhill." But "it's great for business meetings."

SPEC: *Baked mozzarella w/tomato sauce $6.75; Zuppa del giorno $3.75; Scampi all Andrea $16.25; Pizzas $9.75-$11.25*

CECIL'S GRILL   LD   Continental

(C12) 304 E. 42nd St. (1st & 2nd) 212/297-3456

F 6 / S 6 / A 6 / $32   MC V AE DIS

A surprisingly worthwhile dining spot for a hotel restaurant. Cecil's offers an ample bar area and a sunny dining room. A favorite for lunch with the U.N. crowd, while at dinner it's popular with Tudor City and Murray Hill residents. Salad bar at lunch, as well as rich soups add accents to a menu that changes seasonally. Try the gourmet pizzas.

SPEC: *Seared sea scallops $5.75; Smoked duck breast salad $6.75; Jerked red snapper $18.50; Escoveitched grouper $18.50*

CHAT 'N CHEW   LD   American

(F10) 10 E. 16th St. (5th & Union Square) 212/243-1616

F 5 / S 5 / A 5 / $19   AE   **TO/D**

The perfect place for good food "your mother never made you." Guaranteed you won't leave hungry. The decor is sort of "early summer camp." "If you need to feel rural, this could satisfy you." Also a great place to bring the kids who get their own menu and food that's sure to satisfy them and you.

SPEC: *Platter of the Gods (hummus w/toasted roti & marinated vegetables) $6.50; Teenie weenie macaroni & cheese $3.95; "Thanksgiving on a roll" $8.95; Fried catfish po' boy $9.95;*

CHEF 28   LD   Chinese

(E11) 29 E. 28th St. (Park & Mad.) 212/685-8871

F 7 / S 8 / A 6 / $16   MC V D AE   **TO**

They bill themselves as a Gourmet/Contemporary Chinese restaurant oriented toward health, and dining here you'll find out why. No MSG, fresh ingredients, a wide variety of dishes, and a lovely atmosphere that not only caters to your physical health, but your mental health as well.

SPEC: *Vietnamese sesame chicken rolls (4) $3.95; Spicy shrimp wonton dumplings (8) $3.50; Apple chicken $8.25; Crispy Hunan fish $11.95*

Robert Dover
5-time National Freestyle Riding
Champion and 3-time Olympian

"I dine out frequently and my favorite is
Jezebel's, in the theater district. It's wonderful
New Orleans creole and on top of the superb
food, it has a 'Cotton Club' feel, making it seem
as if you're stepping into a different era."

CHUTNEY MARY   LD   Indian

(F10) 40 E. 20th St. (Park Ave. S. & B'way) 212/473-8181

F 7 / S 6 / A 6 / $22   MC V D AE   **TO/D**

To some, this is one of the best Indian restaurants in the city, offering "stimulating food." Organic, fresh, delicious and friendly.
Everything tastes homemade—not too spicy, so it's perfect for
beginners. The nan bread is heaven for the carbojunkie. But one
diner asks, "Where are the customers?"

SPEC: *Trolly-side samosas $4.95; Crispy noodles & puffed rice $4.95;*
Silk & Jewels $9.95; Chicken Sagwala $11.95; Cheese dumplings in
pistachio cream $4.95

CITY CRAB   LD   Seafood

(F11) 235 Park Ave. S. (19th) 212/529-3800

F 6 / S 5 / A 6 / $33   MC V D AE   **TO**

A friendly, informal crab house that's cool in the summer and warm
in the winter. "More of a barn than a restaurant." It's a taste of New
England with that certain sophistication that says, "Only in New
York." "Always fresh and simple as it should be." Others echo the
advice: "Take the next train to Baltimore."

SPEC: *Steamers $8.95; Atlantic salmon pastrami $5.95; Atlantic*
salmon $14.95; Traditional Down-East clam bake $16.95

COFFEE SHOP, THE   BLD   Brazilian

(F10) 29 Union Sq. W. (16th) 212/243-7969

F 6 / S 5 / A 6 / $27   AE

There is a certain faded fabulousness about this hectic hive, but
don't tell them that. "Wonderfully wicked," it's filled with fashionable Flatironers and unsuspecting tourists. "Lots of gorgeous
women." And "Great people watching." But if you're having a bad
hair day, you may want to skip it.

SPEC: *Coconut crisped shrimps $6.95; Bahian dumplings $6.95;*
Grilled breast of chicken w/kale & fresh vegetables $12.95; Bahian
grilled seafood paella for two $16.95 per person

CONFETTI PASTA   LD   Italian

(C10) 5 E. 38th St. (Mad. & 5th) 212/689-3838

F 6 / S 6 / A 5 / $23   MC V D AE DIS   **TO/D**

A video monitor reveals chefs preparing pasta meals. They're cre-
ating made-to-order meals for patrons. An outgrowth of a successful catering business,this restaurant offers the opportunity to
create your own pasta or pizza, then watch someone else do the
handiwork.

SPEC: *Crab cakes $4.95; Little Neck clams baked w/bacon $5.50;*
Franco pizza (beef Bolognese, pepperoni, peppers, onion, mozzarella
& marinara) $8.95

0	1	2	3	4	5	6	7	8	9	10
disappointing		fair		good		very good		excellent		perfect

COURTYARD CAFE   BLD   American

(C11) 130 E. 39th St. (Lex. & Park Ave. S.) 212/779-0739

F 6 / S 6 / A 7 / $31   MC V D AE DIS

Nothing splashy here. But the charming courtyard is a secret nestled in Murray Hill. If you don't tell a soul—NYC bigwigs are regulars here. Check for Bratton and Giuliani between press conferences. "Excellent bar." Service is friendly; the food is well-prepared; the prices are very reasonable; and check out the live jazz on Thursday nights.

SPEC: *Sesame noodle salad $10.50; Caesar salad $7.50; Jamaican jerk chicken sandwich $13.50; Grilled pizza $12; Floribbean roasted mahi-mahi $15.50*

CURRY IN A HURRY   LD   Indian

(E11) 119 Lexington Ave. (28th) 212/683-0900 Fax: 685-6385

F 6 / S 5 / A 3 / $9   MC V D DIS   TO/D

It may have a shlocky fast-food look, but don't let this deter you. "The curry may be fast, but the food's just right." You can either take-out, have it delivered, or, if you're not in a hurry for your curry, there's a bright, comfortable, full-service dining room upstairs.

SPEC: *Chicken Kacchi Biriyan $5.99; Chicken Tikka $3.79; Tandoori platter $5.99; Vegetarian platter $5.49*

DAPHNE'S HIBISCUS   LD   Caribbean

(F11) 243 E. 14th St. (2nd & 3rd) 212/505-1180

F 5 / S 5 / A 4 / $19   TO/D

Down home, authentic Caribbean cooking in a laid back, "tropical atmosphere." The homemade ginger beer and the jerk chicken and pork, along with chef Frank William's coconut bread pudding, are standouts. **Closed: Monday**

SPEC: *Island style fritters $3; Pride of the Caribbean patties $2.50; Jerk chicken and pork $8.95; Fish escovitch $10.95; Coconut bread pudding $2.50*

DOCKS OYSTER BAR   LD   Seafood

(C11) 633 3rd Ave. 40th 212/986-8080
See review on page 244.

DUKE'S   LD   Southern

(F11) 99 E. 19th St. (Park Ave. S. & Irving Pl.) 212/260-2922

F 6 / S 6 / A 5 / $19   MC V D AE

Another winner from savvy restaurateur Andrew Silverman, owner of Steak Frites and Chat 'n' Chew. Duke's perfectly recreates a southern BBQ roadhouse, right down to the old soda machine, Univ. of Tenn 1971-72 football schedule, and the heat on your tongue when you chomp into the brisket.

SPEC: *Roasted corn chowder $3.95; Real Gumbo "Redneck Riviera "style $5.95; Smoked & grilled turkey sandwich $5.95; Beef brisket $7.95; Ribs, brisket & chicken BBQ combo $12.95*

E.   LD   Chinese

(F11) 226 3rd Ave. (19th St.) 212/473-5858

F 4 / S 6 / A 7 / $18   MC V   TO/D

"What Chinese takeout should be." And the restaurant itself, though small, is a pleasant place to sit and eat.. All menu items are made fresh. Dishes not on the menu may be requested.

SPEC: *Salads, priced from $4.95 (w/o topping) to $11.95 (topped w/steamed salmon); Rainbow chicken $7.95; Slippery savory pork $8.25; Happy Gathering $8.95*

EAST   LD   Japanese

(E11) 366 3rd Ave. (26th & 27th) 212/889-2326 Fax: 889-2746
(C10) 9 E. 38th St. (Mad. & 5th) 212/685-5205

F 6 / S 5 / A 4 / $19   MC V D AE   **TO/D**

Sit upstairs if you're looking for an authentic Japanese setting that's quiet and romantic, but be prepared to go shoeless. Known for its Happy Hour sushi menu (between 5 and 6:30 pm, all sushi 1/2 price,) this chain also offers a large variety of non-sushi entrees. "Good Americanized sushi," most say. "At a decent price."
SPEC: *Fashion rolls $5.50; Sashimi $7.50-$15; Sushi super deluxe $17; Yellowtail teriyaki $15*

EAST SIDE DINER   BLD   Diner

(E11) 325 3rd Ave. (25th & 26th) 212/685-1181

F 4 / S 5 / A 3 / $12   Cash only   **TO/D**

With a menu the size of a small novel, you can pretty much name your meal at this "Swiss Army Knife" of diners. It's open 20 hrs. a day, closing only to clean and bake fresh breads and desserts. Great place to go with several others with different food cravings. Folks rave about the "good onion rings."
SPEC: *Mini pita pizzas from $3.95-$4.95; Lamb kebob over rice w/salad $8; Brisket of beef w/potato, vegetable & salad $7.95*

EISENBERG'S SANDWICH   BL   American

(F10) 174 5th Ave. (22nd) 212/675-5096 Fax: 675-0276

F 6 / S 5 / A 7 / $10   Cash only   **TO/D**

1929. The year the stock market crashed and the year Eisenberg's opened its doors to the public. This breakfast-and-lunch-only railroad flat-style American Kosher sandwich shop makes you want to order lunch while writing skits for the Alan Brady Show. There's one counter and a handful of tables. "Best tuna sandwich in NY." "Oatmeal! Pastrami!" shout exuberant diners.
SPEC: *Matzo ball soup $1.85; Eisenberg's Reuben special $5.95; Corned beef, pastrami, Swiss cheese & cole slaw $6.25; Rice pudding $1.50*

EL PARADOR CAFE   LD   Mexican

(D12) 325 E. 34th St. (1st & 2nd) 212/679-6812 Fax: 889-1223

F 6 / S 7 / A 7 / $25   MC V D AE   **TO**

A loyal clientele has frequented this "time warp" Mexican restaurant with a hacienda feel for nearly 40 years now and with good reason. "Great and classy," and the food is consistently good. There are 23 different kinds of tequilas to choose from; daily fish specials; and other regular menu items that dazzle the palate. **Closed: Sunday**
SPEC: *Pickled jalapeños stuffed w/ cheeses or peanut butter $6.50; Grilled skewers of marinated shrimps and scallops $17.75; Camarones salsa verde $17.75*

EUREKA JOE   BLD   American

(E10) 168 5th Ave. (22nd) 212/741-7500

F 6 / S 6 / A 7 / $14   Cash only   **TO/D**

An oasis from the bustling city streets, this gourmet coffee shop serves sandwiches, salads, and "special savories," in a chic, hotel lobby-like atmosphere. Caricatures of the famous line the walls, looking down on diners as they relax on sofas and easy chairs, or make use of the courtesy phones "Great place to do the crossword puzzle."
SPEC: *Roasted vegetable turnover $5; Black bean & vegetable turnover w/blue corn crust $5; Flatiron salad $7.95; Greek salad $7.95*

0	1	2	3	4	5	6	7	8	9	10
disappointing		fair		good		very good		excellent		perfect

EAST 14TH – 42ND STREET

FAGIOLINI'S — LD — Italian

(C11) 334 Lexington Ave.   (39th)   212/883-9555 Fax: 953-1726

F 6 / S 6 / A 6 / $21   MC V D AE DIS   **TO/D**

Meaning "string bean," this narrow, simply dressed restaurant has a clean-cut style and comes highly recommended by hotels in the area. Moderately priced, the presentation is as "pleasant" as the food is delicious. **Closed: Saturday, Sunday lunch**

SPEC: *Green & white fettucine w/portobello mushrooms $9.75; Breast of chicken w/wild mushrooms $10.50; Tiramisu $9.50*

Fiori

FIORI — LD — Italian

(D11) 4 Park Ave. (33rd) 212/686-0226

F 5 / S 8 / A 5 / $21   MC V AE   **TO/D**

A NY landmark and an architect/archeologist's delight. Upon entering, you're immediately under it's spell, since the incredible painted ceiling is hard to miss. It's "pubby" and "casual." And though the food isn't spectacular, it's deemed "uniformly good." **Closed: Saturday & Sunday**

SPEC: *Herb focaccia $2.50; Fried cajun crabcakes $5.95; Penne w/pepper vodka & prosciutto $9.95; Shrimp scampi $11.95*

FRESCO TORTILLA GRILL — LD — Mexican

(E11) 36 Lex. Ave. (23rd & 24th) 212/475-7380

F 4 / S 5 / A 1 / $6   Cash only   **TO/D**

It all began with 1 tiny storefront and in 2 years Fresco Tortilla has expanded to 4 fast food outlets in key locations around Manhattan. Chinese owned and operated, the food is mainly authentic Mexican, though some call it "bogus." Forget Taco Bell and go for the real thing: it's cheaper, fresher, tastes better and delivery is fast!

SPEC: *Fresh flour tortillas w/choice of stuffings $.99-2.19; Quesadillas sincronizadas w/ choice of stuffings $2.19-$3.79; Fajitas by the lb. $12.99*

FRIEND OF A FARMER — BLD — American

(F11) 77 Irving Place (18th & 19th) 212/477-2188 Fax: 529-9178

F 6 / S 5 / A 7 / $22   MC V AE DIS   **TO/D**

Reminiscent of a New England inn, this cozy restaurant "makes you feel like you've left NY." It's filled with wholesome, fresh-baked smells, quaint hanging dried flowers, and Mom's amazing homemade chicken potpie—assuming, of course, your mom could cook. It also has a garden and sidewalk cafe. Some say it "looks better than it tastes."

SPEC: *Eggplant terrine $6.95; Chicken pot pie $8.75/$10.75; Spinach meatloaf $8.50/$10.75; Chocolate brownies $2.50*

106   F = Food   S = Service   A = Atmosphere $ = Average cost of a meal

BENTEL & BENTEL

Gramercy Tavern

GRAMERCY TAVERN   LD   American

(F10) 42 E. 20th St. (Park Ave. S. & B'way) 212/477-1025

F 8 / S 7 / A 7 / $64   MC V D AE

Danny Meyers' spin-off of his well-respected Union Square Cafe has the simple elegance of a French country home. The wait staff is elegantly attired in button-down, collarless shirts with black vests. Comments include, " Splendid "deserves its reputation," and "very good, but not up to the hassle it takes to get in." And "rude, pretentious—you feel like you're putting them out by being there."

SPEC: *Prix fixe 3-course menu $52: Seared tuna w/white beans, lemon & arugula; Roast rabbit w/black olives & sherry vinegar; Lobster & artichoke salad*

GRAMERCY WATERING HOLE   LD   American

(F11) 106 19th St. Park & Irving Pl. 212/674-5783

See Sutton Watering Hole review page 142.

GRAND CENTRAL OYSTER BAR   LD   American

(C10) Grand Central Terminal (Lower Level) 212/490-6650

F 8 / S 6 / A 6 / $32   MC V D AE DIS   **TO**

Top 10 $21-35 Moderate

A NY original. Deep in the cavernous confines of Grand Central Station you'll find some of the best and freshest seafood in town. Nowhere else will you find a better selection of oysters. All smoking of salmon, sturgeon and trout is done on premises. Noisy and crowded, especially during lunch, but if it bothers you, just wear ear plugs, because it's worth defying the sound barrier for seafood like this. **Closed: Saturday & Sunday**

SPEC: *Fried oysters $7.50; Imperial balik salmon $9.95; Smoked salmon $22.95; Lobster (price varies according to season); Bouillabaisse $25.45; Hazelnut chocolate chunk cake $6.25*

HANGAWI   LD   Korean

(D10) 12 E. 32nd St. (Mad. & 5th) 212/213-0077

F 7 / S 9 / A 9 / $36   MC V D AE

The aesthetic of this vegan restaurant is Zennish and the presentation will leave you in awe. There's precision to everything: the setting (black lacquer plates, spoons and chopstick cases); the colorful, delicate quilts that decorate the walls; the bright green and yellow pillows. "Too many little fried things, but aesthetically fun." Be prepared to remove your shoes, which you shouldn't mind since you'll feel quite at home.

SPEC: *Emperor's meal (Prix fixe) $24.95 & $29.95; Vegetarian glory $19.95; Grilled lanceolata $19.95*

0	1	2	3	4	5	6	7	8	9	10
disappointing		fair		good		very good		excellent		perfect

Hangawi

HEARTLAND BREWERY — LD — American

(F10) 35 Union Sq. W. (16th & 17th) 212/645-3400

F 5 / S 6 / A 6 / $24   MC V D AE

The new kid on the block has a lot to offer: Midwestern soul with city slickness. "Real beer made here," (5 homemade,) and an inventive, rich American menu. "Fab place for lunch after green market." "Great beer; above average pub fare." "Best micro-brewery in Manhattan."

SPEC: *BBQ chicken "lolly pops" $6.95; Picnic tortilla $6.50; Meat loaf $11.95; Buttermilk fried chicken $12.95; Aunt Bee's chocolate mud cake $4.50*

HOULIHAN'S — LD — Amer/Continental

(C11) 380 Lexington Ave. (42nd) 212/922-5661
(D10) 350 5th Ave. (34th) 212/630-0339
See review on page 230.

I TRULLI — LD — Italian

(E11) 122 E. 27th St. (Lex. & Park Ave. S.) 212/481-7372

F 7 / S 7 / A 7 / $32   MC V D AE

Named for the stone domed house found in the Puglia region of southern Italy, the decor makes you believe that you're actually in one of them. Appetizer bar, outdoor terrace, and wood-burning fireplace create a country (but not cutesy) feel. "Flavorful country Italian. Great garden." "Delicious food with very warm service."
Closed: Sunday

SPEC: *Grilled homemade game sausages $9; Baby cuttlefish $10; Penna alla Dauna $14; Grilled swordfish $21; Italian crepes, apples & pears, caramel Tuaca sauce $6*

IL MARE — LD — Italian

(C10) 10 E. 38th St. (5th & Mad.) 212/447-1854

F 6 / S 6 / A 6 / $30   MC V D AE   **TO**

Located in the heart of the business district, this is a convenient, classy, and quiet place to dine. The waiters dress in jackets with bow ties, and they all speak Italian. The food is a treat here, and as its name suggests, seafood is their specialty. "A nice dinner date place." **Closed: Sunday**

SPEC: *Roasted fresh peppers and anchovies $7; Striped bass $18; Seafood salad $22; Angel hair pasta w/seafood $18; Zabaglione ali-masala $7*

JACKSON HOLE — BLD — American

(D11) 521 3rd Ave. (35th) 212/679-3264
See review on page 231.

LA COLOMBE D'OR   LD   French

(E11) 134 E.26th St. (Lex. & 3rd) 212/689-0666

F 7 / S 6 / A 7 / $35   MC V D AE

This 20-year old Provencal hideaway strives to be cozy and, for the most part, succeeds. The Napoleon room upstairs puts you in a French country farmhouse mood, and it's good for private parties, and "great for cold, snowy days." Between the food, prepared by chef Matthew Murphy, and the "charming ambiance," The Golden Dove" has much to offer.

SPEC: *Soupe de poissons $5.50; Pates aux tomates $12; Breast of chicken $16.50; Steak frites: onglet grille $18*

LA MAISON JAPONAISE   LD   French/Japanese

(C11) 125 E. 39th St. (Park & Lex.) 212/682-7375 Fax: 599-8083

F 7 / S 6 / A 7 / $25   MC V D AE DIS

Hideki Takami, formerly chef to composer Igor Stravinsky, offers a menu reflecting the influence of French and Japanese cuisine. Located in a charming turn-of-the-century brownstone, amidst a sparse decor, makes for an upscale dining experience. If you can, get a seat in the front, upstairs dining room, near the window overlooking the street. "Consistently good, great value for the money." **Closed: Sunday**

SPEC: *Shumai dumplings $3.50; Escargots Japonaise $4.50; Chicken flambe $13.95; Wasabi mignon $16.95*

LAMARCA   LD   Italian

(E11) 161 E. 22nd St. (3rd) 212/673-7920 Fax: 982-1482

F 8 / S 6 / A 4 / $10   Cash only   **TO/D**

A small, family owned and operated restaurant. The pasta is home-made and the premises so clean you could eat off the floor. But you don't have to. Try the dining room instead, which doubles as an art gallery. Ten bucks will get you a large portion of any pasta, bread, salad, and a non-alcoholic drink. "Hard to beat." **Closed: Sunday**

SPEC: *(Price fixed, includes salad & bread) Fusilli con pesto; Spaghetti alla carbonara; Involtini-prosciutto, tacchino, spinaci $10*

Les Halles

LES HALLES   LD   French

(E11) 411 Park Ave. S. (28th & 29th) 212/679-4111

F 7 / S 6 / A 7 / $34   MC V D AE

Jazz sets the musical tone, and B & W prints of Fernandel, the French equivalent of Jerry Lewis, provide the visuals. "Primo meats!" If you want something not on the menu, check the butcher case up front. If you see something you like, the chef will cook it to order. "Very French, but in France you don't wait if you have a reservation." "Noisy and crowded, service can be distracted."

SPEC: *Terrine du jour $5.75; Warm sausage w/lentils $6.75; N.Y. sirloin $21; Onglet (hangar steak) $18.50; Poulet roti $14.50*

0	1	2	3	4	5	6	7	8	9	10
disappointing		fair		good		very good		excellent		perfect

LIVE BAIT
LD — **Southern**

(E10) 14 E. 23rd St. (Mad. & B'way) 212/353-2400

F 5 / S 5 / A 5 / $23   AE

"Dive" bait is more like it. Trying to be trendy by not really trying after all these years. Still attracts a faux model-y crowd, and acts like a bayou pick-up joint. "Best catch of the day—it's at the bar." Don't go looking for the beautiful people here, unless it's your waiter or waitress…and don't hate them because they're beautiful.

SPEC: *Chicken wings $5.95; Cajun fried calimari $6.95; Pulled Carolina BBQ pork on a bun $7.95; Bible Belt smothered pork chops $11.95; Blue ribbon chicken pot pie $10.95*

LORANGO
LD — **Tex-Mex**

(E11) 323 3rd Ave. (24th) 212/679-1122

F 6 / S 6 / A 5 / $17   MC V AE   **TO**

A Tex/Mex restaurant bar that's always hopping. Its devoted following notes good food, personal service, comfortable decor and a festive atmosphere. The margaritas are "highly recommended" and the $5.95 weekend brunch is a satisfying bargain.

SPEC: *Chalupas $3.75; Chicken quesadilla $6.75; Budin Azteca (torta w/layers of chicken, cheese); Camarones (sautéed shrimp) $12.95; Kahlua mousse $2.95*

LOST & FOUND RESTAURANT
LD — **Italian**

(C11) 329 Lexington Ave. (38th & 39th) 212/889-5599

F 6 / S 6 / A 6 / $24   MC V D AE

We like a restaurant that appreciates its customers, so we look fondly on this one that every 3 months has a "Customer Appreciation" night when they give away prizes of pastas and salads. Of course there's a slight catch—drinks not included. But what the heck. The spot is warm, cozy, friendly, and there's a piano player and singer, as well. **Closed: Sunday**

SPEC: *Baked clams (for 2) $13.95; Pollo alla parmigiana (for 2)$16.95; Scampi marinari (for 2) $22.95; Vitello alla parmigian(for 2) $17.95*

MAYROSE
BLD — **American**

(F10) 920 Broadway (21st) 212/533-3663 Fax: 533-3696

F 5 / S 4 / A 5 / $21   MC V D AE   **TO/D**

Their slogan is "comfortable food," like meatloaf, "mac" and cheese, and chicken soup, aka "penicillin." This upscale diner is a little too expensive for the quality delivered, which is inconsistent—"A little too trendy, with okay food," is how one diner describes it." But folks rave about "the great breakfast." Fine for a quick bite pre- or post-movie.

SPEC: *Penicillin (chicken soup) $3.50; Veggie chili $6.25; Shepherd's pie $9.75; Tabasco & buttermilk fried chicken w/mashed potatoes $9.25; Max's festive chocolate cake $3.75*

MESA DE ESPANA
LD — **Spanish**

(E10) 45 E. 28th St. (Park Ave. S. & Mad.) 212/679-2263

F 7 / S 6 / A 4 / $26   MC V D AE

Generous portions of hearty, Spanish cuisine attract those who appreciate well-prepared classic dishes. Paella is served in any of 4 versions and is one of many palate pleasers.

SPEC: *Sautéed string beans w/Spanish ham $6.25; Paella Valenciana w/lobster $17.25; Mariscadas (shrimps, mussels, clams, scallops) $14.95*

Mesa Grill

MESA GRILL   LD   Southwestern

(F10) 102 5th Ave. (15th & 16th) 212/807-7400 Fax: 989-0034

F 9 / S 8 / A 8 / $40   MC V AE

From Bobby Flay's kitchen to your mouth. The seasoned southwestern "innovative and inventive" cuisine is so thick you can cut it with a knife and you'd better. Furnished with playful cowboy-lassos-horse banquettes, mix 'n match pastel plates, and colossal pillars, Mesa Grill transports the SW to the NE. One diner may have said it all: "Bobby Flay—marry me!"

SPEC: *Quesadillas $11; Shrimp & roasted garlic $10.50; Red snapper $23; Black angus steak w/housemade steak sauce $24.50*

METRONOME   LD   American

(E10) 915 Broadway (21st) 212/505-7400 Fax: 505-5529

F 5 / S 5 / A 7 / $40   MC V D AE DIS

Longing for the glorious Jazz Age of the 1920s? Metronome is anxious to provide it for you by trying hard to summon the ghost of Jay Gatsby. The decor is...well, interesting. And the food? "Wonderful," say some, "horrible" say others. **Closed: Saturday**

SPEC: *Roasted asparagus $9; Salmon & lobster wontons $12; Orrechiette w/broccoli di rape & hot/sweet sausage $18; Frozen white chocolate banana mousse $5.50*

MOLLY'S TAVERN   LD   Irish-American

(E11) 287 3rd Ave. (22nd & 23rd) 212/889-3361

F 4 / S 6 / A 6 / $18   MC V D AE

Sawdust on the floor and a cozy fireplace helps bring you back to a time in Ireland when they named their pubs "Shebeen," Gaelic for ghost, to keep the English away. But today everyone's welcome (even the English), for homemade items like chicken pot pie.

SPEC: *Shepherd's pie $10.25; Chicken pot pie $10.95; Burgers $6.50-$7; Fish & chips $10.50*

MORENO   LD   Italian

(F11) 65 Irving Place (18th) 212/673-3939

F 6 / S 6 / A 6 / $36   MC V D AE

Boasting over 250 parties each year, Moreno (no relation to Rita) has perhaps hosted one of yours with their contemporary Italian cuisine. Three rooms make this possible, and the sidewalk seating makes it nice for a party of two. "Warm, friendly, great place all around." "The owner is a 10."

SPEC: *Scampi salad $12; Arugula al a Milanese $10; Rigatoni con-melanzane $16.50; Pollo arrostito $17.50*

0	1	2	3	4	5	6	7	8	9	10
disappointing		fair		good		very good		excellent		perfect

Barry Slotnick
Attorney

"**Le Cirque**, because of its elegance and service, the consistently good meals and it's appropriate pricing for all amenities, Also, **Coco Pazzo**, because the food's good, the service excellent, the ambiance is fine and everybody's willing to assist with special diet needs."

NOODLES ON 28   LD   Chinese

(E11) 394 3rd Ave. (28th) 212/679-2888 Fax: 679-2895

F 7 / S 6 / A 5 / $16   MC V AE   **TO/D**

This Cantonese/Mandarin restaurant specializes in noodle dishes. But that's not all. This slice of Chinatown in Gramercy, also provides a variety of Chinese specialties such as dim sum and dumplings, along with the more traditional dishes. "A delightful surprise." "Great takeout."
SPEC: *Steamed chicken dumplings $4.50; Shu Mai (Dim Sum dumpling) $3.25; Lobster Cantonese $15.50; House steak, Hong Kong style $13.95*

NOVITA   LD   Italian

(E11) 102 E. 22nd St. (Park Ave. S. & Lex.) 212/677-2222

F 8 / S 7 / A 7 / $30   MC V D AE

Novita's Italian fare sneaks up on diners, then dazzles them with its artistry and inventiveness. Imagine da Vinci reincarnated as a chef, expertly running the kitchen. Then imagine customers departing with Mona Lisa smiles. "Great neighborhood spot, good value."
Closed: Saturday lunch. Sunday
SPEC: *Black farfalle & spicy shrimp $13; Salmon tartare dumplings $10; Char-grilled veal chop $20; Roasted duck w/Barolo sauce $18*

OLD TOWN BAR & RESTAURANT   LD   American

(F10) 45 East 18th St. (Park Ave. S. & B'way) 212/529-6732

F 5 / S 5 / A 6 / $13   MC V AE

"Fun, funky, historic." Old Town opened its doors in 1892 and they're still open. Dark, with the permanent smell of beer in the air, it makes you want to take up drinking in the afternoon. The food is average pub fare, though folks rave about "the great burger"— but obviously the food didn't matter to Woody Allen who shot a scene for "Bullets Over Broadway" here.
SPEC: *Buffalo chicken wings $4.25; Burgers $6-$6.75; Tuna melt $6.75; Chili dog $6.25*

OTTOMANELLI'S CAFE   LD   Italian

(F11) 337 3rd Ave (25th) 212/532-2929
(C10) 301 Madison Ave. (41st) 212/370-5959
See review on page 41.

PARK AVALON   LD   Mediterranean

(F11) 225 Park Ave. S. (18th & 19th) 212/533-2500

F 7 / S 6 / A 6 / $27   MC V AE

This new-ish princess of Park Avenue South is for the "beautiful people" in all of us. Chic, but not so much as to be exclusive. Lightness and high design create a pretty but cool setting to enjoy not outrageously priced Mediterranean cuisine. Some call it "a fun place, with good food and prices." Others call it "boring," and give it "Two thumbs down!"
SPEC: *Tuna handroll $7.50; Pizza's $9.50-$10.50; Tuscan-style roast chicken $12.75; Warm chocolate cake $5.50; Lemon parfait $4.95*

PARK BISTRO   LD   French

(E11) 414 Park Ave. S. (28th & 29th) 212/689-1360

F 7 / S 5 / A 6 / $35   MC V D AE   **TO**

For upscale people or wannabes. Dress up, or dress casual, and bring your wallet to enjoy this full dining experience with a classy, comfortable feel. "Pushy waiters who think they're authentically French." "Excellent food, bad service, stuffy atmosphere." "Haughty attitude."

SPEC: *Warm potato salad w/goat cheese $8; Tomato tart w/basil $7.50; Sautéed skate w/port wine & vinegar. w/cocoa beans $20*

PASTICCIO   LD   Italian

(D11) 447 3rd Ave. (30th & 31st) 212/679-2551 Fax: 685-3932

F 6 / S 6 / A 6 / $26   MC V D AE   **TO/D**

Mauvish in tone, this restaurant has a feel typical of a worldly woman with a tender, motherly way about her. The walls are covered with a hodge-podge of well-arranged children's drawings of, what else? —food! "Romantic setting." "Great food, but overpriced for a neighborhood place."

SPEC: *Roast veal in tuna sauce $7.95; Tortellini in consommé broth $5.50; Filet mignon in Barolo wine sauce $19.95; Meat lasagna $12.95*

Patria

PATRIA   LD   Latin

(F11) 250 Park Ave. S. (20th) 212/777-6211

F 8 / S 7 / A 7 / $41   MC V D AE

"Funky food, funky drinks, funky restaurant." If you desire Nuevo Latino cuisine, you'll find it here under the innovative eye of chef Douglas Rodriguez. Meaning "homeland," Patria's contemporary and colorful decor entices the spirit into the delicate flavors of Central and South America. For dessert, have a cigar, a chocolate one with its very own sugar-shaped matches. A feast for the eyes. A trip for the senses. "If only it were more affordable."

SPEC: *Ecuadorian ceviche $12; Venezuelan empanada $9; Guatemalan chicken $19; Swordfish $23; Giraldi puro de chocolate (chocolate cream filled cigar cookie w/white mocha ice cream) $8*

PAUL & JIMMY'S RISTORANTE   LD   Italian

(F11) 123 East 18th St. (Park Ave. S. & Irving) 212/475-9540

F 6 / S 6 / A 5 / $26   MC V D AE   **TO**

This nice, but nothing special family owned restaurant in Gramercy, is pleasant enough for your traditional Italian meal. But don't ask for Paul and Jimmy because they haven't been around for 26 years.

SPEC: *Fresh minestrone $4.75; Pollo alla griglia $13; Lobster tails $19.50; Torta di ricotta $4.75; Zuppa inglese (rum cake) $4.75*

PEDRO PARAMO LD Mexican

(F12) 430 E. 14th St. (1st & Ave. A) 212/475-4581

F 7 / S 7 / A 4 / $21 MC V **TO/D**

The only fault of this friendly little family run Mexican restaurant is it's out of the way location. But their slogan is, "If you can't go to Mexico, come to Pedro Parama," for its traditional homestyle cooking. "Excellent, simple, authentic Mexican."

SPEC: *Ceviche $6.25; Marinated octopus $7.50; Alambres de camarones $12.50; Sautéed chicken w/Mexican cactus hearts $9.75; Natilla $2.75; Chocolate mousse cake w/Kahlua $3.75*

Pete's Tavern

PETE'S TAVERN LD Italian

(F11) 129 E. 18th St. (Irving Pl.) 212/473-7676

F 5 / S 5 / A 6 / $28 MC V AE **TO/D**

Honest Abe was president when this bar/restaurant first opened its doors. Step back in time with the original 1864 fixtures and furniture. "An eatery for drinks," serving primarily Italian fare. It's also heavy on the usual array of pub grub. Good enough for O. Henry, who supposedly wrote "The Gift of the Magi" here, so it should be good enough for us. "Great spot to watch games on TV."

PIGALLE LD French

(E11) 111 E. 29th St. (Park Ave. S. & Lex.) 212/779-7830

F 8 / S 7 / A 8 / $29 MC V D AE

This little "slice of Paris" tucked away in Murray Hill, makes you feel like you've won a treasure hunt. Stepping inside transports you to France in a snap. It's more informal than it looks, and successfully promotes a cozy, secure family feeling. "Real people with great attitudes." **Closed: Saturday, Sunday lunch.**

SPEC: *Pate $7.50; Lasagna $6.75; Skate fish raie $16.75; Rabbit $16.75; Duck $17.75*

RAY BARI PIZZA LD Pizzeria

(F11) 220 Park Ave. S. (18th) 212/505-8000

See review on page 176.

ROLF'S LD German

(E11) 281 3rd Ave. (22nd) 212/477-4750

F 8 / S 5 / A 8 / $27 MC V AE **TO**

A popular place for "solid German food." The decor is lush and the decorations change four times a year. "A must see at Christmas." They also showcase a famous person each year, from Marlene Dietrich to Sinatra to Madonna (gee, we didn't know they were German.) Very accommodating, even to serving smaller portions for the "less hungry."

Rolf's

ROYAL CANADIAN PANCAKE HOUSE · BLD · American

(F11) 180 3rd Ave. (17th) 212/777-9288
See review on page 239.

RUSSELL'S AMERICAN GRILL · BL · American

(D11) 45 Park Ave. (37th) 212/685-7676

F 5 / S 5 / A 5 / $28   MC V D AE

Hankering for a satisfying nosh? Check out this spot for breakfast or lunch. No dinner, but they do serve light evening fare in the bar, a cozy spot fitted out like a gentleman's library.

SPEC: *Caesar salad $10; Farfalle w/ocean shrimp & Norwegian salmon in lobster safron broth $13.95; 8 oz burger $11*

SAL ANTHONY'S · LD · Italian

(F11) 55 Irving Place (17th & 18th) 212/982-9030

F 6 / S 6 / A 7 / $22   MC V D AE DIS

In O. Henry's former home, enjoy reasonably priced "honest" Italian food for an excellent value. Look for the romantic, twinkling, lighted trees outside the cafe. A number of separate rooms make for a perfect private party. "Good for lunch." "Predictable," mumble some dissenters.

SPEC: *Caesar salad $6.95; Fritti di calamari $6.95; Linguine al Sal Anthony's $10.95; Trotello al Rosmarino $12.50; Ricotta cheese cake $3.95*

SECRET HARBOR BISTRO · BLD · American

(D11) 303 Lexington Ave. (37th) 212/447-7400

F 5 / S 8 / A 6 / $20   MC V D AE DIS   **TO**

This unassuming bistro draws patrons from the hotel directly above it, as well as from among local residents. Moderately priced, the staff is multilingual and friendly enough to be on a first name basis with many of their regular diners.

SPEC: *Artichoke & spinach dip w/baguettes $4.50; Breaded ravioli w/tomato sauce $5.25; Prime rib $12.95; Seafood platter $14.95*

SILK · LD · French/Japanese

(E11) 378 3rd Ave. (27th & 28th) 212/532-4500 Fax: 532-4947

F 8 / S 7 / A 7 / $32   MC V D AE

In a tasteful, golden room, with satin banquettes and subtle oriental touches, Silk serves innovative French-Asian fusion cuisine. The neighborhood may be a little out of the way and nondescript, but the food certainly isn't. "Unusual but excellently flavored." "Unique, inventive food—great bar."

SPEC: *Crab meat fritter $8; Grilled tuna steak $20; Grilled jumbo prawns w/lotus leaf $20; Caramelized apple & raisin spring roll, pineapple confit & cinnamon ice cream $7*

0	1	2	3	4	5	6	7	8	9	10
disappointing		fair		good		very good		excellent		perfect

DONTÉ BURSE

Silk

SILVER SWAN   LD   German

(F10) 41 E. 20th St. (Park & B'way) 212/254-3611

F 7 / S 6 / A 7 / $28   MC V D AE DIS

This sweet, quiet German dining room is as serene as a swan. The bar, with its 75 bottles of beer on the wall (and 8 on tap), and its international microbrewery menu, is open to the wee hours of the A.M. "If your parents are coming in from Pa., this is a good place to take them." Go for the sauerbraten, stay for the nacht (night).
SPEC: *Pickled red beet salad $3; Potato pancakes $5.95; Wienerschnitzel $15.95; Sauerbraten $14.95*

SOTTO CINQUE   LD   Italian

(E11) 417 3rd Ave. (26th) 212/685-2037
See review on page 179.

STEAK-FRITES   LD   French

(F10) 9 E. 16th St. (5th & Union Sq. W) 212/463-7101

F 7 / S 6 / A 6 / $24   MC V D AE   TO

There's a lyrical Parisian feel in this French bistro. Try the dish that the restaurant is named for and study the mural on the dining room wall depicting caricatures of colorful French friends of the artist. Look for the sign of the smoking cow. "Great steak." But some feel "the place has taken a nose dive."
SPEC: *Mussels w/broth $6; Black Angus steak frites $17.50; Crisp skin salmon $13.50; Profiteroles $5.50; Napoleon $5.50*

STELLA DEL MARE   LD   Italian

(F11) 346 Lex. Ave. (39th & 40th) 212/687-4425

F 8 / S 7 / A 7 / $36   MC V D AE DIS   TO/D

"Wrong neighborhood, great restaurant." "Excellent seafood." The service is impeccable, the atmosphere formal and traditional. A single long-stemmed red rose graces every table. The waiters, all in jacket and tie, are professionals. There's live piano in the downstairs lounge in the evenings.
SPEC: *Mussels in white wine $7.50; Charcoal broiled salmon $23; Strawberries w/zabaglione $7.50*

TAMMANY HALL   LD   Italian

(E11) 393 3rd Ave. (27th & 28th) 212/696-2001 Fax: 696-9450

F 7 / S 7 / A 8 / $30   MC V AE

Sleek architecture of stainless steel and huge slabs of cherry mahogany create a feel of opulence. The tables are separated by sinuously curving wood partitions, whereas the horse-shoe bar is a great place to hang out and meet people. The kitchen serves up regional Italian and continental cuisine.
SPEC: *Salmon carpaccio $8.95; Rigatoni w/arugula, plum tomatoes & smoked mozzarella $11.95; Osso buco $19.95*

TEMPO   LD   Italian

(E10) 30 E. 29th St. (Park Ave. S. & Mad.) 212/532-8125

F 7 / S 7 / A 7 / $32   MC V D AE

Tired of lunch in the office? Move the meeting over to Tempo, the Italian restaurant with a corporate attitude. "A real gem—cuisine and service excellent." It's quiet and cool. Perfect place to work on any "big deal" with its boardroom chic.
SPEC: *Fish carpaccio $7.95; Fusilli Mataroccu $13.95; Pollo Nicola $18.95; Torta di cioccolata $6;*

TING   LD   Chinese

(D11) 435 Park Ave. S. (29th & 30th) 212/696-5628

F 6 / S 8 / A 1 / $18   MC V AE   **TO/D**

This small, storefront establishment boasts "fastest kitchen," "most selections," and "microwavable containers." In most cases you're probably better taking out, since the uninspiring ambiance leaves much to be desired. The delivery area is larger than most, thanks to mopeds, so give it a try.
SPEC: *Temple duck $9.95; Duck seafood combo $12.95; Seafood in Phoenix nest $12.95; Peking duck dinner (whole) $24*

TURKISH KITCHEN   LD   Turkish

(E11) 386 3rd Ave. (27th & 28th) 212/679-1810

F 7 / S 7 / A 7 / $21   MC V D AE DIS   **TO**

Classy, but sensual, this unique restaurant is a rich-colored red, except for the elegant white linen tablecloths and the waiters dressed in chef-like, double-breasted white uniforms, minus the hat. Go there on Wednesday evening and enjoy the live, traditional-style Turkish music which goes wonderfully well with the genuine Turkish cuisine. "Put it on your list to try." **Closed: Lunch Saturday and Sunday**
SPEC: *Fried Calamari w/garlic sauce $5.50; Phyllo rolls stuffed w/feta & pan fried $4; Baby lamb grilled, served w/rice $10.50; Sword fish charcoal grilled $11.50*

Union Square Cafe

UNION SQUARE CAFE   LD   American

(F10) 21 E. 16th St. (5th & Union Sq. W) 212/243-4020

F 8 / S 8 / A 7 / $42   MC V D AE

Top 10 $36-55

Expensive

Danny Meyers' sensational downtown American bistro receives rave reviews, like "flawless," from nearly every end of the spectrum. Every aspect of the meal is "almost perfect" and an "experience." Chef Michael Romano's creative wizardry produces superb dishes with beautiful presentations. "Deserves its success." The crowd is hip and beautiful, making it one of the places to be seen in New York.
SPEC: *Baked lobster $24.50; Grilled steak $23.50; Grilled salmon $22.50; Earth & surf $19.50*

0	1	2	3	4	5	6	7	8	9	10
disappointing		fair		good		very good		excellent		perfect

VERBENA   LD   American

(F11) 54 Irving Place (17th & 18th) 212/260-5454 Fax: 260-3595

F 8 / S 7 / A 7 / $38   MC V D AE

This newcomer to historic Irving Place has already drawn much praise. Request a table in the "wonderful," "incredible," back herb garden. Some find the service "snooty," while others say, "nice space, nice people." Go figure. If you're looking for a place to stay, try the quintessential Manhattan inn of the same name, upstairs.

SPEC: *Butternut squash ravioli $9; Sautéed sweetbreads $23; Farm-raised breast of chicken w/fallen corn soufflé & succotash $22; Warm blueberry tart $8*

VILLA BERULIA   LD   Italian

(D11) 107 E. 34th St. (Park & Lex.) 212/689-1970

F 6 / S 7 / A 6 / $28   MC V D AE DIS   **TO**

Good place to stop for an Italian meal in the Empire State Building vicinity. Quite formal with its gracious, if somewhat "haphazard service." Lovely fresh flowers, and white linen tablecloths. The food is generally good, particularly the specials, but some details are off-key, like the "piped-in radio music" and fake whipped cream. **Closed: Sunday**

SPEC: *Minestrone soup $5; Tuna w/balsamic vinegar $20; Anglotti $9.95; Chocolate mousse cake $4*

WATER CLUB, THE   LD   American

(D12) 500 E. 30th St. (East River) 212/683-3333

F 7 / S 5 / A 8 / $40   MC V D AE

Regardless of theme (nautical: semaphore flags hang from the ceiling and model ship hulls tacked to the wall), or cuisine (tasty creatures from the sea), "Buzzy" O'Keefe's NY classic is worth the trip simply for the incredible, panoramic view of the East River and beyond. There's also a separate comfortable, clubby bar/lounge that seems right out of a New England country club. Service can be "spotty," but the food presentation is as spectacular as the sight of glowing boats gliding down the river.

SPEC: *Classic crab cake $12; Shellfish gumbo $9; Red snapper w/lobster dumplings $26; Maine lobster P/A; Milk chocolate torte $7*

YAMA   LD   Japanese

(F11) 122 E. 17th (Lex & 3rd) 212/475-0969

F 5 / S 4 / A 5 / $25   MC V AE

Tucked away at basement level, this place has a clean-cut, compact, Japanese style. The key is the sushi bar, which is the heart, if not the soul. The generous portions of fresh sushi will draw you back. But get there early. A line of loyal customers that stretches out the door forms nightly after 7pm. **Closed: Sunday**

SPEC: *Broiled yellowtail collar $7; Pan-fried dumplings $5; Sushi $2-$4.75; Beef teriyaki $8.75; Yasai tempura $8; Udon $9.50*

ZEN PALATE   LD   Asian

(F11) 34 Union Sq. E. (16th) 212/614-9291 Fax: 614-9401

F 7 / S 7 / A 7 / $14   MC V D AE   **TO**

A New Age diner serving vegetarian dishes with a mix of Thai, Chinese, and Japanese flavors. "An oasis in the hectic city." "Service is quick, portions moderate, presentation delightful." Tofu-based "meat" doubles for the real thing. "Sometimes you forget you're eating vegetarian food." "Go upstairs! It's worth the few extra dollars."

SPEC: *Vegetarian ham $7.45; Stir-fried rice fettuccini $6.50; Eggplant in garlic sauce $6.50; Sweet & sour sensation $6.50.*

EAST 43RD–59TH STREET

ADRIENNE BLD American

(A10) 700 5th Ave. (55th–Penninsula Hotel) 212/903-3918

F 7 / S 7 / A 8 / $50 MC V D AE DIS

A spacious "elegant" hotel restaurant that is particularly popular for power breakfast and business lunches. The cuisine is New American, and if you're looking for someplace different to have dinner before the theater, this is a good bet."

AH CHIHUAHUA LD Mexican

(A12) 330 E. 53rd St. (1st & 2nd) 212/888-6807

F 7 / S 5 / A 6 / $22 MC V AE DIS

Quietly nestled on an inconspicuous midtown side street, this small Mexican eatery is a tasty respite from the NY workday hustle-bustle. Styled from a Texas original, this diamond-in-the-rough transports to just south of the Mexican border. Consistent and authentic-style, ample portions are well-served and quickly delivered. **Closed: Sunday**

SPEC: *Quesados $5.25; Tacos Chihuahua $9.95; Burritos frijol $8.95; Fajitas pollo $13.95*

AKBAR LD Indian

(A11) 475 Park Ave. (57th & 58th) 212/838-1717 Fax: 750-6746

F 6 / S 7 / A 6 / $30 MC V AE DIS **TO/D**

Akbar attracts its own breed of moguls to enjoy deliciously spiced foods, imported stained glass ceilings, and an interior color scheme signifying hard work and prosperity. For a little enlightenment, Saturdays' spiritual bunch offers tarot card readers, palmists and psychics.

SPEC: *Grilled scallops $9.50; Bater masala (quail) $17.95; Tandoori lamb chops $21.95; Aloo jeera (diced potatoes) $11.95*

AL BUSTAN LD Middle Eastern

(B11) 827 3rd Ave. (50th & 51st) 212/759-8439 Fax: 759-0050

F 7 / S 7 / A 7 / $32 MC V D AE

Featuring Lebanese cuisine, with a bit of eastern flair, Al Bustan delivers "good food for a decent price." The dining room is bright and airy, which is nice if you like to feel as if you're a specimen under a microscope. Still, it's a "great place to have a business meeting" or a funky, casual meal.

SPEC: *Prix-fixe lunch $16.95; Tabouleh; Fattoush; Minced lamb;Marinated chicken cubes; Grilled salmon +$3*

ALLEGRIA LD Italian

(B11) 66 W. 55th St. (6th Ave.) 212/956-7755

F 6 / S 7 / A 7 / $32 MC V D AE DIS **TO/D**

Mediterranean sprightliness in this mid-town oasis. A large outdoor cafe and offerings of light, fresh fare distinguish Allegria from the usual NYC micro-cafe. "The real thing" attracts a bustling "Let's do lunch" crowd and bold bright murals give Allegria "a happy feel."

SPEC: *Grilled shrimp w/white beans $10; Slices of turkey topped w/green sauce $8.95; Grilled tuna $18.75; Grilled sliced sirloin steak $21.50; Tiramisu $5.50*

0	1	2	3	4	5	6	7	8	9	10
disappointing		fair		good		very good		excellent		perfect

AMBASSADOR GRILL   LD   Continental

(B12) 1 U.N. Plaza (1st & 2nd–Hyatt Pk Plaza Hotel) 212/702-5014
F 7 / S 7 / A 7 / $40   MC V D AE DIS

A favorite of out-of-towners staying at the hotel, as well as diplomats and others associated with the U.N. across the street. To some, the stark, modern decor with plenty of mirrors, is "a turn-off," and "too gimmicky," while others find it "comfortable" and "interesting."
SPEC: *Prix fixe: Crabmeat & taro root salad; Smoked trout salad; Red snapper. Grilled sirloin of beef; Scallopine of veal $29.95*

ARIA   LD   Italian

(B11) 253 E. 52nd St. (2nd) 212/888-1410
F 6 / S 7 / A 8 / $34   MC V D AE DIS

Quiet, subdued and pleasant. Aria boasts "a great room" and fine Northern Italian cuisine with lots of updated touches at prices that don't spoil the fun. The mood here is subtle, the service friendly and the quality reliably comforting.
SPEC: *Tuscan bean soup $6.50; Beef carpaccio $9.50; Grilled salmon $19.95; Roast veal chop $26.75*

B.T. GRILL, THE   LD   American

(B11) 252 E. 49th St. (2nd & 3rd) 212/758-8320
F 6 / S 6 / A 8 / $40   MC V D AE

It's all here in this chic little steakhouse—art deco, art nouveau, lots of marble and a cool bistro-feel. Wonderful food, in this distinctly casual, yet smart, offshoot of The Box Tree restaurant. The same high standards apply here. **Closed: Saturday & Sunday**
SPEC: *White bean soup $7.50; Crabmeat sauté $14.50; Shepherd's pie $12; T-Bone steak $26; Venison saddle $38*

BAR AND BOOKS   D   American

(B12) 889 1st Ave. (50th) 212/980-9314
F 5 / S 6 / A 6 / $20   MC V D AE

Look for "entrepreneur" co-owner Mark Grossich enjoying sagacious conversation and a tasteful Jamaican cigar in a library motif setting. A handsome bar is aligned below street level windows in a darkly furnished, bookcased walled, classic "cocktail lounge." Excellent appetizers, elegantly served, and live entertainment await in a smoke-filled, smoker's paradise.
SPEC: *Appetizers only.*

BENIHANA OF TOKYO   LD   Japanese

(A11) 120 E. 56th St. (Park & Lex.) 212/593-1627
See review on page 199.

BICE   LD   Italian

(A10) 7 E. 54th St. (Mad. & 5th) 212/688-1999
F 6 / S 5 / A 6 / $45   MC V D AE

It's the clientele— "too many beautiful people"—that makes Bice, not the food. This "loud and crowded" Italian eatery has become one of Manhattan's hot spots despite its "bad attitude" and "expensive food." While it's "good for business meetings", you should go to Bice to drink, not to dine...unless, of course, it's on your company.
SPEC: *Baked eggplant w/mozzarella $12; Linguine w/clams $20; Grilled New Zealand venison chops $30; California squab $24; Banana mousse $8*

BILLY'S   LD   American

(B12) 948 1st Ave. (52nd & 53rd) 212/753-1870

F 5 / S 6 / A 6 / $29   MC V D AE   **TO**

"125 years old and still alive." Billy's opened its doors in 1870, making it the oldest family owned restaurant in New York City. A handsome mahogany interior and an "old time saloon bar" with working gaslights, "reliable" Billy's still recreates a turn-of-the-century world. A "great neighborhood hangout," with traditional American fare. There is even a "good quality chicken breasts on greens" to appease the more health conscious palate.
SPEC: *Chopped chicken livers $5.75; French onion soup $4.95; Lamb chops $23; Scallops $17.50*

BOX TREE, THE   LD   French

(B11) 250 E. 49th St. (2nd & 3rd)   212/758-8320 Fax: 308-3899

F 7 / S 7 / A 8 / $92   MC V AE

"Very romantic" and "very pretty," begins to describe this "exquisite" townhouse, deftly turned into a country inn. Antiques, fine art and back-lit Tiffany windows surround a player piano and softly padding waiters. Three working fireplaces add a warm glow to the "excellent service and atmosphere." A European trained chef turns out "classic" French and expensive fare. **Closed: Saturday lunch**
SPEC: *5 course pre-fixe dinner: Snails in pernod butter gratine; Medallions of veal w/wild mushroom; Roast pheasant w/juniper berry*

BROADWAY DINER   BLD   Diner

(A11) 590 Lexington Ave. (55th) 212/486-8838

F 5 / S 6 / A 4 / $16   Cash only

Tourists fill the East Side version of the original West Side diner on weekends while during the week, the lunch crowd lines up out the door. The reward?... Tasty fare served in "gargantuan portions." At night, the "West Side branch is a lot hipper," hosting a downtown crowd.
SPEC: *Turkey burger $6.50; Grilled chicken breast w/guacamole $9.95; Chicken pot pie $8.50; Grilled vegetable platter oriental w/brown rice $7.95*

BRUCE HO AND THE FOUR SEAS   LD   Chinese

(A11) 116 E. 57th St. (Park & Lex.) 212/753-2610 Fax: 688-6092

F 5 / S 6 / A 4 / $35   MC V D AE   **TO/D**

The personable Bruce Ho, an icon in "exquisite Chinese cuisine" since 1964, makes his new customers feel like regulars and the regulars feel like new. Simple decor and cooking upon request, a task not many undertake, contribute to its longevity. No jacket, but Mai Tai required.
SPEC: *Chef's special mixed platter $8; Veal medallions $28; Steamed salmon $19.75; Malaysian shrimp $21.50*

BRUNO RISTORANTE   LD   Italian

(A11) 240 E. 58th St. (2nd & 3rd) 212/688-4190 Fax: 688-4342

F 7 / S 7 / A 7 / $35   MC V D AE DIS   **TO**

Art deco and cosmopolitan, this combination of Northern and Southern Italian boasts a celebrity clientele like the cast of an all-star movie. A split personality gives it a smaller, more elegant downstairs dining room where the waiters serve in flocks, and a more lively second story where, "The experience is the upstairs piano room." **Closed: Sunday**
SPEC: *Fettuccini w/portobello mushrooms & cognac sauce $18.75; Marinated, broiled veal chop w/sautéed hot cherry peppers $28.50*

0	1	2	3	4	5	6	7	8	9	10
disappointing		fair		good		very good		excellent		perfect

BULL AND BEAR — LD — American

(B11) 301 Park Ave. (49th –Waldorf Hotel) 212/872-4900

F 5 / S 6 / A 6 / $42   MC V D AE DIS

With its dark-wood paneling, antique clock and muted air, the Bull and Bear emits a touch of "Old World" class that some will find charming, while others will just find stuffy. But the "business boys" who feel that it's "great for luncheons and meetings," don't seem to mind. And it's a familiar, New York, classic.

SPEC: *Smoked Faroe island salmon $11.50; Aged black angus strip steak (12 oz) $28; Charbroiled marinated flank steak (10 oz) $26*

CAFE CENTRO — LD — French

(B10) 200 Park Ave. (45th & Vanderbilt) 212/818-1222

F 7 / S 7 / A 7 / $34   MC V D AE

Always crowded, this bistro serves up delightful meals to a hip clientele. There's a great beer garden for Happy Hour, as well as a huge room for private parties. The wait staff is friendly and attentive. No wonder it's become one of New York's new power scenes. It may be "loud!" but it's a "great addition to Grand Central."

SPEC: *Grilled Lyonnaise sausage $6.50; Mallard duck foie gras $9.95; Chicken tagine $18.50; Osso buco of monkfish $18.50; Coconut mousse bomb $7*

CAFE DUPONT — LD — Continental

(A12) 1038 1st Ave. (56th & 57th) 212/223-1133

F 7 / S 7 / A 7 / $30   MC V D AE DIS   TO

If atmosphere means little, but quality food means a lot, Cafe DuPont is for you. So small you have to walk outside to change your mind, this Sutton Place store front eatery is a favorite with upscale neighborhood diners for their incredible gourmet food.

SPEC: *Mesclun salad w/shallot oil vinaigrette $6; Escargot $8; Duck breast w/pear ginger sauce $18.50; Rack of lamb $24*

CAFE S.F.A. — L — American

(B10) Saks 5th Ave. 611 5th Ave. (50th—8th fl.) 212/940-4080

F 6 / S 6 / A 6 / $25   MC V D AE DIS   TO

The ladies who lunch, lunch happily here. And those that occupy window-side tables have a bird's-eye view of Fifth Ave. and Saks' other famous neighbors—the gardens of Rockefeller Center and the soaring spires of St. Pat's. An imaginative menu. Smart service. A convenient counter accommodates single shoppers. But " long waits" can be off-putting at popular hours.

SPEC: *Sweet corn & Maryland crab chowder $5.95; Ginger chicken dumplings $6.50; Polenta torte $11.25; Paillard of veal $14.95*

CAPTAIN'S TABLE, THE — LD — Seafood

(B11) 860 2nd Ave. 46th 212/697-9538

F 6 / S 6 / A 6 / $30   MC V D AE   TO/D

This seafood stop has a tired look, but "good" food. It's the kind of place your grandparents would take you to. Diners select their meals from large platters before it's cooked. Choose your sea creatures carefully, though, as some selections can be rather pricey.

SPEC: *Snails Bourguinon $7.50; Grilled yellowfin tuna $19.95; Swordfish steak $19.95; Trout almondine $15.95; Fried shrimp wrapped in jalapeño peppers $16.95*

CHIAM LD Chinese

(B11) 160 E. 48th St. (Lex. & 3rd) 212/371-2323 Fax: 935-0012

F 7 / S 7 / A 7 / $34   MC V D AE   **TO/D**

The blend of both worlds, featuring light Hong Kong-style cuisine with an international spin. The setting is subdued and utterly civilized. Not for glitz-seekers. But the restraint is satisfying in every way. "A cut above, but not miles beyond." For wine connoisseurs, special tasting events. And for the romantically inclined—a table can be arranged in Chiam's wine cellar—the perfect place to "pop the question."

SPEC: *Hacked chicken in sesame sauce $8.25; Aromatic beef $9.25; Salt-baked calamari kowdoon $14.95; Beijing pork filets $14.95; Banana flambé $6*

CHIN CHIN LD Chinese

(B11) 216 E. 49th St. (2nd & 3rd) 212/888-4555

F 7 / S 7 / A 7 / $28   MC V D AE   **TO/D**

The brothers Chin provide diverse "Hong Kong food with NY style," while adding a modern twist. Exquisite art deco interior design reflects a tasteful timelessness. Antique family photos convey an appreciation of family and history. A dining experience pleasurable to all the senses.

SPEC: *Peking duck $35; Cha Cha shrimp $18; Hong Kong pork filets $15.50; Mama Chin beef $17.50*

CHRIST CELLA LD American

(B11) 164 E. 46th St. (Lex. & 3rd) 212/697-2479

F 7 / S 7 / A 6 / $44   MC V D AE

Although the steaks and chops are well-prepared and hearty, the meals are "expensive." For the most part, the crowd is older: some diners are from the newer, NY power scene, while others look as if they have a few more years behind them. With, "great grilled steaks and fish," the food is "solid," and served in large portions.

SPEC: *Tuna tartar $15.75; Sirloin steak $29.95; Calf's liver $30.95; Filet mignon $29.95; Lamb chops $29.95; Fudge cake $9.75*

CHRISTO'S LD American

(B11) 541 Lexington Ave. (49th & 50th) 212/755-1200

F 5 / S 7 / A 7 / $40   MC V D AE DIS

This unpretentious steakhouse/sports bar, serves the normal fare. During the day, the clientele is primarily business; at night, tourists or New Yorkers looking for a carnivorous meal. It's divided into three areas—the grill, the main dining room, and the bar. "The waiters know service with a smile." But, the only place safe from television monitors is the main dining room.

SPEC: *Shrimp cocktail $11.95; Prime sirloin steak $29.95; Prime "T" bone steak $29.95; Chicken w/lemon sauce $19.95; Cheesecake $4.75*

CLARKE'S LD American

(A11) 915 3rd Ave. (55th) 212/759-1650

F 5 / S 5 / A 6 / $16   MC V D AE

Clarke's (don't call it P.J.'s), is a "great," "old-time bar" that has been a neighborhood watering hole since the 1890s. Distinctly nestled among glass and chrome skyscrapers, you'll find a "fine," "standard menu" and "the best hamburgers in town." It's a "great neighborhood place" with "good value," and you can still catch a shining star or two sequestered within the crowds.

SPEC: *Vichyssoise $3.80; Hamburgers $6.10-$7.10; Cold poached salmon w/sauce verde; Chili $5.60*

0	1	2	3	4	5	6	7	8	9	10
disappointing		fair		good		very good		excellent		perfect

COMING OR GOING · BLD · American

(A10) 38 E. 58th St. (Mad. & Park) 212/980-5858 Fax: 750-3944

F 6 / S 6 / A 7 / $37 MC V D AE **TO/D**

This small but "adorable place," is a little gem and "mid-town sleeper," in a large neighborhood setting. "Lovely at dinner," every table is decorated with a candle in a different style holder. The walls are adorned with various one-of-a-kind small mirrors. There is also "good food," with everything, including home-grown herbs, made on premises. **Closed: Sunday (Saturday during summer)**
SPEC: *Baked wild mushrooms $7.95; Braised lamb shank $18.95; Free range chicken $19.95; Valrhona chocolate soufflé cake $7.25*

DAWAT · LD · Indian

(A11) 210 E. 58th St. (2nd & 3rd) 212/355-7555 Fax: 355-1735

F 7 / S 7 / A 7 / $31 MC V D AE **TO/D**

This "excellent" Northern Indian restaurant is fit for a raja. It's the gift of chef, Madhur Jaffrey, cookbook author, TV personality, and film actress. The food is "great," "innovative" "gourmet Indian" with "a good selection of different tastes." "A step above the rest," Dawat is still acclaimed by New Yorkers to have: "The best Indian food in the city!"
SPEC: *Baghari Jhinga (shrimp, garlic & curry leaves) $9.95; Salmon in a banana leaf $22.95; Leg of lamb $22.95; Carrot halva $4.95*

DENIZ · LD · Mediterranean

(A12) 400 E. 57th St. (1st & Sutton) 212/486-2255

F 7 / S 5 / A 6 / $28 MC V D AE **TO**

Newly emerging on the Upper East Side, Deniz is spacious and ready for business. Their motto: "Fish fresher than ours is still in the sea." The palate experiences an explosion of savor—Mediterranean style. The Ottoman decor, accents your dining experience with tranquility.
SPEC: *Char grilled mashed eggplant salad $6.50; Stuffed mussels $7.50; Grilled red snapper $19.50; Octopus a la Turk $14.50*

EAST · LD · Japanese

(B11) 137 East 47th St.   (Lex & Third) 212/980- 7909
(C11) 210 East 44th St.   (2nd & 3rd) 212/687- 5075
See review on page 105.

EDWARDIAN ROOM · BLD · Continental

(A10) 768 5th Ave. (59th–Plaza Hotel) 212/759-3000

F 6 / S 7 / A 8 / $51 MC V D AE

This "beautiful, large dining room," set in "stately," "old, elegant style," soars with cathedral ceilings, dark wood accents and lavish wall trimmings. The service is "slow but elegant," the wait staff surprisingly friendly and the food "upscale." With a menu that changes both daily and seasonally, there's also a handsome prix-fixe lunch and several special dinners served throughout the year.
SPEC: *Venison carpaccio w/asparagus $14.50; Roasted free-range chicken $26; Roast rack of lamb $29; Green tea creme brulee $8*

Rolanda Watts
Syndicated talk show host

"**Box Tree**. Not only are the food and service totally superb, but it is truly the most romantic restaurant on the continent. Just imagine relaxing over a 5-course meal and later sauntering upstairs to enjoy a glass of brandy in one of the secluded, fire-lit rooms."

EL RIO GRANDE   LD   Tex-Mex

(C11) 160 E. 38th St. (3rd Ave.) 212/867-0922

F 6 / S 5 / A 6 / $24   MC V D AE   **TO**

Split into Texan and Mexican halves, divided by the kitchen, you can be escorted across the border from one "country" to another. The Texan side is a bit more casual with a smoking dining room area and an immense, flying bull hanging over the bar. There's "good food," "good margaritas," and the closer you get to the weekend, the bigger the singles scene.

SPEC: *Stuffed jalapeño $8.95; Wild Bill's wings $4.50; Pechugas del pollo $13.95; Flan $3.25; Banana piñata $5.25*

EQUINOX CAFE & RESTAURANT   BLD   Italian

(B11) 541 Lexington Ave. (49th–Doral Inn Hotel) 212/593-4725

F 3 / S 3 / A 3 / $23   Cash only   **TO/D**

The neon wattage in this cafe/restaurant is sure to wake you up. The decor screams Miami beach, but the cuisine, which is undistinguished, is Italian/American. And, if you're in dire need of film, postcards, or a NY T-shirt, they've got you covered.

SPEC: *Pollo al rosmarino $9.75; Pollo alla citron $9.75; Canelloni verdi $7.95; Bistecca alla griglia $17.50; Fruit pie $3*

Eros

EROS   D   Mediterranean

(A12) 1078 1st Ave. (58th & 59th) 212/223-2322

F 7 / S 7 / A 7 / $32   MC V AE DIS

A campy Greek/Mediterranean den that's full of delights, from its gold ceiling to its high back plush, pale green loveseats and lounge chairs for cozy, exotic dining. The menu is inspired and interpretive. Get psyched about Eros. Go, and don't look back.

SPEC: *Grilled sardines $8.75; Octopus, squid & shrimp salad $9.50; Taverna-style chicken $17.50; Rabbit stifado $19.50*

FELIDIA   LD   Italian

(A11) 243 E. 58th St. (2nd & 3rd) 212/758-1479

F 8 / S 7 / A 7 / $39   MC V D AE

One of the loveliest settings in the area. The dark wood paneling, fresh flowers and lovely "winter garden window" bespeak the air of elegance in this posh, brownstone setting. Owner Lidia Bastianich has created a perfect spot for Triesta-style, "delicious Italian fare," with "polite, educated service." Uniquely suitable for either daytime "business clientele," or an "almost perfect," "sometimes magical," romantic evening.

SPEC: *Calamari $12; Grilled polenta w/warm octopus salad $10; Pan roasted monkfish $28; Butterflied breaded veal chop $28*

0	1	2	3	4	5	6	7	8	9	10
disappointing		fair		good		very good		excellent		perfect

Vincent Sardi
Owner of Sardi's Restaurant

"**Gino** is unique. It's one of the few old style Italian restaurants which retains its personality, cuisine and clientele. Even though Gino's retired, the restaurant goes on as usual. And occasionally, when he does come in, he's hailed as a celebrity."

57/57	BLD	American

(A10) 57 E. 57th St. (Mad. & Park) 212/758-5757

F 8 / S 7 / A 8 / $44   MC V D AE

The Temple of Dendur meets the 20th Century in this elegant, I.M. Pei-designed monument. Muted, mellow and relaxing in every way. Chef Susan Weaver prepares an enticing menu of New American cuisine, which also includes interesting "light alternative" selections. There's a spacious European-style bar and piano music nightly. Jazz on Friday and Saturday nights. Not just for tourists or hotel guests, to be sure.

SPEC: *Grilled portobello mushrooms $6; Tuna & ratatouille $24; Herb roast rack of lamb $30; Devil's food cake $8;*

FITZER'S	BLD	Irish-American

(A11) 687 Lexington Ave. (56th & 57th) 212/355-0100

F 4 / S 6 / A 7 / $24   MC V D AE DIS

Located inside the Fitzpatrick Hotel, Fitzer's offers a quiet respite from the hustle and bustle of the 57th street area. With its dark, carpeted interior, chandeliers, and wood-paneled bar, it has a calming influence, at least until Happy Hour when it gets crowded with thirsty after-work singles.

SPEC: *Fried chicken tenders $6; Oak smoked Irish salmon $10.50; Irish shepherd's pie $10; Seafood goujons $10; Corned beef & cabbage $10.50; Baileys ice cream sandwich $7*

Top 10 $56+

Very
Expensive

FOUR SEASONS—THE POOL ROOM	LD Continental

(B11) 99 E. 52nd St. (Park & Lex.) 212/754-9494

F 8 / S 9 / A 9 / $62   MC V D AE

One of the most famously elegant restaurants in the world. Next to the grill room there's a "much more exciting" pool room with "best seating near the pool" or "on the balcony overlooking the entire restaurant." Trees depicting the four seasons and "floating curtains" complete the environmental melange. First-class continental cuisine is always impeccably served in first-rate, cosmopolitan style.

SPEC: *Tuna carpaccio $17; Crab meat salad $18.50; Medallions of veal $36.50; Pepper tuna $37.50 Sautéed calf's liver $35*

Top 10 $36-55

Expensive

FOUR SEASONS—THE GRILL	LD	Continental

(B11) 99 E. 52nd St. (Park & Lex.) 212/754-9494

F 8 / S 8 / A 7 / $42   MC V D AE

Though The Grill is better known for "power lunches," it still leaves its mark as one of the preeminent dining experiences in the city. There's the "impressive NY design," and "perfect, classic bar." But some call the "decor very '70s," "cool and uncomfortable," and suggest it "be brought into the '90s." The ambiance may be "a bit stiff," for some, "but there's great food" and "classic, elegant service."

SPEC: *Prix-fixe: Penne, crayfish & wild leeks; Herb baked monkfish $36.50; Curried breast of capon $29.50; Roasted leg of rabbit $33.50; Passionfruit brulee; Hazelnut chocolate torte*

Fresco

FRESCO **LD** **Italian**

(B10) 34 E. 52nd. St. (Mad. & Park) 212/935-3434

F 7 / S 7 / A 7 / $44 MC V D AE

Not the hippest of restaurants, nor is it a power scene, but it is a "great place for business lunch or a casual date." The majority of selections here come from the Tuscany region and the portions "are huge."

SPEC: *Stuffed portabello mushroom $9; Rigatoni w/broccoli & grilled chicken $18; Bass aqua pazza $26; Fennel crusted loin of veal $26*

FU'S **LD** **Chinese**

(B11) 972 2nd Ave. (51st & 52nd) 212/517-9670

F 6 / S 6 / A 5 / $24 MC V D AE **TO/D**

There are plenty of Chinese restaurants around, but only a handful could be called romantic. This is one them. Fu's is small, but the interior is elegant and the staff is friendly and helpful. And, if you call ahead, they'll even pre-fix a dinner for you. How's that for cooperation?

SPEC: *Grand Marnier shrimp $7; Peking duck $28.95; Crispy orange beef $13.95; Lichees $2.75; Fu's cheesecake $3.50*

GAUGUIN **LD** **Asian**

(A10) 768 5th Ave. (5th & CPS–Plaza Hotel) 212/319-0404

F 3 / S 5 / A 5 / $40 MC V D AE

Formerly Trader Vic's, this South Pacific-style bar is fun and reasonably priced. Regrettably, Gauguin does not live up to it's predecessor's reputation. It's made to feel like a tropical island with a bridge walkway, tikki torches and low-level lighting. The dining room is spacious and there's a huge bar at one end of the room, with an incredible selection of exotic drinks. So at least enjoy an exciting, evening, hip 20's and 30's scene.

SPEC: *Lobster spring rolls $9; Seafood shu-mai dumplings $7; Pu pu platter (for 2 or more) Sesame chicken, lobster spring rolls, maple glazed ribs, salt & pepper calamari $10 per person*

GIAMBELLI 50TH **LD** **Italian**

(B11) 46 E. 50th St. (Mad. & Park) 212/688-2760

F 6 / S 7 / A 7 / $35 MC V D AE DIS

It's "expensive," "overpriced," and some claim there's "poor quality food and service." But this midtown ristorante oozes history and still garnishes high ratings. There's an "incredible wine list" and "great fresh fish." "The owner makes you feel welcome," and the wait staff is nice. But the food has a very tired taste and look to it.

SPEC: *Prix-fixe lunch $27: Special antipasto; Baked large green egg noodles; Ravioli; Baked chicken and meat stuffed cannelloni; Chicken cacciatora; Broiled spring lamb chops; Chocolate cake*

0	1	2	3	4	5	6	7	8	9	10
disappointing		fair		good		very good		excellent		perfect

GIRAFE   LD   Italian

(A11) 208 E. 58th St. (2nd & 3rd) 212/752-3054

F 8 / S 8 / A 7 / $34   MC V D AE DIS

Fond of wildlife? Check out this ristorante in the shadow of Bloomie's. "Fun, especially for a long lunch." Just look for the giraffe sculpture outside this pretty, little spot. Lots of large portraits of creatures of the wild, the four-legged kind, surround you while you feast on first-rate Northern Italian fare. Lots of neighborhood regulars and some NYC bigwigs frequent this subdued, subtle spot. **Closed: Sunday**

SPEC: *Gamberi Girafe $13; Caprese $10.50; Grilled salmon $24; Scallopine di pollo umberto $19.50 Fragole $8; Zabaglione al marsala $10*

GLOUCESTER CAFE   BLD   Seafood

(B10) 37 E. 50th St. (Park & Mad.) 212/750-2233 Fax: 750-2252

F 4 / S 2 / A 5 / $32   MC V D AE DIS

A NY institution since 1948, the huge space that was once Gloucester House was completely gutted (except for the butcher block) to make room for the new, nouvelle cuisine. The menu is as dazzling as the art deco decor with many interesting and imaginative alternatives to seafood.. Tired of trying to figure out who's who? Try chillin' with your own private VCR (plus headphones) on the upper level.

SPEC: *Lobster club sandwich w/ smoked bacon & key lime spread $12.50*

HARRY CIPRIANI   LD   Italian

(A10) 781 5th Ave. (59th & 60th) 212/753-5566 Fax: 308-5653

F 7 / S 6 / A 7 / $49   MC V D AE DIS

In! Glitzy! A hot, happening "classy" spot for NYC's power elite. This vivacious base of the international set—kin to the famed Harry's Bar in Venice—is so Hemingwayesque. They claim the best power lunch in N.Y. You'll find Ron, Tom, Warren, The Donald and Marla. And if you have to ask who—don't bother to go. It's very "clubby," but that's part of the fun.

SPEC: *Polenta w/duck ragu $10.95; Salmon in wine w/zucchini $32.95; Monkfish alla Livornese $32.95*

HATSUHANA   LD   Japanese

(B10) 17 E. 48th St. (Mad. & 5th) 212/355-3345 Fax: 308-0001

(B11) 237 Park Ave. (46th) 212/661-3400

F 6 / S 4 / A 2 / $40   MC V AE D

"Still the best, freshest sushi in the city." Although pricey, the food is prepared with great care, so the fish seems to melt in your mouth—not in your...There are, however, some complaints about "poor" service. After a meal here you might become a sushi addict.

SPEC: *Shrimp & vegetable tempura $8; Sushi $18; Sashimi special (8 varieties of sliced raw-fish) $28; Chirashi special $27*

HOULIHAN'S   LD   Amer/Continental

(A11) 677 Lexington Ave. (56th) 212/339-8858

(A10) 767 5th Ave. (58th & 59th) 212/339-8850

See review on page 230.

Il Gabbiano

IL GABBIANO   LD   Italian

(A11) 232 E. 58th St. (2nd & 3rd)   212/754-1033 Fax: 754-6783

F 7 / S 7 / A 7 / $35   MC V D AE DIS   **TO/D**

Everything's cooked to order in this cozy East Side favorite where the recent renovation means comfortable seating, soft light and lots of fresh flowers daily. Steady customers get more than tasty dishes. If Il Gabiano rates high on your list, you may be in for a VIP card, which means 25% off each check.

SPEC: *Carpaccio of smoked salmon $11.95; Buffalo mozzarella w/roasted peppers & tomatoes $10.95; Broiled salmon $24.95; Black linguine lobster $23.95*

IL NIDO   LD   Italian

(A11) 251 E. 53rd St. (2nd & 3rd Aves.) 212/753-8450

F 8 / S 7 / A 6 / $44   MC V D AE

Il Nido is not without its charms: the stunning trattoria design, for instance. And the "wonderful" cuisine is rated high. But the curtness of the wait staff can be a turnoff, particularly when combined with the high prices. Twenty bucks or more for a plate of pasta? Crack open the Spaghetti-O's, Marge.

SPEC: *Roast peppers w/anchovies; Macaroni & bean soup $8; Lobster, shrimp, clams & mussels $37; Chocolate torte $7*

IL TOSCANACCIO   LD   Italian

(A10) 7 E. 59th St. (5th & Mad.) 212/935-3535

F 8 / S 7 / A 7 / $36   MC V D AE

"Like dining in Tuscany." That's just the effect Pino Luongos had in mind for his new restaurant. Suave and elegant in a very European way, it features a bar and lounge upstairs. Downstairs, there's a room with comfortable chairs, love seats and ottomans, as well as a wonderful mural wickedly depicting famous Italians like Sophia Loren and Catherine de Medici enjoying a meal together.

SPEC: *Tuna tartare $8.50; Linguine w/scallops, mussels, clams & calamari $16; Grilled marinated baby chicken $20.50*

IL VIGNETO   LD   Italian

(A12) 1068 1st Ave. (58th & 59th) 212/755-6875

F 6 / S 6 / A 5 / $22   MC C AE   **TO/D**

The food must be decent if Ford models patronize this handsome, serene "tiny, cute" and "undiscovered" Italian restaurant. Soft colored tan walls and floors, casual and relaxed feel, make it enticing to anyone who is looking for a tasty, moderately priced and quick Italian lunch or dinner.

SPEC: *Sicilian eggplant salad $5.75; Insalata di Caesar $4.50; Risotto w/baby shrimp; Chicken w/eggplant, prosciutto, mozzarella, marsala & mushrooms $11.75*

0	1	2	3	4	5	6	7	8	9	10
disappointing	fair		good			very good		excellent		perfect

INAGIKU

LD   **Japanese**

(B10) 11 E. 49th St. (Mad. & 5th) 212/355-0440

F 7 / S 6 / A 6 / $40   MC V D AE

This fixture at the Waldorf Hotel offers a refuge from the "mean streets" where kimono-clad waitresses, subtle decor, and soft interior light create a soothing ambiance so rare in "The Naked City." A tempura bar and rooms for truly Japanese dining (you sit on the floor.) Shabu-shabu and teriyaki prepared tableside.

SPEC: *Tempura appetizer $8.50; Yakitori (grilled chicken on skewers) $7; Ishiyaki steak $25; Seafood ishiyaki $29; Kuri zenzal $6.50*

JUBILEE

LD   **French**

(A12) 347 E. 54th St. (1st & 2nd) 212/888-3569

F 7 / S 6 / A 6 / $29   MC V D AE

This newish bistro has the intimate feel of a French country inn. There's a fireplace to add to the ambiance but, alas, it doesn't work. "Consistent value in every category." "The chef is talented and the people care." A first-rate menu + stylish presentation + scrumptious desserts = a cause for Jubilation!

SPEC: *Truffled chicken liver paté $7; Curry mussels $8.50; Shrimp cannelonis w/lobster sauce $14*

L'ENTRECOTE

D   **French**

(A12) 1057 1st Ave. (57th & 58th) 212/755-0080

F 7 / S 8 / A 7 / $35   MC V D AE

Enchanting, cozy restaurant ("only 34 seats") with a bistro flair. With French artifacts and wine bottles adorning the walls, you can close your eyes and almost fool yourself into thinking you're in Paris. Especially since the restaurant is small enough to allow smoking. **Closed: Sunday**

SPEC: *Escargots $7.75; Caesar salad $5.75; L'entrecote $20.75; Steak au poivre $21.75; coupe aux marrons $6.25; Profiteroles $6.25*

Top 10
$56+
Very
Expensive

LA GRENOUILLE

LD   **French**

(B10) 3 E. 52nd St. (5th & Mad.) 212/752-1495

F 9 / S 8 / A 8 / $75   MC V D AE

Another one of NY's classic French spots. The decor features charming arrangements of fresh flowers, lovely white tablecloths, and well-suited waiters. The dining room feels like a French castle garden. The meals are gastronomical fantasies. The clientele is upscale, but not snobby. There's a splendid small dining room on the 2nd floor available for private parties. **Closed: Sunday & Monday & August**

SPEC: *Prix fixe lunch $42; Prix fixe dinner $75*

LA MAGANETTE

LD   **French**

(B11) 825 3rd Ave. (50th) 212/759-5677 Fax: 759-9048

F 4 / S 4 / A 2 / $27   MC V AE

It's old. It's tawdry. It's overpriced. It does have a nice outdoor dining space and a great dance club downstairs. But the food is mundane, the dining room devoid of ambiance, and the wait staff lacks personality.

SPEC: *Grilled portobello mushrooms $5.95; Scaloppinne alla Maganette $16.95; Combination la Maganette $19.95; Veal rollatina margherita $21.95*

LA MANGEOIRE **LD** French

(A11) 1008 2nd Ave. (53rd & 54th) 212/759-7086

F 6 / S 6 / A 6 / $37   MC V D AE

This small country French cottage is "an outstanding find" that "deserves better recognition." It's no Bouley, but it offers a moderately priced meal in a casual, friendly setting. There are 2 small dining rooms, a cute bar in back, and "beautiful flowers all over." There's a limited but well-priced wine list, and there are well-prepared and reasonable prix-fixe menus.

SPEC: *Mediterranean-style fish soup $8.50; Beef daube & spinach ravioli $9; Seafood pasta $18; Roasted monkfish, Bouillabaisse style $20; Rabbit Provencale $22.50*

LASAGNA RISTORANTE Italian

(B11) 941 2nd Ave. (50th)   212/308-5353 Fax: 308-5846

F 6 / S 5 / A 5 / $20   MC V D AE DIS   **TO/D**

The decor is simple: ceiling fans with terra-cotta style motif, and there's a hint of America in both atmosphere and cuisine. With 13 lasagna dishes and more than 15 pasta variations to choose from, Italy is more than represented at this friendly, inexpensive midtown restaurant. Save room for the tiramisu! It's fluffily prepared by the proprietor's charming wife, Ricki.

SPEC: *Penne primavera w/smoked salmon $5.95; Four cheese lasagna $9.95; Linguine w/mixed seafood 13.95; Tiramisu $4.50*

LE CHANTILLY **LD** French

(A11) 106 E. 57th St. (Park & Lex.) 212/751-2931

F 7 / S 6 / A 6 / $60   MC V D AE

This namesake of the ultra-chic French race track oozes romance and class. Chef David Ruggerio whips up delicious classic French meals offered in a bright and elegant dining room with well-spaced tables, tablecloths and fresh flowers. Waiters speak French and have a charming way of explaining the evening's selections.

SPEC: *Prix fixe dinner: Tuna tartare; Hot pumpkin soup; Grilled red snapper; Spring lamb loin; Spiced duck; Humphrey Bogart's hat of white chocolate & bourbon $53*

LE COLONIAL **LD** Vietnamese

(A11) 149 E. 57th St. (3rd & Lex.) 212/752-0808 Fax: 752-7534

F 7 / S 7 / A 8 / $28   MC V D AE

The walls are adorned with lovely, pre-war photos of Vietnam and its proud heritage. The upstairs cocktail lounge offers a romantic ambiance, with comfortable couches and Oriental rugs. And, if you're lucky, you might bump into Madonna, one of the celebrities who's been spotted here.

SPEC: *Soft salad rolls w/shrimp $6.50; Charcoal grilled baby back ribs $7.50; Crisp-seared whole red snapper P/A; Ginger marinated roast duck $16*

LE PERIGORD **LD** French

(B12) 405 E. 52nd St. (1st Ave.) 212/755-6244

F 7 / S 7 / A 6 / $60   MC V D AE

Elegant in every way, from the staff to the chef, to the food, to the unequivocal setting. This scene is fashionable and upscale. The wait staff doesn't just serve diners, they mingle with them. Serving only the finest dishes—excellent cuts of meat and rare catches of fish—Le Perigord is a true culinary experience.

SPEC: *Prix-fixe ($52) Duck liver w/Sauterne jelly $15; Bay scallops; Dover sole; Bass; Beef stew; Rabbit; Veal kidney; Crepes soufflés +$5*

0	1	2	3	4	5	6	7	8	9	10
disappointing		fair		good		very good		excellent		perfect

GAYLE GLEASON

Le Train Bleu

LE TRAIN BLEU — L — Continental

(A11) Bloomingdale's, 1000 3rd Ave. (59th & 60th) 212/705-2100

F 5 / S 5 / A 7 / $30 MC V D AE DIS

Toot! Toot! All aboard! Peckish Bloomie's shoppers in search of a civilized nosh make whistle-stops here. This romantic, carefully wrought recreation of an elegant European dining car is a mirror of times past. It's pure theater. Look for attentive service and quality food. But if you're looking for the French countryside passing by—will the Queensboro Bridge really suffice?

SPEC: *Texas sweet potato bisque $4.75; Smoked Petrossian salmon $9; Baked filet of lemon sole $15.75; Barbequed L.I. duck breast $16*

LEOPARD, THE — LD — French

(B11) 253 E. 50th St. (2nd & 3rd) 212/759-3735

F 8 / S 7 / A 8 / $49 MC V D AE

This French-Continental offers a fun, eclectic atmosphere to its patrons. The petite townhouse has a small dining area with an enormous vase of flowers in the center. The starch white walls are complemented with elegant accent pieces. The menu is well-priced. The food delicious. Could we ask for more?

SPEC: *Complete dinner, including unlimited wine $49; Lobster crepe; Goose liver pate; Roasted boneless duck; Sautéed veal chop; Poached fillet of salmon; Filet mignon; Chocolate mousse cake*

LES SANS CULOTTES — LD — French

(A11) 1085 2nd Ave. (57th & 58th) 212/838-6660 Fax: 644-8247

F 6 / S 6 / A 6 / $21 MC V D AE

Culture shock is what you get when you step off bustling 57th street and into this charming, unpretentious old French countryside restaurant. The tablecloths are blue checked, there's a dining area on the main floor, and a quirky, old staircase leading up to a 2nd, more intimate, dining room. The menu is rather limited, but the prix-fixe meal is very French and very reasonable. "Great value."

SPEC: *Prix fixe dinner (including appetizer, entree and dessert) $19.95; Duck w/cherry sauce; Salmon w/basil sauce*

$56+

Very
Expensive

LESPINASSE — LD — French Asian

(A10) 2 E. 55th St. (Mad. & 5th–St. Regis) 212/339-6719

F 9 / S 8 / A 8 / $58 MC V D AE

This showcase for fine food and service is also one for fine prices. Chef Gray Kunz prepares Asian-accented French cuisine for his guests with an extreme air of style and grace. "Master Kunz, über alles!" The tastes are very complex, making it like a voyage into the culinary unknown. With huge arches and elegant wing-back chairs, the dining room has a Louis XV motif.

SPEC: *Herb risotto & mushroom fricassee $21; Bell pepper gumbo $16; Roast guinea hen $31; Grilled halibut $35; Crispy black bass $33*

LEXINGTON AVENUE GRILL   BLD   American

(B11) 569 Lexington Ave. (Loew's N.Y. Hotel- 51st) 212/753-1515

F 6 / S 6 / A 6 / $29   MC V D AE DIS

Boisterous, touristy, but convenient, especially if you're staying at the Loews NY hotel. This American-style grill boasts a chef formerly of the Rainbow Room. The menu's broad and the prices fair. And for sports fans there are 9 TVs in the bar area. For this, thank Bab Costas who does his broadcasts from here on occasion.
SPEC: *Wild mushrooms & asparagus $7.95; Smoked duck salad $7.50; Barbecued pork tenderloin $17.95; Pan roasted chicken breast $16.95*

LIPIZZANA   LD   Viennese

(A11) 987 2nd Ave. (52nd & 53rd) 212/753-4859

F 6 / S 6 / A 5 / $27   MC V D AE   **TO/D**

If you've got a hankering for Viennese food and you're stumped as to where to satisfy your craving, this is the place. The menu is chock full of Austrian specialties (fortunately, with translations). The interior is light and airy and the large upstairs room is perfect for corporate parties or wedding receptions. And the thin-crusted pizza, a remnant from the location's former tenant, Rocky Lee's, lives on. Hmm, doesn't sound Viennese to us.
SPEC: *Herring trio $6.25; Weisswurst und knackwurst $6.50; "Alt Wiener" Tafelspitz (boiled beef, chives & apple horseradish sauce) $17.95; "Fiaker goulash" $14.50*

LOBBY LOUNGE   LD   Amer/Continentl

(A10) 57 E. 57th St. (Mad. & Park) 212/758-5700

F 6 / S 7 / A 8 / $36   MC V D AE

This civilized, sophisticated spot offers an instant "getaway" feeling in the midst of the throbbing city. An all-day dining menu, brunch and mid-afternoon tea are all offered. Or just drinks. There's piano music and a sense of "Old World elegance."
SPEC: *Onion soup w/brie croutons $8; Grilled vegetable sandwich $18; Seared salmon steak $22; Chicken paillard $21*

LUTÈCE   LD   French

(B11) 249 E. 50th St. (2nd & 3rd) 212/752-2225

F 7 / S 7 / A 7 / $68   MC V AE D

For decades this has been considered one of the city's finest, but with a new owner and chef it's questionable as to how long Lutèce can retain this glory. Many say it's slipped in recent years. The setting is still lovely, but the food is "tired." Right now, the restaurant lacks an identity. But it's probably worth waiting until the old Lutèce fades and the new one comes a bloom. "Pray for it."
SPEC: *Prix fixe dinner $60: Cassolette de crabe "Wielle France"; Sole e la manche belle meuniere; filets D'agneau; Mignon de boeuf en feuillete; Gateau chocolate, etc.*

MAGGIE'S PLACE   LD   Irish-American

(B10) 21 E. 47th St. (Mad. & 5th) 212/753-5757 Fax: 753-5765

F 5 / S 6 / A 6 / $28   MC V D AE DIS   **TO**

A classic Irish pub a cut above the rest, with a beautiful dark wood bar downstairs and restaurant upstairs. Maggie's Place offers an interesting choice: You may choose pub grub or, if you move upstairs and dine in the restaurant, you can choose from a far more sophisticated menu. "Great burgers." **Closed: Sunday**
SPEC: *Dublin fish & chips $13; Steak & mushroom pie $11; Irish lamb stew $12; Medallion of veal au Chambord $19; Triple chocolate truffle cake $5*

0	1	2	3	4	5	6	7	8	9	10
disappointing		fair		good		very good		excellent		perfect

MARCH   D   American

(A12) 405 E. 58th St. (1st & Sutton) 212/754-6272

F 8 / S 8 / A 7 / $65   MC V D AE

In one of the most romantic spots in the city, chef/owner Wayne Nish creates a culinary symphony for his guests, with an exciting array of American cuisine. The menu changes frequently, if not daily. The meals are prix-fixe with plenty of choices. The wait staff is "impeccable" and setting, especially the outdoor garden, is "beautiful."

SPEC: *Prix-fixe menu*

MEE NOODLE SHOP AND GRILL   LD   Chinese

(B11) 922 2nd Ave. (49th) 212/888-0027

F 6 / S 5 / A 3 / $15   AE   **TO/D**

Expect lines pouring onto 2nd Avenue at lunch and a crowded, noisy dinner. The exposed kitchen takes up 1/3 of the seating(limited to 35) and accounts for 50% of the cacaphony. But for family style, Chinese, deliciously steaming soups (they're a meal) and innumerable noodle combinations, this unpretentious gem is "always fast, reliable and satisfying."

SPEC: *Egg scallion pancakes (2) $2.10; Tofu vegetable soup $3.50; Crispy chicken $7.95; Hunan pork w/black bean and shrimp chili sauce $9.25; Grilled assorted seafood kabob $10.95*

MELTEMI   Greek

(A12) 905 1st Ave. (51st) 212/355-4040 Fax: 752-5914

F 6 / S 5 / A 3 / $15   AE   **TO/D**

Delights from an historic culture come directly to you Greco-Roman style. The dining room has a colosseum-like entrance along, with paintings and collages of Greece past and present. Vivacious in color, artistic in design, the cuisine of primarily seafood is presented in "good taste and style." The staff is helpful and attentive, giving you a real "family" feel.

SPEC: *Charcoal grilled octopus $9.95; Charcoal grilled whole fish w/virgin olive oil & oregano $18.95; Homemade pastries $3.95*

METROPOLITAN CAFE, THE   LD   American

(A12) 959 1st Ave. (52nd & 53rd) 212/759-5600

F 6 / S 6 / A 6 / $20   MC V D AE   **TO**

If you're on First Avenue, in midtown, looking for someplace to eat—someplace big but "unspectacular," with an extensive menu with "huge portion" healthy salads. Look no further. They also serve hearty meat and potato dishes. There's a garden cafe and a new glass-enclosed, sunny atrium..

SPEC: *Santa Fe corn & chile cream chowder $2.95; New Mexican cheese fondue $5.95; Pan sautéed flounder fillets $13.50; Metropolitan beef fajitas $12.95; Hazelnut bomb $4.75;*

MICHAEL'S PUB   LD   Continental

(A11) 211 E. 55th St. (2nd & 3rd) 212/758-2272

F 7 / S 7 / A 7 / $35   MC V D DIS

Long known by New Yorkers as the place to catch Woody Allen joining in Monday night jazz performances. But it's also a place for business people to grab pub dishes like steaks, kidney pies and broiled fish. The rare Wood-man showing is said to be worth the $35 prix-fixe dinner. But the pub fare is not so exciting without him. The aura is "male and upscale."

MITSUKOSHI LD Japanese

(A11) 461 Park Ave. (57th) 212/935-6444

F 7 / S 6 / A 6 / $40   MC V D AE   **TO**

A great place for a Japanese business dinner. The restaurant has a unique entrance as guests must go down a glass-enclosed escalator to reach the dining room. The food is "quite authentic and high quality." The decor is simple and the noise level low.
SPEC: *Yakitori $7; Beef kaminari zuke $9; Chicken teriyaki $18; Shabu Shabu $29; Lobster tail tempura $27; Hiyashi shiruko $6.50*

MONKEY BAR D American

(A10) 60 E. 54th St. (Park & Mad.- Hotel Elysee) 212/753-1066

F 7 / S 7 / A 9 / $38   MC V AE

If you see five large, red columns in front of you, you're in the right place. Legend has it this hip spot was named for the actress Tallulah Bankhead's monkey who periodically escaped and went cavorting about the premises. Unlike that monkey, the restaurant is under control. Early on, business folk come for grilled seafood specials. At night, yuppies line the tables like moths around lampposts, drinking and checking each other out while ordering the famous house dessert, made, of course, from bananas.
SPEC: *Ricotta ravioli $9; Grilled stuffed squid $8.50; Chili rubbed swordfish $23.50*

MONTEBELLO LD Italian

(A11) 120 E. 56th St. (Park & Lex.) 212/753-1447

F 6 / S 8 / A 7 / $38   MC V D AE

Some call this an "elegant and relaxing oasis," while others find the atmosphere "hum-drum" and the food "reliable," but "nothing special." The linen tablecloths and dark-wood accents give a homey feel, and the wait staff is friendly and obliging. Montebello may seem "passe" to some, but it does have its loyal adherents.
SPEC: *Insalata montebello $7.50; Muscoli riviera $8.75; Angelhair w/crab meat $20.75; Gamberi montebello $23.75*

MORTON'S OF CHICAGO LD American

(B10) 551 5th Ave. (45th) 212/972-3315

F 7 / S 8 / A 7 / $46   MC V D AE

Originally established in Chicago in '78 and only recently blown our way, this classy steakhouse is a reminder of America at the turn of the century. An open kitchen lets you sneak a peak at where it all happens as do illuminated pig lanterns on each table. The "knowledgeable wait staff" may be nice enough to describe the various dishes displayed for you on a cart...but are they willing to wheel you out on one? **Closed: Lunch Saturday & Sunday**
SPEC: *Cockenoe oysters on half shell $9.95; Shrimp Alexander $11.95; Double filet mignon $28.95; Porterhouse steak $29.95; New York cheesecake $5.25*

MR. CHOW D Chinese

(A12) 324 E. 57th St. (1st & 2nd) 212/751-9030

F 7 / S 6 / A 7 / $48   MC V D AE

Upscale, three-course, designer Chinese restaurant, tastefully and conservatively decorated. Its celebrity list is as long as a lo mein noodle, starting with De Niro and ending with Pacino. It's far more pricey than its counterparts, but the food is better and the ambiance far more elegant. Make reservations, because "showing up without one is considered an insult." "Love that chow at Mr. Chow."
SPEC: *Prawn w/sesame on toast $7.75; Salt & pepper shrimps $14.75; Peking duck $48; Drunken fish $23.50*

0	1	2	3	4	5	6	7	8	9	10
disappointing		fair		good		very good		excellent		perfect

JOHN ESPINOSA

Mr. Chow

NEARY'S LD American

(A12) 358 E. 57th St. (1st and 2nd) 212/751-1434

F 6 / S 6 / A 6 / $24 MC V D AE **TO**

Jimmy Neary is known as the Mayor of 57th Street. And his traditional "friendly and comfortable" pub as the Irish "21." The luck of the Irish has shined on many famous patrons like Helen Hayes, Hugh Carey and Frank Gifford. Serving good, solid, homestyle American and Irish-American food, Neary's is a "great neighborhood gathering place."

SPEC: *Smoked Wild Irish salmon $8.95; Broiled lamb chops w/mint jelly $18.95; Corned beef and cabbage $14.95; Rice pudding $2.95; Peach melba $2.95*

NICHOLSON CAFE Amer/Continental

(A12) 323 E. 58th St. (1st & 2nd) 212/355-6769

F 7 / S 8 / A 8 / $43 MC V D AE

Like a plant that rarely blooms, this limited hours dining room reveals spectacular beauty when it does. When it's open, which is haphazard and completely at the whim of owner, John Nicholson, patient diners are rewarded with one of the city's most romantic settings with food to match. Save yourself the trouble and call first.

SPEC: *Prix fixe menu only, entrees include free range roast chicken, fillet of salmon, roast leg of lamb, crab cakes and filet mignon $42.50*

NONNA LD Italian

(A11) 115 E. 57th St. (Park & Lex-The Galleria) 212/826-1021

F 7 / S 7 / A 5 / $24 MC V D AE

This open, friendly spot blends right into its structure, the courtyard of the Galleria on 57th. It's warm and welcoming just like an Italian grandmother (nonna) should be. The perfect after work gathering spot or setting for a special party or event. And there's Nonna To Go, a take away counter for those in a rush. "Super for a lunchtime office getaway."

SPEC: *Grilled calamari on frisee $6.75; Risotto w/porabello mushroom $11.50; Codfish provençal $14; Fruit tart $4.50*

THE OAK ROOM AND BAR LD Continental

(A10) 768 5th Ave. (59th -Plaza Hotel) 212/546-5330

F 5 / S 6 / A 7 / $47 MC V D AE

The world famous Oak Room continues to be one of NY's biggest power scenes. With high ceilings, dark wood chairs, and large tables, the room has an elegance appropriate for the blue-blood. And with such a pricey menu, it takes a blue-blood to eat here. The wait staff is very formal, but why is the service "so poor"?

SPEC: *(Pre-theater menu) Lobster bisque; Wild mushroom ravioli; "Black Angus" London broil; Veal paillard; Pan seared chicken breast; Creme brulee; Fresh fruit tart $42*

OPUS II   D   American

(A11) 242 E. 58th St. (2nd & 3rd)   212/753-2200 Fax: 688-4342

F 7 / S 7 / A 6 / $36   MC V D AE DIS   **TO**

Steaks one notch up from "pretty good," Opus may also glean its loyal clientele by serving huge portions at a fixed price. The limited menu is announced by the waiter in a modern, art deco atmosphere that thankfully steers clear of the old boys club feel that haunts so many steakhouses. **Closed: Sunday**
SPEC: *Prix-fixe dinner w/choice of steak, veal, lamb, pork, chicken, lobster ($10 extra) $29.95*

OTABE   LD   Japanese

(A10) 68 E. 56th St. (Park & Mad.)   212/223-7575

F 8 / S 7 / A 7 / $42   MC V D AE

This Japanese restaurant has its fans and its detractors. Some say it's "Extraordinary," and the "best Japanese in NY." While others feel it offers little more than a "fun atmosphere," and that it's "not worth the money."
SPEC: *Beef tataki $6; Sashimi $8–$16; Tuna & yellowtail sushi $13; Saon teriyaki $18; Shrimp tempura $12.50*

OTTOMANELL'S CAFE   LD   Italian

(B12) 237 Park Ave. (45th)   212/986-6886
(A12) 951 1st Ave. (52nd & 53rd)   212/758-3725 Fax: 980-2250
See review on page 41.

PALM   LD   American

(B11) 837 2nd Ave. (44th & 45th)   212/687-2953

F 7 / S 7 / A 6 / $40   MC V D AE

This age-old bistro-steakhouse embodies the notion of the NY power scene. Portions are huge and service very fast. The $19.95 prix-fixe lunch is a steal. "Steak and lobster are the best," and "food is the reason to go." The decor is basic, with wood floors and cartoon drawings adorning plaster walls. Upstairs, there's a nice room for private parties.
SPEC: *Clams oreganato $10; Crabmeat cocktail $14.50; New York strip $28; Steak a la Stone $30; Double steak (36 oz for 2) $56*

PALM COURT, THE   BLD   Continental

(A10) 768 5th Ave. (59th-Plaza Hotel)   212/546-5350

F 8 / S 7 / A 7 / $38   MC V D AE

The Palm Court retains the stately grace and elegance associated with The Plaza. Diners sit amid a lavish garden with fresh flowers. It's a great place to go for Sunday brunch or evening tea. "Great dessert and after dinner drinks." The crowd is older—often out-of-towners—but the good food and service make this a lovely New York staple.

PALM TOO   LD   American

(B11) 840 2nd Ave. (44th & 45th)   212/697-5198
See review above.

Anne Rosenzweig
Owner/chef of Arcadia and
Lobster Club

"For really delicious roasted meats in the simplest surroundings, try **Wing Wong** (102 Mott St. 212/274-0696). Great homey Mexican food is found at **Gabriela**. And the **Savoy**, for a supernal New York experience, with a sensitive chef and the best vegetables."

0	1	2	3	4	5	6	7	8	9	10
disappointing		fair		good		very good		excellent		perfect

Geoffrey Bradfield
President, Spectre-Bradfield Inc.

"New Yorkers are inclinded to be rather territorial, and living in a city where dining out is the norm, one tends to gravitate toward favorite local haunts. High on my list would be: **Harry Cipriani**, **Ici** and **Brio**. Not only is the cuisine superb, but I'm always made to feel most at home."

PAMIR   LD   Afghani

(A12) 1065 1st Ave. (58th) 212/644-9258
See review on page 172.

PANDA RESTAURANT   LD   Chinese

(A12) 987 1st Ave. (54th) 212/752-8822

F 5 / S 6 / A 3 / $19   MC V   **TO/D**

Where can you find discerning Sutton-placers eating an informal Chinese meal? Lacking colorful decor, the one room dining area is sparse but pleasant. The atmosphere is friendly, and so is the evening staff. Most importantly, the food is delicious, served in ample portions.
SPEC: *Hack chicken $3.95; Chicken & shrimp Szechuan style $10.55; Peking duck (for 2) $22; Pineapple chicken $10.55*

PAPER MOON MILANO   LD   Italian

(A10) 39 E. 58th St. (Mad. & Park) 212/758-8600 Fax: 758-4306

F 7 / S 8 / A 7 / $34   MC V D AE   **TO/D**

Foreign businessmen, fashion models and "suits" favor this "elegant" Northern Italian restaurant. Hundreds of black and white photos of Milan adorn the walls constantly reminding you of the restaurant's namesake. There's also a roomy bar with a twist of art deco, and a huge window which allows you to people watch.
SPEC: *Mixed grilled vegetables $12; Risotto alla milanese $20; Pizzas $15-$17; Mixed sorbet $8*

PEACOCK ALLEY RESTAURANT   BLD   French

(B11) 301 Park Ave. (Waldorf-49th) 212/872-4895 Fax: 486-5124

F 7 / S 8 / A 9 / $54   MC V D AE DIS

Like dining at your grandmother's house if your grandmother is a bejeweled dowager. This NY institution, where once society's "peacocks" paraded, still meets the standards of the "whole 400." Yet it still has that Cole Porter feeling. A harpist plays at dinner. Two beautiful and understated private rooms are perfect for business or personal entertaining. And don't miss afternoon tea served, lobby side, in the grand continental tradition.
SPEC: *Three foie gras $22; Poached foie gras w/asparagus & fresh morels $16; Muscovit duck $28; Sautéed veal chop $33*

PEN & PENCIL   LD   American

(B11) 205 E. 45th St. (2nd & 3rd) 212/682-8660

F 7 / S 7 / A 7 / $42   MC V D AE DIS   **TO/D**

Although relatively few writers we know could afford this steak house, the Pen & Pencil does have a worldly charm about it worth writing home about. Formal, but still friendly, the service, comfortable booths and caricature paintings on the walls lend a welcome touch of class
SPEC: *Blue claw lump crabmeat $12.95; Cold seafood sampler $16.95; Sirloin steak $29.75; Triple American lamb chops $29.75; Peanut butter & jelly sandwich served w/split of Veuve Cliquot $57.85*

PESCATORE   LD   Italian

(B11) 955 2nd Ave. (50th & 51st) 212/752-7151

F 7 / S 6 / A 7 / $24   D AE   **TO**

For those of us who don't speak Italian, "pescatore" means fish, so it stands to reason that this restaurant specializes in food from the sea. With its classy, beautiful interior, it's a great place to take somebody you want to impress, whether it's a client or a hot date. And if fish isn't your thing, there's also a large selection of pasta and pizza to choose from.

SPEC: *Tuna carpaccio $7; Raw seafood platter $25; Monkfish rolled in grape leaves stuffed w/shitake mushrooms $18; Sautéed French turbot $21*

RAFFAELE   LD   Italian

(A12) 1055 1st Ave. (57th & 58th) 212/750-3232

F 7 / S 7 / A 9 / $31   MC V AE

This intimate contemporary Italian bistro right off the 57th Street nexus of power and fashion is refreshing. With a whiff of an art deco decor and light, Raffaele attracts all of the heavy hitters of the neighborhood like Eileen Ford and Bill Blass.

SPEC: *Lunch: Antipasti $6.50; Linguine al verzo $11; Pollo concarciofi $12.50;Scaloppina marsala $13.50*

RAY BARI PIZZA   LD   Pizzeria

(A11) 930 3rd Ave. (56th) 212/755-2390

See review on page 176.

ROSA MEXICANO   D   Mexican

(A12) 1063 1st Ave. (58th) 212/753-7407 Fax: 421-4091

F 7 / S 6 / A 6 / $35   MC V D AE   **TO/D**

Not south of the border, but just south of the 59th Street bridge lies one of the best finds for Mexican cuisine in Nueva York. Chef/owner Josephina Howard has built "a little hacienda" on the East Side, but be advised: this is classic Mexican eating. Some of what passes for Mexican cuisine elsewhere has been sent packing. The "best guacamole on the planet," is prepared at your table, and fresh tortillas are made in front of your eyes.

SPEC: *Guacamole $9; Roasted & pickled green chilies filled w/sardines $5.75; Beef short ribs, marinated in beer & lemon $9.50; Tripe stew $16.50*

ROYAL CANADIAN PANCAKE HOUSE   BLD American

(A11) 1004 2nd Ave. (53rd) 212/980-4131

See review on page 239.

RUSTY STAUB'S ON 5TH   LD   American

(B10) 575 5th Ave. (47th) 212/682-1000

F 8 / S 7 / A 7 / $32   MC V D AE   **TO/D**

Batter up! Die-hard Met fans will swoon as they enter this temple to the "great American pastime" Surprisingly, for a sports-themed restaurant, the wine list here is "impressive." Patrons come from far and wide for Rusty's legendary rib recipe and chef Patricia Kelly's imaginative American menu. Rusty's friends (i.e., baseball legends) drop by and he does his cable broadcast from here, too.

SPEC: *Sweet corn & seafood chowder $6; Barbecued Canadian babyback ribs $18.95; Grilled chicken paillard $16.95; Gingersnap bread pudding $6.50*

0	1	2	3	4	5	6	7	8	9	10
disappointing		fair		good		very good		excellent		perfect

SAN GIUSTO LD Italian

(B11) 935 2nd Ave. (49th & 50th) 212/319-0900

F 6 / S 6 / A 6 / $34 MC V D AE DIS **TO**

Large, gilt-edged mirrors, framed portraits and attractive design lend San Giusto an inviting elegance. A favorite for business folk, but in a city filled with Italian restaurants this one simply doesn't stand out enough to go out of your way to visit. But if you're a connoisseur, the wine list is extensive.

SPEC: *Escargot w/cognac & garlic $8.75; Pollo san Daniele $18.75; Saltimbocca romana $19.75; Linguine ale vongole $17; Thin pancakes w/chocolate or marmalade $6.75*

San Martin

SAN MARTIN LD Mediterranean

(B11) 143 E. 49th St. (Lex & 3rd) 212/832-9270 Fax: 832-0888

F 7 / S 8 / A 7 / $32 MC V D AE DIS **TO/D**

While catering primarily to an international clientele, San Martin's still manages to capture the feel of a New York bistro. The long tube of a room benefits from good lighting, a staff that is "simpatico," and a fine Spanish/French/Italian menu.

SPEC: *Arugulas de Aguinaga (baby eels) $6.75; Paella Valenciana $18.75; Bistecca al Pepe Rosso $18.75; Zabaglione $4.50*

SERYNA LD Japanese

(A10) 11 E. 53rd St. (Mad. & 5th) 212/9809393

F 7 / S 6 / A 8 / $42 MC V D AE

A Japanese restaurant named after a Greek mermaid? Why not? Step off the street, into the vest pocket park, past a refreshing waterfall, to find this serene haven. Don't miss the sections of the actual Berlin Wall, set off as a freestanding sculpture. Inside, enjoy this retreat, which is the only US outpost of this Tokyo chain, famous for its shabu-shabu and Ishiyaki, both delectably prepared right at your table. **Closed: Sunday**

SPEC: *Fluke & pimento $15.65; Tender beef-sashiomi $11; Dover sole $28; Swordfish teriyaki $25; Shabu-Shabu $28*

SHUN LEE PALACE LD Chinese

(A11) 155 E. 55th St. (Lex. & 3rd) 212/371-8844

F 7 / S 6 / A 6 / $40 MC V AE D **TO**

The "best," classiest, "old style" Chinese food in Manhattan. The atmosphere is modern, yet retains oriental authenticity. "Dependable" Hunan and Szechuan offerings even include specials requiring 24-hour preparation. Busy with business folk and locals, duck and fish dishes are popular. "You'll never eat takeout again."

SPEC: *Giant prawns in black bean sauce $12.95; Hot & sour cabbage $6.95; Beggars chicken $37.25; Hunan lamb $18.75*

SMALL CAFE, THE LD Continental

(B11) 330 E. 56th St. (1st & 2nd-Sutton Hotel) 212/753-2233

F 5 / S 5 / A 4 / $26 MC V D AE DIS

If you're looking to escape from New York, but can't quite make it past the 59th Street Bridge, this is the perfect alternative. Eat in a tranquil indoor garden setting that will definitely calm your nerves. The food is good, the crowd upscale and the ambiance quaint and natural.

SPEC: *Prix fixe dinner menu $19.95*

Smith & Wollensky

SMITH & WOLLENSKY LD American

(B11) 797 3rd Ave. (49th) 212/753-1530

F 8 / S 7 / A 6 / $44 MC V D AE

Another NY power restaurant that serves up hearty fare at heart-stopping prices. "Should be renamed Smith and Expensive." The majority of diners are male bankers and lawyers "You can feel the power in the room." The decor is simple with several small dining areas and a huge bar. But it's the steaks, "the biggest in town," that pack them in.

SPEC: *Split pea soup $4.50; Slice steak $29.75; Prime rib of beef $29.75; Veal chop $29.75; Cheesecake $6.75; Bourbon pecan pie $7*

SOLERA LD Spanish

(A11) 216 E. 53rd St. (2nd & 3rd) 212/644-1166 Fax: 644-3379

F 8 / S 8 / A 8 / $52 MC V D AE

A pricey but supremely elegant and inviting stop for "new interpretations" of regional Spanish cuisine. The small enclosed patio with a skylight features the best seat in the house. Hot and cold tapas bar. "Spanish at its best." **Closed: Sunday**

SPEC: *Prix-fixe (examples) Rabbit terrine; Catalan sal-doc; Red snapper; Poached rainbow trout; Prime lamb chops; Chicken chorizo vegetable paella $45*

SORELLE LD Italian

(A12) 994 1st Ave. (54th & 55th) 212/753-0520 Fax: 371-5874

F 7 / S 7 / A 5 / $19 MC V D AE DIS **TO/D**

The owner, Stephanie Guest, is actress Joan Bennett's daughter, so she has decorated this casual, relaxed, cheery neighborhood restaurant with posters, photos, and movie memorabilia. The weekend, all-you-can-eat brunch at $9.95, is a real bargain, especially in this toney part of town.

SPEC: *Broccoli rabe $5.95; Black pasta w/shrimp, scallops, clams, mussels & fresh tomato $12.95; Pollo alla vodka $13.95; Tiramisu $4.95; Torta di cioccolata $4.95*

0	1	2	3	4	5	6	7	8	9	10
disappointing	fair		good		very good			excellent		perfect

SPARKS STEAK HOUSE   LD   American

(B11) 210 E. 46th St. (2nd & 3rd) 212/687-4855 Fax: 557-7409

F 7 / S 7 / A 6 / $46   MC V D AE

At lunch you'll find wall-to-wall business suits at this midtown institution, often referred to as the "best steakhouse in Manhattan." A "saloony" feel surrounds diners—dark woods and brass. Steaks are served plain or fancy and sizzled to perfection. The award-winning wine list never ends. Clientele includes N.Y. power mavens, celebrities and a broad cross-section of visitors from around the world.

SPEC: *Crab meat & bay scallops $12.95; Baked clams & shrimp scampi $10.95; Extra thick veal loin chop $18.95; Rib lamp chops (3) $29.95; Prime sirloin steak $29.95*

Top 10
$21-35
Moderate

SUSHISAY   LD   Japanese

(B10) 38 E. 51st St. (Mad. & Park) 212/755-1780

F 8 / S 7 / A 6 / $34   MC V D AE   **TO**

The best sushi in New York, according to many afficionados. This jewel is the sole US location of a Tokyo-based chain. Service is deft. The atmosphere polite. And there's a sushi bar for those enjoying the sushi experience solo. But no, there's no American-style liquor bar. Saki and Japanese beer only. "Expensive, but always satisfying." "Sushi heaven." **Closed: Sunday**

SPEC: *Fresh sea urchin $8; Taraba crab $15; Sashimi $11-$50 (chef's recommended selection); Sushi $18-$30; Sushisay dinner selection $40*

SUTTON WATERING HOLE   LD   American

(A11) 209 E. 56th St. (2nd & 3rd) 212/355-6868

F 5 / S 3 / A 6 / $22   MC V AE D DIS

The decor is somewhat schizophrenic. Dark wood, dimly lit, and an inexplicable touch of Africa, what with a map of that continent on one of the wood beams that separates diners from one another. And yet the atmosphere, despite waiters who "tend to forget you are there," is homey and relaxed, the food good, and the prices reasonable.

SPEC: *5-Alarm onion rings $3.50; Popcorn shrimp $5.75; Wild mushroom ravioli $10.50; Safari chicken $10.95*

SWING STREET CAFE   LD   Italian

(B11) 253 E. 53rd St. (2nd & 3rd) 212/754-4817 Fax: 486-7324

F 6 / S 6 / A 6 / $23   MC V D AE DIS   **TO/D**

Little sister to Aria next door. Smaller, less expensive (though the food is just as good), more informal, with almost a garden-like feel. There are two levels, and the higher you go the quieter and airier it is.

SPEC: *Caesar salad $5; Penne puttanesca $9.95; Grilled swordfish $13.50; Grilled veal $13.50; Chocolate cake $4.50*

TATOU   LD   American

(B11) 151 E. 50th St. (Lex. & 3rd) 212/753-1144 Fax: 753-0589

F 5 / S 5 / A 6 / $40   MC V AE

One of those restaurants that has little or no appeal. They market themselves as a dinner club, yet fail to have any real name acts. The dining room is quite large and grand, with a huge stage similar to the burlesque theaters. The New American cuisine is decent, but over-priced. The wait staff can be "haughty." Occasionally there's a good jazz band that enlivens the place, but nothing comes without a price as there is a cover for the music plus the cost of the meal.

SPEC: *Chilled asparagus salad $10.50; Yellowfin tuna tartar $9; Broiled veal chop $28.50; Curry marinated rack of lamb $29*

TOMMY MAKEM'S RESTAURANT   LD   Irish-American

(A11) 130 E. 57th St. (Lex. & Park) 212/759-9040 Fax: 753-5182

F 4 / S 7 / A 7 / $25   MC V D AE   **TO**

On any given evening you can't see across the bar as young, clean-cut Upper East Siders congregate at Tommy Makem's to lift a glass...or two...or three. In grand style, the interior of this rather upscale Irish pub is adorned in...what else?...green, making it very cozy and inviting...especially if you're a devoted fan of ales, including Guinness Stout, Bass, Harp or John Courage. "Great Sheperd's pie." **Closed: Sundays July 4-Labor Day**

SPEC: *Irish oak smoked salmon $9.25; Chicken & leek pot pie $11.95; Fish & chips $11.95; Shepherd's pie $11.95*

TOP OF THE SIXES   LD   American

(A10) 666 5th Ave. (52nd & 53rd) 212/757-6662 Fax: 751-4989

F 6 / S 7 / A 8 / $50   MC V D AE DIS

The best view for the buck in NY. The crowd is a bit stodgy and staid and there's no flair with the food or the wait staff, but the fare is decent and the price fair. "Go for the view." "Elegance at its best."
SPEC: *Lobster salad $14; Salmon crabcake $11.50; Asian style duck $24; Chipolte marinated rack of American lamb $28.50*

TOWNHOUSE RESTAURANT, THE   LD   Amer/Cont'l

(A11) 206 E. 58th St. (2nd & 3rd) 212/826-6241

F 7 / S 6 / A 7 / $29   MC V D AE   **TO**

Not only are you no longer in Kansas, you're hardly in the '90s. Men wearing ties and packed wallets in a sophisticated, "very comfortable," low-lighting atmosphere. Handsome fellows serving mostly other men in a "gay friendly," moderately priced environment. "Good for Sunday brunch!"
SPEC: *Potato leek soup $5; Beef carpaccio $7.50; Chicken filets dipped in flour & egg $15; Grilled pepper crusted pork tenderloin $16*

TRATTORIA PESCE PASTA   LD   Italian

(A12) 1079 1st Ave. (59th) 212/888-7884
See review on page 95.

TRE COLORI   LD   Italian

(A12) 316 E. 53rd St. (1st & 2nd) 212/355-5360

F 5 / S 6 / A 4 / $25   MC V D AE DIS   **TO/D**

A neighborhood trattoria where the three colors of the Italian flag are saluted by the Northern Italian fare. A pleasant but modest restaurant which rightly claims "homestyle cooking at affordable prices."
SPEC: *Mozzarella in carozza (w/anchovy sauce or marinara) $5.25; Roast cornish hen $9.95; Filet of sole w/rugola, radicchio, chopped tomatoes in pink sauce $12.95*

TROPICA   LD   American

(B10) 200 Park Ave. (45th & Vanderbilt) 212/867-6767

F 8 / S 7 / A 8 / $38   MC V D AE

This "favorite" Key West-inspired seafood spot has a casual and relaxing ambiance but remains "impressive and hard to top." The clientele is hip and savvy. The chef churns out innovative combinations pleasing to most palates and with "wonderful presentation." "Convenient and friendly," it's a great place to stage your own "power lunch."
SPEC: *Grilled foie gras $13.75; Breast of jerked chicken, quesadilla $16.95; Red snapper $21.75; Fruit couscous $6.50*

0	1	2	3	4	5	6	7	8	9	10
disappointing		fair		good		very good		excellent		perfect

TRUFFLES   LD   Continental

(B11) 227 East 50th St. (2nd & 3rd) 212/750-5315 Fax: 750- 0092

F 6 / S 7 / A 6 / $40   MC V D AE DIS   **TO/D**

Specializing in both truffles: the mushroom-like delicacy, and truffles, the chocolate, this warm, little restaurant with snippets of poetry stenciled on its golden walls, provides just the right atmosphere for indulgence. The original artwork that surrounds you is for sale, and changes every two months. A favorite of international travelers who stay at nearby hotels. **Closed: Sunday**

SPEC: *Stuffed roast quail $11; Foie gras de moulard $19; Breast of pheasant $27; Tournedos Rossini $35; Stuffed poached pear $5*

VONG   LD   Thai

(A11) 200 E. 54th St. (2nd & 3rd) 212/486-9592 Fax: 980-3745

F 8 / S 7 / A 8 / $50   MC V D AE

Chef Jean-Georges Vongerichten produces innovative, "wild and delicious" Thai-French cuisine. This sleek midtowner has a very upscale setting. The clientele is hip. The atmosphere is a little noisy, but fun. The dining room is flashy with high ceilings, black marble walls, large fresh flower arrangements, and a secluded bar area. The "unique food combinations" are beautifully presented, but the service can be "too cool and unfriendly."

SPEC: *Lobster & daikon roll $14; Quail rubbed w/Thai spices $10; Duck breast $24; Crisp squab w/pancakes $25; Pineapple fried rice $5*

WOLLENSKY GRILL   LD   American

(B11) 205 E. 49th St. (2nd & 3rd) 212/753-0444

F 7 / S 7 / A 6 / $27   MC V D AE   **TO**

As the son of the power palace Smith & Wollensky around the corner, the Grill offers a similar menu at lower prices. There's a nice outdoor area with green umbrellas and cute tables for "a good lunch." The food is the same quality as its parent, only a little less upscale...and the crowd is younger and hipper. "A good stop for a steak and a glass of cabernet."

SPEC: *Pea soup $4.75; Fried blossom onion $6.75; Wollensky burger $9.75; Steamed lobster $19.50; Chocolate mousse cake $6.50*

WYLIE'S STEAK & RIB HOUSE   LD   American

(B12) 891 1st Ave. (50th) 212/751-0700 Fax: 688- 0417

F 7 / S 6 / A 5 / $17   MC V D AE DIS   **TO/D**

Wylie's is "simple," and "casual," so bring the family. And get ready to do some serious chowing down on "healthy portions" of BBQ chicken, "great ribs and onion loaf," steak and anything that can be thrown on the barbie. There are also some "strong Texas style drinks" waiting to be downed if you're really singles minded, or ready to leave the kids at home.

SPEC: *Baby back ribs $14.95; BBQ chicken $7.95; 18 oz. T-Bone steak $14.45; Chinese roast pork on garlic bread w/duck sauce $7.95*

ZARELA   LD   Mexican

(B11) 953 2nd Ave. (50th & 51st) 212/644-6740 Fax: 980-1073

F 8 / S 7 / A 7 / $28   D AE   **TO**

Ready to party, Mexican style? Zarela's is the place. Decked out like a fiesta, complete with crepe paper designs and mariachi music, Zarela's also delivers impeccable "real Mexican, not American style" fare. Receives raves from most diners as some of the "best Mexican food in the U.S." If you're looking for a tad quieter evening, ask for a table upstairs, though be prepared to share conversation with those seated next to you, since tables are very close together.

SPEC: *Poblano relleno $8.95; Roasted duck $15.95; Roasted marinated pork $12.95; Camarones poblanos $13.95*

ZEPHYR GRILL   BLD   Continental

(B12) 49th & 1st (Beekman Tower Hotel) 212/223-4200

F 8 / S 8 / A 7 / $31   MC V D AE   **TO**

Take a ride on the Zephyr, the luxury train from L.A. to Chicago.
Attentive waiters serve multi-cultural dishes in a comfortable,
"art deco" setting. Have a beer dinner (4 courses—and all the
micro-brewed beer you can drink,) or whatever the chef might be
offering that day.
SPEC: *Five tiny taste teasers $4.75; Smoked Irish salmon $8.50;
Seared raw tuna $16.50; Pork tenderloin brochettes $13.75*

ZONA DEL CHIANTI   LD   Italian

(A11) 1043 2nd Ave. (55th) 212/980-8686 Fax: 980-0508

F 7 / S 7 / A 7 / $23   MC V AE   **TO/D**

Last year the 2nd Avenue Brasserie changed its name and its menu
and this is what it came up with. And as good as that restaurant
was, this "favorite neighborhood" reincarnation is even better. The
food is uniformly good, creatively prepared and served, and the wait
staff is kind, helpful and generous. The sunken dining room is airy,
yet also intimate and romantic. There's a pleasant outdoor cafe and
an occasional wine tasting dinner.
SPEC: *Cured meats w/shaved parmesan & arugula $8; Charcoal
grilled Atlantic salmon $14; Charcoal grilled spring lamb fillet $15.75*

EAST 60TH – 86TH STREET

A TAVOLA   BLD   Italian

(E17) 1095 Lexington Ave. (76th & 77th) 212/744-1233

F 5 / S 6 / A 5 / $25   MC V AE   **TO/D**

From the outside, and from within, this looks like any coffeeshop,
but the family that's run it for years serves up Italian food that truly
pleases knowing palettes...and their wallets. The presentation isn't
fancy, but the Italian cuisine is of consistently "fine quality."
SPEC: *Broccoli rabe $6; Veal stew $12; Chicken cutlet alla Mario
$12.50; Broiled veal A Tavola $14.95*

ALLORA   LD   Mediterranean

(E17) 1321 1st Ave. (71st) 212/570-0384

F 6 / S 5 / A 5 / $25   D AE   **TO/D**

Giant windows open onto the sidewalk, and the typical bag-o-garlic
and bottles of herbs sunk in olive oil remind you that it is, yes, a
Mediterranean spot. Pasta is homemade and fish specialties
abound. Subtle angels dance on the palely painted walls and fruit
desserts like sorbet are well presented.
SPEC: *Calamari fritti $6; Octopus oreganetta $10; Fettuccine con
pollo $9.50; Ravioli verdi $9.50; Pizza pescatore $12*

ANGELS   LD   Italian

(F17) 1135 1st Ave. (62nd & 63rd) 212/980-3131

F 6 / S 6 / A 5 / $20   MC V AE DIS   **TO/D**

NY may be dangerous to some, but not here, where an angel
watches over you while you eat. Cutely decorated with cherubs and
other heavenly spirits, this "wild" Italian restaurant serves large
portions of good, solid food, as evidenced by the ever-present line
outside. The 2 dining areas are "cramped," but for many it's the "#1
pasta joint on the Upper East Side."
SPEC: *Stracciatella soup $3.50; Narragansett "Hot Tails" $6.95;
Chicken San Ricardo $13.95; Tiramisu $3.95*

0	1	2	3	4	5	6	7	8	9	10
disappointing		fair		good		very good		excellent		perfect

ANTICO CAFFE
LD   **Italian**

(E17) 1477 2nd Ave. (77th) 212/879-4824

F 6 / S 4 / A 6 / $19   Cash only   **TO/D**

Very hip and trendy, in a Soho-like style, this Italian restaurant is just one of the many new, "in" spots to eat at on the Upper East Side. Small and terribly cramped is its downfall, along with the inconsistency of the food. But it's a great place to take a date, or to be seen. The outside seating is a major plus, though some cite "rude servers."

SPEC: *Minestrone soup $3.50; Pizzas $7.95; Black pasta w/mushrooms, green peas, chicken, sage, parmeggiano cheese $8.95*

ARCADIA
LD   **American**

(F16) 21 E. 62nd St. (Mad. & 5th) 212/223-2900

F 7 / S 7 / A 7 / $65   MC V D AE

From her midtown brownstone, Anne Rosenweig churns out an impressive array of New American cuisine. The dining room is elegant, with fresh flowers, dark wood accents, and globe lights. The tables are cramped, but a beautiful landscaped mural wraps around the dining room, adding its charm. The wait staff can be "snobby," but the clientele is "down-to-earth."

SPEC: *Pre-fixe menu; Corn cakes w/creme fraiche & caviar +$5; Crispy roast chicken; Carmelized loin of tuna; Chimney smoked lobster; Warm chocolate bread pudding $58*

Arizona 206

ARIZONA 206
LD   **Southwestern**

(F17) 206 E. 60th St. (2nd & 3rd) 212/838-0440 Fax: 988-3703

F 7 / S 6 / A 6 / $43   MC V D AE DIS

If you're looking for innovative, great Southwestern food served in a warm, homey atmosphere (complete with fireplace and lounge chairs) that takes you back to your days in Arizona, would you look across from Bloomingdale's? That's what you'd find here and, if you can't quite come up with the big bucks this restaurant will set you back, visit the smaller, more casual cafe next door. The menu is different, but the food is just as good.
Closed: Sunday lunch

SPEC: *Lamb taquitas $10; Grilled quail $12; Pan roasted monkfish $24; Grilled rabbit loin $26; Chile-crusted venison loin $27; Chocolate espresso "Bomba" $8.50*

ARRIBA ARRIBA!
LD   **Mexican**

(D17) 1463 3rd Ave. (82nd & 83rd) 212/249-1423
See review on page 197.

Asia

ASIA LD Asian

(F17) 1155 3rd Ave. (67th & 68th) 212/879-9888

F 5 / S 6 / A 6 / $31   MC V D AE   **TO/D**

Asia takes ancient Chinese secrets one step beyond by combining neighboring Asian influences and producing unexpectedly interesting dishes. Its dining rooms, separated by 2 spectacular "very relaxing," 500 gallon fish tanks are otherwise spacious and modest. "Big on hype and 'attitude,' but good food."

SPEC: *Chicken w/basil & lemongrass $13.50; Seafood platter w/ginger scallion sauce $17.95; Pad Thai noodles $10*

AUREOLE LD American

(F16) 34 E. 61st St. (Mad & Park) 212/319-1660

F 8 / S 8 / A 8 / $65   MC V D AE

Located in a beautiful duplex townhouse, overlooking a scenic garden, Charlie Palmer's highly rated restaurant wows diners with "creatively prepared," and "wonderfully" served meals. The cost is high, but the consensus is: "Save up your money and treat yourself to a little slice of heaven!"

SPEC: *Salmon & lobster wontons $10; Seared veal medallions $24; Pan seares salmon fillet $19*

Top 10 $56+
Very Expensive

B.G.'S STEAKHOUSE D American

(E17) 1373 1st Ave. (74th & 75th) 212/717-6039

F 4 / S 5 / A 3 / $22   MC V D AE DIS   **TO/D**

Unadorned and affordable, this new East Side eatery harkens back to a largely bygone tradition in NY: the solid, no frills, neighborhood fish and steak place with a friendly bar. "Everyone talks to everybody here," is how B.G.s explains it.

SPEC: *Escargots $4.95; Grilled eggplant $3.95; Grilled aged N.Y. steak & grilled shrimp $167.95; Grilled swordfish steak $11.95*

BALUCHI'S LD Indian

(D17) 1565 2nd Ave. (81st & 82nd) 212/288-4810

F 7 / S 7 / A 6 / $19   MC V AE   **TO/D**

At this popular, local haunt, diners relax on embroidered chairs under a red and black beamed ceiling. The decor is somewhat unusual and the dining area is more spacious than most Indian restaurants. "Impeccable service of the 'Raj,'" is the kind of praise offered.

SPEC: *Chicken malai kabab $6.95; Tandoori vegetable platter $7.95; Chicken tikka masala $10.95; Rogan josh (lamb in cardamom sauce) $10.95*

0	1	2	3	4	5	6	7	8	9	10
disappointing		fair		good		very good		excellent		perfect

Wendy Monitz
Actress on Guiding Light

"The West Bank Cafe is among my favorites. The food is terrific, the prices are reasonable, and it has a great atmosphere. Owner Steve Olson is a courteous and attentive host to all his customers. I should know, because I worked there when I was a struggling actress."

BANGKOK HOUSE — LD — Thai

(E17) 1485 1st Ave. (77th & 78th) 212/249-5700

F 8 / S 6 / A 7 / $26 MC V AE **TO/D**

Dine here in exotic, shadowy candle light amid lavender walls and mirrors...and a menu that goes from inexpensive to I-hope-some-one-else-picks-up-the-tab. Attracts diners from all over the city. Boasts extremely fresh and well-prepared food.
SPEC: *Satay $.95; Thai spring rolls $4.95; Steamed filet of red snapper w/chopped shrimp & ginger $17.50; Pineapple shrimp $12.75*

BAR AND BOOKS — American

(E17) 1020 Lexington Ave. (73rd) 212/717-3902
See review on page 120.

BARAONDA — LD — Italian

(E17) 1439 2nd Ave. (75th) 212/288-8555 Fax: 717-4249

F 6 / S 6 / A 7 / $36 Cash only **TO/D**

The eyes feast first at Baraonda, "a downtown restaurant that's uptown," where every inch of wall is covered by faux Picasso drawings and painted slogans. Fresh flowers at each table make for a Northern Italian meal in a bright, colorful, even happily wacky setting. Several different languages spoken here, since the crowd is international, "fashionable and very good-looking."
SPEC: *Sautéed baby artichokes $8.50; Caesar salad $7.50; Linguine w/mixed seafood $16; Grilled salmon $19; Dark chocolate tarte w/raspberry sauce $7*

BEACH CAFE — LD — Continental

(E17) 1326 2nd Ave. 212/988-7299 Fax: 861-3450

F 5 / S 4 / A 5 / $25 MC V AE **TO**

Good, solid continental cuisine has brought diners to this classic New York cafe for 30 years. A varied menu lets you order a burger while everyone else enjoys the seafood specialties. Check out the bar and you'll find a mix of ties and T-shirts and a friendly setting that won't drive you nuts. "A sure bet—it's next to OTB."
SPEC: *Gorgonzola garlic bread $5; Grilled vegetables di stagione $7.50; Chicken pot pie $12.50; Sliced steak plate $12.50; Key lime pie $4.50*

Top 10
$0-20
Inexpensive

BELLA DONNA — LD — Italian

(E17) 307 E. 77th St. (1st & 2nd) 212/535-2866

F 7 / S 6 / A 5 / $15 Cash only **TO/D**

If you're looking for pasta and/or pizza and you're just too lazy to leave the neighborhood, this "way too small," restaurant is "delicious, cheap, friendly, noisy," but bright. It's also quick and inexpensive. Bringing your own wine, which is encouraged, will keep the bill down even more.
SPEC: *Crostini $5; Insalata Mediterranea $5; Ravioli artichokes $9.95; Rigatoni w/prosciutto parma and mushrooms $8*

BELLISSIMA   LD   Italian

(F17) 1179 2nd Ave. (62nd & 63rd) 212/751-1536 Fax: 751-1746

F 7 / S 7 / A 3 / $18   Cash only   **TO/D**

Modestly decorated with original brick walls and a rare collection of late '40s oak stained wooden tables and chairs, Bellissima is best known for its delivery service within a radius of over 40 blocks. It's the Italian version of a Chinese restaurant—prompt service, affordable prices and...very good food...except you won't be hungry half an hour later. Beautiful.

SPEC: *Fried calamari $4.50; Linguine & clam sauce $8; Nick's farfalle $7.75; Ravioli $8.95; Napoleon $4.25*

BIG SUR BAR AND GRILL   D   American

(D17) 1406 3rd Ave. (80th) 212/472-5009

F 4 / S 5 / A 7 / $25   MC V AE

It's hip, it's hot, it's all happening at Big Sur, the 'in spot" of the moment. The newest, trendiest restaurant/bar to hit the Upper East Side in a while is a place for the young and single, and those who need to be "seen." But some call it "a waste of a good corner." No lunch—that's decidedly unhip—but there is a Saturday and Sunday brunch.

SPEC: *Crispy vegetable spring rolls $8; Chesapeake crab cakes w/corn relish $9; Roast chicken w/garlic mashed potatoes $14; Pan roasted duck $16*

BLUE MOON MEXICAN CAFE   LD   Mexican

(E17) 1441 1st Ave. (75th) 212/288-9811

F 5 / S 5 / A 5 / $19   MC V D AE DIS   **TO/D**

This Mexican restaurant is big on the singles scene and cheap on prices. "Hot salsa, cool drinks." The frozen margaritas will turn your typical conservative Upper East Sider into a wild and carefree animal. "Watch out for stale tortillas." But don't be surprised to find a couple of New York Rangers hanging out.

SPEC: *Papa rellena (stuffed potato) $6.95; Fiesta platter $10.95; Blue Moon giant burritos $8.95; Fajitas $11.95-$12.95*

BLUE PLATE   LD   American

(E17) 1484 2nd Ave. (77th & 78th) 212/249-3000

F 6 / S 6 / A 5 / $22   MC V AE   **TO**

One of two new kids on the block (the other being Fork University). Too early to tell much, but the food is solid, tasty American, and the service is not only friendly and casual, but sincere which, believe us, isn't all that common. The dominant color theme is...what else? blue and white walls; blue glasses; blue candle holders; and, yes, blue plates.

SPEC: *Crispy seafood dumplings $5.95; Roast boneless breast of chicken $9.95; Meatloaf w/mashed sweet potatoes $9.95; Banana split $4.95*

BOONTHAI   LD   Thai

(D17) 1393A 2nd Ave. (72nd & 73rd) 212/249-8484

F 6 / S 6 / A 4 / $23   MC V D AE   **TO/D**

Small and leisurely, this neighborhood Thai offers an odd meeting place for East and West. If you're racing to a movie but hanker for Pad Thai not popcorn, Boonthai cooks up a popular Early Bird Special timed specifically for the film crowd.

SPEC: *Bar-B-Q squid $8.95; Soft shell crab curry or garlic $16.95; Satay (chicken or beef) $8.95*

0	1	2	3	4	5	6	7	8	9	10
disappointing		fair		good		very good		excellent		perfect

BORDER CAFE LD Southwestern

(D17) 244 E. 79th St. (2nd & 3rd) 212/535-4347

F 4 / S 5 / A 4 / $20   MC V D AE DIS   **TO/D**

The Arizona decor, great Margaritas, tasty vegetarian and low-fat dishes are what keep customers coming back for more. Though it may have "the hum-drummest chicken this side of Tallahassee," it's a "10 for kids." But if you think you see a salamander running past you, you've had too much to drink.

SPEC: *Frozen margarita sm. $5.50, lg. $7.50; Sizzling fajitas $11.95-$13.95; Border bananas $3.25; Sopapillas $3.25*

BRIGHTON GRILL LD American

(E17) 1313 3rd Ave. (75th & 76th) 212/988-6663 Fax: 439-9730

F 6 / S 6 / A 6 / $25   MC V D AE   **TO**

An upscale, "unpretentious and likable" neighborhood restaurant where the food is good and the hostess knows everyone. Spacious and large, you feel like you're in a fish tank due to the large, beautiful hand-painted mural of sea creatures on each wall.

SPEC: *Marinated squid salad $5.95; Grilled jumbo lemon pepper-shrimp $6.25; Fillet of sole $12.95; Paella $14.95; Garlic mashed potatoes $2.50*

Cafe Nosidam

BRIO LD Italian

(F17) 786 Lexington Ave. (61st & 62nd) 212/980-2300

F 7 / S 7 / A 7 / $32   MC V D AE   **TO/D**

Want to take a Bloomingdale's shopping break? Try this "lively," cozy, romantic Southern Italian restaurant in the shadow of the famed department store. The waiters are knowledgeable and congenial, giving it the feel of your own "friendly" neighborhood eatery.

SPEC: *Caponata (eggplant in sweet/sour sauce) $8.50; Black linguine w/peppers & shrimp $14.50; Cornish hen $14.50; Tiramisu $5*

BROTHER JIMMY'S D Southern

(E17) 1461 1st Ave. (76th) 212/545-7427

F 6 / S 5 / A 4 / $20   MC V D AE   **TO/D**

Porky pig might run for his life, but you'd be too full from dinner to catch him. "Triple fat overload" portions of ribs and mashed potatoes are big enough to scare any cardiologist. This college and 20-something bar/restaurant has made a name for itself by their food and "in" scene.

SPEC: *1/2 BBQ chicken $9.50; Rib platter $13.95; Outerbank burrito (vegetarian) $7.95; Brother Jimmy's dry rub ribs $13.95*

BURRITOVILLE LD Tex-Mex

(E17) 1489 1st Ave. (77th & 78th) 212/472-8800
See review on page 77.

CAFE GRECO LD Mediterranean

(E17) 1390 2nd Ave. (71st & 72nd) 212/737-4300 Fax: 737-0817

F 6 / S 6 / A 6 / $26 MC V D AE **TO/D**

It's seafood Mediterranean style in this family owned and operated cafe. "Simple fare well done, room to hear your guests," and
"well-spaced tables." The pastel decor will almost make you feel
the Mediterranean breeze. Cafe dining in front lets you view the
action on 2nd Ave., while the back room is more formal with a
garden view.

SPEC: *Spanakopita $5; Greek salad $5; Lamb chops $18.95; Chicken
marsala $12.95; Striped sea bass $15.95*

CAFE NOSIDAM LD Italian

(F16) 768 Madison Ave. (65th & 66th) 212/717-5633 Fax: 717-4436

F 8 / S 7 / A 7 / $35 MC V AE **TO/D**

"A real sleeper." The clientele isn't the only thing that can never be
too rich or too thin at Cafe Nosidam, Madison spelled backwards.
The new American/Italian food, a lotta mahogany, and the chance
to break bread with celebs, keeps us looking forward to going back.
Cafe Nosidam will leave you dethgiled.

SPEC: *Grilled octopus $12; Lobster ravioli $18; Veal chop $25.95;
Tiramisu $6.50; Flourless chocolate-Grand Marnier mousse
cake $7.50*

The Pierre

CAFE PIERRE BLD French

(F16) Pierre Hotel (61st & 5th Ave) 212/940-8185 Fax: 750-0541

F 7 / S 7 / A 7 / $45 MC V D AE

The Cafe Pierre is synonymous with quiet elegance. Very uptown.
Very stately. An old New York standby since 1930, and richly subtle
in every way. European standard of service and food. And cheek-to-
cheek dancing on Thursday, Friday and Saturday nights. Definitely
not for the "yeah-yeah" crowd.

SPEC: *Smoked & fresh salmon rillette w/caviar creme fraiche $12;
Fillet of red snapper $25; Grilled filet of beef l$28; Chocolate
meringue & caramel ice cream sandwich $8*

CAFFE BUON GUSTO LD Italian

(E17) 236 E. 77th St. (2nd & 3rd) 212/535-6884

F 6 / S 6 / A 4 / $22 Cash only

The food here is definitely worth the trip, whether it be from across
the street or from across town. It's probably one of New York's best
kept secrets. But make a reservation, because there's almost
always a wait.

SPEC: *Caesar salad $5.75; Ravioli $8.95; Pasta alla vodka $8.95;
Swordfish Livornese $15.95; Chocolate almond cake $3.50*

0	1	2	3	4	5	6	7	8	9	10
disappointing		fair		good		very good		excellent		perfect

CAFFE GRAZIE   LD   Italian

(D16) 26 E. 84th St. (Mad. & 5th) 212/717-4407

F 6 / S 4 / A 6 / $27   AE   **TO/D**

Possibly the most lemon-yellow room in NY, and one of the few places in the city that actually merits the description "cheery." Good prices and friendly staff. Ask to be seated upstairs, where the ceilings are high, the fireplace warm, and the feel romantic. For even higher ceilings, there's limited dining at the outdoor cafe—one table available on the sidewalk.

SPEC: Minestrone $5; Stracciatella (soup) $4.50; Grilled chicken lasagna $15; Ahi tuna steak $17.50

DONTE BURSE

Caffe Med

CAFFE MED   LD   Italian

(F17) 1268 2nd Ave. (66th & 67th) 212/744-5370

F 6 / S 6 / A 7 / $22   AE

This cafe, imported straight from Italy, lock, stock and dessert case, should put you in a romantic, Europhile mood, even with the bold jazz mural that wraps incongruously around the room. Every single dolci is imported from Milan—including the sorbets and gelati. Bring a loved one, or bring a book. Good people watching from the outdoor cafe.

SPEC: Robiola salad $7.50; Carpaccio palmito (raw filet mignon) $10.75; Di Parma focaccia $9.75; Tiramisu "Cream brulee" cheese cake $5

CALIFORNIA PIZZA KITCHEN   LD   Pizzeria

(F17) 201 E. 60th St. (2nd & 3rd) 212/755-7773 Fax: 755-7785

F 6 / S 5 / A 5 / $14   MC V D AE DIS   **TO/D**

"The United Nations of pizza." Perhaps the only restaurant in town that pages you by your own personal beeper to let you know your table's ready. "Feels like the burbs in decor." The food is good and priced well. Salads and pizzas (27 varieties) are original and tasty. Be prepared to wait, but it's worth it.

SPEC: Focacci w/checca $1.95; Spinach artichoke dip $4.95; BBQ chicken pizza $8.95; Hawaiian pizza $8.50; Myer's rum chocolate pecan pie $4.50

CAMPAGNOLA   D   Italian

(E17) 1382 1st Ave. (73rd & 74th) 212/861-1102

F 6 / S 6 / A 6 / $38   MC V D AE DIS   **TO**

A glass arch entrance gives way to a spacious country-like dining room. After all, "campagnola" means countryside...where you can expect good Northern Italian food, nightly piano playing, and celebrity sightings. Psst...there's also free tastings at the antique wooden bar.

SPEC: Linguine ai fruiti di mare $18.95; Grilled veal chop $26.95; Rack of lamb $28.95

Candle Cafe

CANDLE CAFE BLD Vegetarian

(E17) 1307 3rd Ave. (74th & 75th) 212/472-0970 Fax: 472-7169

F 6 / S 6 / A 6 / $18 MC V D AE DIS **TO/D**

The courts may have O.J., but Candle Cafe has the juice. This health conscious, conscience conscious cafe brings you down to earth, then feeds you. "You feel good about yourself after—like a tough workout." Amid fall colored tapestries, the candlelight glow illuminates patrons as eclectic as the dishes they're eating. The only thing remotely "animal" in this place is likely to be your dinner guest.

SPEC: *Sampler plate of bean pate, hummus, miso tahini $5.95; Seitan peppersteak $10.95; Casserole of the day $10.95; Chocolate cake $4.75; Fruited cheesecake $4.75*

CANYON ROAD D Southwestern

(E17) 1470 1st Ave. (76th & 77th) 212/734-1600

F 6 / S 5 / A 6 / $26 MC V AE

With its cozy, lodge-like, New Mexican feel, Canyon Road offers a wonderful array of "fun food," like soft swordfish tacos and spicy peanut shrimp. Prices are reasonable and patrons hungry. Friday night's the big one, so it's best to make reservations. Watch out for the frosty fruit flavored margaritas, they're a real shock to the system.

SPEC: *Spicy peanut shrimp $6.95; Taos turkey & turkey sausage chile $3.95; Soft tacos of fresh swordfish w/pico di gallo $13.95*

CARLYLE, RESTAURANT AT THE BLD French

(F16) 35 E. 76th St. (Mad.-Carlyle Hotel) 212/744-1600

F 8 / S 8 / A 8 / $55 MC V D AE

A grande dame restaurant in a grande dame hotel. How perfect! This smartly run, clubby spot caters to uptown girls and guys with deep pockets and lots of time to linger over a meal, or afternoon tea. And the divinely chic surroundings cosset with a wonderful sense of belonging—truly elegant service and style. Civility reigns at the Carlyle—as does entertainer Bobby Short.

SPEC: *Smoked Scottish salmon $19.50; Maryland crab cakes $24; Dover sole $35; Filet mignon $29.75; Grilled shrimp $27.50*

CHELSEA PASSAGE L American

(F16) 10 E. 61st St. (Mad.–Barney's NY Uptown) 212/826-8900

F 3 / S 4 / A 2 / $20 MC V D AE

No more than a place for a quick bite while taking a respite from shopping. The menu is limited; the space little more than a corner carved out of the second floor of the store; and the prices are high for what amounts to little more than an ordinary sandwich or an ordinary salad. If you must be seen in this bore of a bistro, simply have a coffee. It's the respectable thing to do.

0	1	2	3	4	5	6	7	8	9	10
disappointing		fair		good		very good		excellent		perfect

CHINA FUN   LD   Chinese

(F17) 1239 2nd Ave. (65th) 212/752-0810 Fax: 752-0821

F 6 / S 4 / A 4 / $13   MC V AE   **TO/D**

If the old fortune rings true for Chinese food: that the excellence of a restaurant's take out is judged by the sheer number of bicycles parked outside—then China Fun is the hands down winner. They get you in and out as quickly as the food comes and, with a large menu, the choices will dazzle you.

SPEC: *Roast pork, roast chicken and roast duck noodle soup $5.95; Warm noodle in light peanut & garlic sauce $4.50*

CI VEDIAMO   LD   Italian

(D17) 1431 3rd Ave. (81st) 212/650-0850

F 5 / S 5 / A 6 / $27   AE   **TO**

Yet another "hip," and bustling Upper East Side spot. Ci Vediamo ("See you") has a quick, open bistro bar downstairs and a romantic setting upstairs with subtle corners, velvet brocade curtains, and intimate tables.

SPEC: *Black ravioli w/lobster $10.95; Penna alla Giuliano $9.95; Linguini Ci Vediamo $13.95; Costola di Vitello $18.95*

COCO PAZZO   LD   Italian

(E16) 23 E. 74th St. (Mad. & 5th) 212/794-0205

F 7 / S 7 / A 7 / $48   MC V D AE

The name means "Crazy chef." The soft lighting, tan walls, yellow and blue color scheme help add an open, cheerful feeling to the restaurant, something sometimes lacking in the management and staff. Still, it's rated "one of the best." They serve more than 80 different wines and the food makes up for the occasional snotty attitude. "Lots of celebs." Make reservations and remember to bring your patience and a sense of humor.

SPEC: *Sautéed chicken livers $9; Spaghetti con vongole $17; Whole roasted fish of the day $28; Sautéed tenderloin of veal filled w/vegetables & mozzarella $25*

COCONUT GRILL   LD   American

(E17) 1481 3rd Ave. (77th) 212/772-6262

F 6 / S 6 / A 5 / $20   MC V AE

Certainly nothing to go coconuts over. The most exciting thing about this bar/restaurant is the people watching scene. They get a huge hip and young crowd for brunch. Still, it's "always fun," and though the food is "inconsistent," it offers a "great weekend brunch, with outdoor seating."

SPEC: *Sweet potato fries w/maple dipping sauce $4.50; Sesame skewered chicken $4.95; California-style stir fry $10.95*

CONTRAPUNTO   LD   Italian

(F17) 200 E. 60th St. (3rd Ave.) 212/751-8616 Fax: 988-3703

F 6 / S 6 / A 5 / $30   MC V D AE DIS

Overlooking 3rd Avenue, this comfortable, glass-enclosed 2nd story restaurant offers an upscale respite for shoppers and movie-goers. Filled with "pretty people," and "overpriced" but "always good," pasta, this is part of a trio of restaurants in the same building—Yellowfingers and Arizona 206.

SPEC: *Focaccia $3.50; Caesar salad $7.50; Fettuccine sorrentina $15.50; Seared red snapper $17.50; Hazelnut mascarpone torte $6.50*

CORTINA　　　　LD　　　　Italian

(E17) 1448 2nd Ave. (74th & 75th) 212/517-2066

F 5 / S 5 / A 5 / $20　　MC V AE

Perfectly acceptable, but nothing to write home about. This small homogenous Italian cafe won't break your wallet, but it won't knock your socks off either. Go for the gelato and a cappuccino for an afternoon or late night snack.

SPEC: *Mushroom risotto $7; Rigatoni w/creamy vodka sauce $5.95; Chicken breast $12; Hot cinnamon dessert crepe $6.25*

DALLAS BBQ　　　　LD　　　　American

(E17) 1265 3rd Ave. (72nd) 212/772-9393
See review on page 62.

DANIEL　　　　LD　　　　French

(E16) 20 E. 76th St. (Mad. & 5th) 212/288-0033 Fax: 737-0612

F 8 / S 8 / A 8 / $75　　MC V D AE

Elegant without being stuffy, Daniel holds its balance between the serious and the romantic. You can enjoy gourmet French cooking from three prix-fixe meals (a tasting of 8 courses.) Reservations a must, but if you get there early, sink into one of the plush chairs in the bar/lounge for a drink and contemplate the wonderful meal that awaits. **Closed: Sunday**

SPEC: *Three prix-fix meals $64, $74, $94, of 8 courses change daily; Prix-fixe lunch $33*

DEMARCHELIER　　　　LD　　　　French

(D16) 50 E. 86th St. 212/249-6300

F 7 / S 6 / A 6 / $35　　MC V D AE

With its authentic, stylish wood paneling this "very French bistro" is a "good" bet "after visiting the Metropolitan Museum of Art." The staff is either "warm and welcoming" or "unless they know you, forget it."

SPEC: *Onion soup $6.25; Garlic sausage w/warm potato salad $8.50; Grilled chicken $17.75; Steak tartare $18.50; Crêpes Suzette $6.75*

DIVINO RISTORANTE　　　　LD　　　　Italian

(D17) 1556 2nd Ave. (80th & 81st) 212/861-1096 Fax: 861-1753

F 6 / S 7 / A 6 / $26　　MC V D AE DIS　　**TO/D**

If you're indecisive about where to eat, but know it has to be Italian, Divino is the place. With 3 restaurants on the same block, there's a choice of upscale, just plain relaxed, or takeout. The Ristorante is more formal and slightly more expensive than the Cafe. An older crowd leans toward the restaurant, while the Cafe next door attracts a younger crowd. And for takeout, there's Gastronomia, also with a few tables if you prefer to eat in.

SPEC: *Cold veal, tuna sauce $7.25; Risotto del giorno $15.25; Baked red snapper $21.95; Chocolate rum cake $4.25*

DOLCETTO　　　　LD　　　　Italian

(D17) 1378 3rd Ave. (78th & 79th) 212/472-8300

F 7 / S 7 / A 7 / $26　　MC V D AE DIS　　**TO**

The handsome, soft and soothing decor of wood floors and sand-tan wall paper, makes for a comfortable dining experience. Dolcetto is warm and gracious, offering Italian cuisine at reasonable prices. recommended are the prix-fixe meal, and "the early bird" special, as "great steals."

SPEC: *Antipasto $6.75; Insalata inverno (potato, onion & string beans) $6.50; Swordfish $15.95; Tiramisu $6*

0	1	2	3	4	5	6	7	8	9	10
disappointing		fair		good		very good		excellent		perfect

DUE **LD** Italian

(D17) 1396 3rd Ave. (79th & 80th) 212/772-3331

F 7 / S 7 / A 7 / $26   Cash only

European in style and clientele, and friendlier than many Italian restaurants springing up all over the Upper East Side. Due has a charming, wholesome feel to it others lack. The food is Northern Italian, and the handsome decor and outside dining help enhance its growing reputation. "Good pasta, excellent grilled portabello."

SPEC: *Sautéed chicken livers $6.50; Grilled eggplant stuffed w/ricotta $6.75; Pollo scarpariello $12.50; Ravioli Piemontese $10.50*

E.A.T. **BLD** Amer/Continental

(D16) 1064 Madison Ave. (80th & 81st) 212/772-0022

F 6 / S 5 / A 5 / $30   AE   **TO/D**

Okay, so it's good, even a little piece of "heaven." But 14 bucks for an egg salad sandwich? You gotta be kidding. It's easy to resent the prices while loving fresh, well-prepared food. Still, many say, "I'll pay the price. It's worth it." The clientele here is, shall we say, on the affluent side. Ironically, E.A.T. furnishes bread to many retail shops, where it's cheaper than from the source.

SPEC: *Chicken vegetable soup $8; Tower of bagel $16; Grilled chicken salad $16; Focaccia sandwich $12; Smoked salmon $24*

E.J.'S LUNCHEONETTE **BLD** Diner

(E17) 1271 3rd Ave. (73rd) 212/472-0600

See review on page 228.

EAST **LD** Japanese

(D17) 1420 3rd Ave. (80th & 81st) 212/472-3975

(F17) 354 E. 66th St. (1st & 2nd) 212/734-5270

See review on page 105.

EAST RIVER CAFE **LD** Italian

(F17) 1111 1st Ave. (60th & 61st) 212/980-3144 Fax: 980-3171

F 5 / S 5 / A 4 / $23   MC V AE   **TO/D**

This typical Upper East Side eatery –"Average all the way."– features friendly service and your choice of 15 pastas for $8.95 and up, as well as other pricier dishes. The bar scene is rather active and Wednesdays through Sundays there's a piano player.

SPEC: *Supreme salad $5.95; Seafood cous-cous $15.75; Black fettucine $12.95; Mushroom ravioli $10.95*

EAST SIDE GOURMET **LD** Chinese

(E17) 1433 2nd Ave. (74th & 75th) 212/535-1471

F 5 / S 3 / A 3 / $15   AE   **TO/D**

Your average Szechuan/Hunan restaurant with a somewhat unusual Americanized name and an even more unusual offer that keeps the dinner crowd lined up out the door. Free wine for those who eat in, but with only 12 tables it's best to get there early.

SPEC: *Sesame chicken $8.75; Szechuan double taste (chicken & shrimp) $9.75; Seafood deluxe $10.95*

ELIO'S D Italian

(D17) 1621 2nd Ave. (84th & 85th) 212/772-2242 Fax: 988-0514

F 7 / S 7 / A 6 / $35 MC V D AE

"A fun" thing to do here is to "try to get the waiters to smile." Another "fun" thing to do is to eat. The food is well-prepared, but the decor is nothing special, what with tables placed close together. Some "can't figure out why it's so popular," since "it's nothing great." But others find it "consistently excellent."

SPEC: *Roast peppers and anchovies -$6.50; Bresaola valtellina $10; Fried zucchini $6; Pasta al pesto $14; Grey sole a piacere $17; Scaloppine piccata $16*

ENTOURAGE SPORTS CAFE D American

(D17) 1571 2nd Ave. (81st & 82nd) 212/535-3700

F 5 / S 6 / A 4 / $15 AE **TO/D**

Your basic friendly sports bar, best known for its Buffalo chicken wings, also available as takeout/delivery from Entourage Wings & Things up the block. With 6 TVs, one a giant screen, it's likely you won't miss much on-field action. Drawing primarily from the neighborhood, there are a surprising number of female patrons. A good sign for the male sports fan looking for more than game action.

SPEC: *Buffalo chicken wings $6.95; Beer battered mushrooms $6.95; Marinated steak teriyaki $11.95; Chocolate cake $3.50*

ERMINIA D Italian

(D17) 250 E. 83rd St. (2nd & 3rd) 212/879-4284

F 7 / S 6 / A 6 / $45 MC V D AE

Tucked away in a small corner of the Upper East Side, this truly romantic spot is a perfect place for that special someone. With the ivy-covered entrance, this ristorante oozes romance and charm. The wine list is extensive; the food out of this world. Make reservations, since it fills up fast, especially on weekends.

SPEC: *Mozzarella Erminia $8.95; Zuppa di pesce $26.95; Costolette di agnello $23.95; Grilled lobster P/A*

Etats-Unis

ETATS-UNIS D American

(D17) 242 E. 81st St. (2nd & 3rd) 212/517-8742

F 8 / S 7 / A 7 / $40 MC V D

Eating at this tiny and casually elegant "special place in its own image," where the menu changes daily, is like attending a dinner party thrown by your coolest friend. You just wish your friend could cook like this. Though the name leads you to believe the "heavenly" food is French, it's not. The name was chosen by owner Tom Rapp, a former architect, because he modeled it after a small, family-owned restaurant in France.

SPEC: *Lobster & avocado Salad $12; Mesclun salad $8; Chocolate soufflé $9.50; Poached pear, chocolate & vanilla custard tartlette $8*

0	1	2	3	4	5	6	7	8	9	10
disappointing		fair		good		very good		excellent		perfect

FIRENZE   D   Italian

(D17) 1594 2nd Ave. (82nd & 83rd) 212/861-9368

F 7 / S 6 / A 7 / $26   MC V D AE   **TO**

If you're looking to take someone on a special date, and you've got a hankering for Northern Italian, Firenze fits the bill. Small, attractive, with a pleasantly romantic atmosphere, chef/owner Anthony Pagano offers a somewhat limited but sufficient menu. If the atmosphere doesn't earn you points, the food will, though some find it "over-priced."

SPEC: *Mussels $7.50; Fettuccine w/four cheeses $11.50; Shrimp sautéed in white wine $18.75; Milanese style veal off the bone $19.95*

FORK UNIVERSITY   LD   American

(E17) 1490 2nd Ave. (76th & 77th) 212/988-5300

F 6 / S 6 / A 5 / $24   MC V D AE

Your GPA will be high because everyone's an expert on eating, right? This newcomer is dependable, relaxed, and foregoes the frat atmosphere that might make some uncomfortable. The small outdoor cafe is perfect for summer, spring, or fall treat. The bar scene is "de rigeur," for late night shmoozing. 1/2 the menu is vegetarian and the chef is formerly from the Russian Tea Room, so expect a creative, eclectic, health conscious fare.

SPEC: *Grilled vegetable salad w/goat cheese $5.95; Pizzas $8.95-$12.95; Vegetable strudel w/sautéed greens $8.95; Marinated roast chicken w/mashed potatoes $13.95*

Gino

GINO   LD   Italian

(F17) 780 Lexington Ave. (60th & 61st) 212/758-4466 Fax: 421-8961

F 6 / S 7 / A 7 / $30   Cash only

Last year Gino celebrated its 50th anniversary qualifying it as a "landmark" in the restaurant world. With a loyal following of diners who appreciate its Southern Italian cuisine, it's certainly worth a visit if you're in midtown and have a hunger for pasta.

SPEC: *Special antipasto $7.25; Baked artichoke $8.25; Fettuccine w/porcini $11.95; Scampi a la Gino $21.50; Torta di Ricotta $3.95*

GIRASOLE   LD   Italian

(D17) 151 E. 82nd St. (Lexington) 212/772-6690

F 7 / S 8 / A 7 / $35   AE   **TO**

Girasole means "sunflower" in Italian, and diners with a subtle eye may notice the motif carved into the wood pattern of the floor and staircase. Italian specialties from all regions are served to Park Ave. diners and occasional crowds of investment bankers. The wine list is exhaustive, and the wait staff very courteous.

SPEC: *Grigliata di verdura $7; Crostini di polenta al gorgonzola $5; Oizeochiette con zucchini e melanzane $14.50; Sardinian pasta $15.50; Homade gelati $5*

GOOGIE'S   BLD   Diner

(E17) 1491 2nd Ave. (78th) 212/717-1122

F 6 / S 6 / A 6 / $22   Cash only   **TO/D**

Modern '50s style restaurant, funky and art deco, Googie's is a hip, "lots of fun," American/Italian diner that has quickly become an "in" spot for brunch and a great place to take kids, who'll love the toothpick-thin fries. The food is okay, but the atmosphere is far more filling and satisfying.

SPEC: *Chicken skewers w/sundried tomato & basil pesto on shoe-string fries $6.75; Tuscan style meatloaf $10; Googie's sundaes $4.95*

HEIDELBERG RESTAURANT   LD   German

(D17) 1648 2nd Ave. (85th & 86th) 212/628-2332

F 5 / S 6 / A 6 / $26   MC V D AE DIS   **TO**

If you're from Germany, or been there recently and want to relive fond memories, this throwback is the place to go. Sauerbraten, schnitzels and all kinds of sausages are available, along with a fine selection of German beers. But one diner wonders, "Is it a misprint or a misnomer? It should read 'Hindenburg.'"

SPEC: *Oxenmaul Salad (marinated tongue & onions) $5.95; Sauerbraten $15.25; schnitzens (3 types) $15.25-$16.25; Schwartzwaelder kirsch torte $4.75; Palat schinken $5.95*

HI LIFE RESTAURANT & LOUNGE   LD   American

(E17) 1340 1st Ave. (72nd) 212/249-3600 Fax: 717-5471

F 7 / S 6 / A 6 / $20   MC V D AE   **TO/D**

Reminiscent of a '30's style jazz club. As a restaurant/cocktail lounge, Hi Life's strong points are its diverse menu, fully equipped sushi bar, 10 beers on tap, live DJ and weekend band. Hollywood-like with its booths, palm trees and soft pink light, it might seem you've wandered into an old Cary Grant film. It's "surprising to find such good food in a place known mainly for monstrous martinis."

SPEC: *Char-grilled filet mignon $8.50; Sushi & teriyaki veggie kebob $6.75; Steamed red snapper $15; Rosemary chicken $14; Chocolate mud pie $5.50*

DONTE BURSE

Hosteria Fiorella

HOSTERIA FIORELLA   LD   Italian

(E17) 1081 3rd Ave. (63rd & 64th) 212/838-7570

F 7 / S 6 / A 6 / $32   MC V D AE DIS   **TO**

Charming and huge, this Tuscany-style restaurant is a real pleaser to anyone who enjoys great Italian food. Known for their antipasto and seafood dishes—"We mourn the passing of the tuna burger"—it's a festive, romantic place to delight in. One of the few restaurants to serve complimentary chocolate covered strawberries after the meal is completed. An especially nice and classy touch.

SPEC: *Antipasto platter $12.95; Rigatoni melanzane $15.95; Grilled scampi $22.25; Filet mignon of tuna $23.25*

0	1	2	3	4	5	6	7	8	9	10
disappointing		fair		good		very good		excellent		perfect

HUNTERS AMERICAN BAR & GRILL   LD   American

(D17) 1387 3rd Ave. (79th) 212/734-6008

F 5 / S 5 / A 6 / $19   MC V AE   **TO**

In the '90s, when instant gratification takes too long, it's nice to find a restaurant like this where there are no gimmicks or quirkiness. Late in the evening, they shut down the back of the restaurant and bring out backgammon and chess sets for customers to use.
SPEC: *Fried mozzarella sticks $3.50; Herb roasted half chicken $8.95; Meatloaf $7.95; Mashed potatoes $2.50; Apple crustada w/ice cream $3.95;*

HURRICANE ISLAND   LD   American

(E17) 1303 3rd Ave. (74th & 75th) 212/717-6600 Fax: 794-9477

F 5 / S 5 / A 5 / $30   MC V D AE   **TO**

Everything's fishy about this place. Hurricane Island, an actual island owned by proprietor Jim Gaston, is a Maine incarnate with fresh lobsters frequently flown in and a pearl of a selection of oysters. Weather report: secure your bib and be blown away.
SPEC: *Oysters $7.95; Maine lobster $17.95 per lb.; Jambalaya $14.95; Brown Betty $4.75; California carrot cake $4.75*

ICHIBAN   LD   Japanese

(F17) 1193 1st Ave. (64th & 65th) 212/734-2100

F 5 / S 6 / A 5 / $20   MC V D AE   **TO/D**

Ichiban means "#1", but this is really nothing more your average Japanese sushi joint. They have good intentions, but they just don't knock themselves out to knock your socks off. **Closed: Sunday**
SPEC: *Tempura $5.25; Gyoza (seafood dumplings) $4; Chicken teriyaki $9.95; Salmon teriyaki $12.95; Yokan (red bean cake) $2*

ICI   LD   French

(E16) 19 E. 69th St. (5th & Madison) 212/794-6410

– / – / – /   MC V AE   **TO/D**

Another new, small, intimate very French bistro off Madison Avenue where fashionable and hip uptowners lunch and sup. There's a decided continental feel and the service can be great… except when it's not.

IL MONELLO   LD   Italian

(E17) 1460 2nd Ave. (76th & 77th) 212/535-9310

F 7 / S 7 / A 7 / $41   MC V D AE

It means "Little Rascal," but unless the little rascal in question is Macaulay Culkin, this would probably be a tad too expensive. However, for all of the big rascals of the Upper East Side and environs, this is a handsome, sophisticated restaurant with an "elegant interior" as well as outdoor dining.
SPEC: *Roasted peppers w/anchovies $10; Macaroni & bean soup $7; Clams in broth $21; Sautéed breast of duck $24*

IL PELLICANO   D   Italian

(F18) 401 E. 62nd St. (1st & York) 212/233-1040

F 8 / S 7 / A 8 / $21   MC V D AE   **TO**

Owner Dogan Ozdenak, a Turkish ex-soccer player and former cook for Malcolm Forbes, lures diners with excellent grilled seafood and attentive service. The space is cozy, romantic and intimate with fresh flowers and antiques scattered throughout.
SPEC: *Grilled calamari salad $6.95; Tuna over house salad $10.95; Swordfish w/fresh vegetables $14.95; Torta profiteroles $6.95*

Nicholas Pileggi
Author of Wiseguys and screenplays for Goodfellas and Casino

If you're in Little Italy, you must try **Paolucci's** (149 Mulberry St., 212/925-2288.) My favorite dish, not surprisingly, is Pork Chops Pileggi, which is served with sauteed peppers, onion and potatoes. Excellent.

ISLE OF CAPRI LD Italian

(F17) 1028 3rd Ave. (61st) 212/758-1828

F 3 / S 5 / A 5 / $34   MC V D AE

Located a stone's throw from Bloomingdale's, this Northern Italian restaurant has been around for 40 years. Once inside, you feel as if you've landed in Palermo, with its charming, classic Italian interior. Possibly good for a shopping break that will take you into another kinder, gentler world. But some warn that it's "way over-priced."
Closed: Sunday
SPEC: *Pasta & bean soup $7.25; Antipasto caldo $10; Veal chop $23; Vitello Francese $17; Semifreddo cioccolato $6*

ISTANBUL KEBAP Turkish

(D17) 303 E. 80th St. (1st & 2nd) 212/517-6880

F 7 / S 7 / A 5 / $16   AE   **TO/D**

Considering the neighborhood and the quality of the food, the prices at this Turkish restaurant are surprisingly reasonable and the cuisine "interesting." The room is small, only a dozen tables in all, but the decor is strikingly handsome, what with oriental rubs and cloths adorning walls and tables.
SPEC: *Cacik (yogurt mixed w/cucumbers, garlic & herbs) $3.75; Musaka $9.95; Karisik (combo platter of grilled specialties $12.95; Kadayif (shredded wheat w/walnuts & honey) $3.50*

J.G. MELON LD American

(D17) 1291 3rd Ave. (74th) 212/650-1310

F 6 / S 6 / A 5 / $20   Cash only   **TO**

The "hamburgers and cottage fries" are great at this Upper East Side pub that's making ready to celebrate its 25th anniversary. The decor is dominated by—yes!—melons, pictures of over 150 of them; and there's actually a working jukebox.
SPEC: *Hamburger $4.95; Roast rock cornish hen, potato & salad $10.95; Chef's salad $8.75; Chocolate chip cake $4.50*

JACKSON HOLE LD American

(F17) 232 E. 64th St. (2nd & 3rd) 212/371-7187
(D17) 1611 2nd Ave. (83rd & 84th) 212/737-8788
See review page 231.

JIM MCMULLEN RESTAURANT LD American

(E17) 1341 3rd Ave. (76th & 77th) 212/861-4700 Fax: 717-5181

F 5 / S 6 / A 5 / $23   MC V D AE   **TO**

Typical of an Old NY style restaurant, Jim McMullen's caters to an attractive, conservative, strictly Upper East Side crowd. If you're looking for a place to take your family, including Grandma and Grandpa, this is it. Maybe it "ain't what it used to be," but while you're there it's a good bet you'll also find a celebrity or two at a nearby table, or perhaps a model chewing on a celery stalk.
SPEC: *Charred tuna $6.75; Asparagus vinaigrette $5.50; Chicken pot pie $11.75; Day boat scallops $15.25; Brownie ala mode $4.50*

0	1	2	3	4	5	6	7	8	9	10
disappointing		fair		good		very good		excellent		perfect

JO JO — LD — French

(E17) 160 E. 64th St. (Lex. & 3rd) 212/223-5656

F 8 / S 7 / A 7 / $40   MC V D AE

In his second eatery, chef Jean-George Vongerichten (Vong's) serves up light French bistro food. In this elegant townhouse that "feels like Paris," you'll find a healthy meal at a nice price. "The food is good, sometimes great!" But some diners say "it's a little too frantic" and "service is sometimes a little snippy."
SPEC: *Tuna $10; Foie gras $16; Codfish $19; Lobster $27; Lamb $25; Squab $24*

JOHN'S PIZZERIA — LD — Pizzeria

(F18) 408 E. 64th St. (1st & York) 212/243-1680
See review on page 86.

L'Absinthe

JUANITA'S — LD — Tex-Mex

(E17) 1309 3rd Ave. (75th) 212/517-3800

F 5 / S 5 / A 5 / $18   MC V AE   **TO/D**

Slightly dull and dark—this non-authentic Mexican restaurant is, to some diners, "past its prime." Known more for its hopping bar scene than for its food which, though pleasing, is undistinguished. If you're a sports fan, bring your autograph book, since many professional football players, past and present, dine here. **Closed: No lunch Monday**
SPEC: *Bean nachos $4.75; Fajitas $13.75; Blackened red fish $13.50; Chili butter chicken $12.50; Juanita's supreme (fried tortilla w/vanilla ice cream & butterscotch or chocolate sauce) $5*

KIOSK, THE — LD — American

(E17) 1007 Lexington Ave. (72nd & 73rd) 212/535-6000

–/–/–/   MC V D AE

Designed by its adept and popular owners—Nell Campbell is one—The Kiosk successfully mixes downtown flair with uptown glare... and heavy metal... copper and zinc table tops, that is. International newspaper headings trim the perimeter of the back room where hordes find themselves getting down uptown.
SPEC: *Peppered tuna w/quinoa $21; Grilled free range chicken w/spinach & mashed potatoes $17.50; Grilled sea bass $21*

KLEINE KONDITOREI   **LD**   German

(D17) 234 E. 86th St. (2nd & 3rd) 212/737-7130 Fax: 879-6515

F 5 / S 5 / A 3 / $26   MC V AE   **TO**

Called "the best German in the city," it's a real time capsule that opened first as a bakery in the '20s, then turned into a restaurant shortly after WWII. "Renovate, already," say some. Regulars include some of the neighborhood's oldest—and at times crankiest—residents, as well as immigrants looking for the food and restaurants they remember from the past.

SPEC: *Calf's brains w/eggs $5.75; Sauerbraten $14.75; Kasselerrippchen $13.75; German sausages $12.25; Apple pancake $11.75; Somloi galuska $4.50*

L'ABSINTHE   **D**   French

(F17) 227 E. 67th St. (2nd & 3rd) 212/794-4950

F 7 / S 6 / A 6 / $35   MC V AE

The magic of the Muppets at the nearby Henson Studio is felt down the street for adults as they are transported to a classic Paris bistro. The large wood and glass doors open onto the street, giving it a sidewalk cafe feel. The staff is friendly, the ambiance relaxed, and the food exemplary.

SPEC: *Endive salad w/smoked duck breast $7.50; Escargots $9.50; Swordfish steak $22; Loin of lamb $23.50*

L'ARDOISE   **LD**   French

(F17) 1207 1st Ave. (65th & 66th) 212/744-4752

F 6 / S 4 / A 4 / $26   Cash only   **TO**

The writing's on the board...chalkboard, that is. And there are loads of them at this humble French place with a serious menu and great sense of humor. Pour example: Frunch—French brunch. And chalk one up for a high-spirited maitre d' who serves as live entertainment.

SPEC: *Sardines $15; Loin of beef $15; Duck $15*

La Folie

LA FOLIE   **LD**   French

(D17) 1422 3rd Ave. (80th & 81st) 212/744-6327

F 6 / S 4 / A 6 / $35   MC V D AE   **TO**

Striving for a Parisienne feel and making it! This bistrot francaise with an American twist has the je ne sais quois of the City of Lights on 3rd Avenue. Very elegant. Very beautiful. Very French. The decor— sofas, faux marble columns, tapestries, lovely flowers and fine soft lighting, as well as the international mix of diners, adds to the sense that you've left the crowded, gritty streets of this city and somehow made it to Paris. Seafood is a specialty of the chef.

SPEC: *Terrine de foie gras $12; Vegetable tart $7.50; Atlantic salmon $18.50; Pan roasted sea bass $19; Moroccan spiced tuna $19.50*

0	1	2	3	4	5	6	7	8	9	10
disappointing		fair		good		very good		excellent		perfect

LA GOULUE LD French

(F16) 746 Madison Ave. (64th & 65th) 212/988-8169

F 5 / S 3 / A 6 / $37 MC V D AE

La Goulue is a recent transplant to Madison Ave. Adorned like an original Parisian bistro, with incandescent lights and Art Nouveau, it continues to dish out deliciously delicate fashion plates. But diners complain you "don't get good service unless you're a regular."

SPEC: *Salmon tartare $9.50; Warm potato and "coach farm" goat cheese tart tatin w/smoked duck breast $9.50; Cold Maine lobster $25; Steak au poivre $26*

LA GRANITA LD Italian

(E17) 1470 2nd Ave. (77th) 212/717-5500

F 5 / S 5 / A 4 / $22 Cash only

This is the new Romanesque restaurant on the block. Be prepared: the space is small and cramped. But on the positive side, it has an upstairs, equipped with a fireplace, large windows that look out onto the street, and a special glass-enclosed smoking section.

SPEC: *Prosciutto della casa $6.50; Verdure alla griglia $7.50; Risotto w/spinach, arugula & basil puree $11.50; Cornish hen $13; Crême brulee $5*

LE BISTROT DE MAXIM'S LD French

(F16) 680 Mad. Ave. (61st & 62nd) 212/980-6988 Fax: 750-0103

F 6 / S 8 / A 8 / $42 MC V D AE

The night they invented champagne, they invented it in the famed original in Paris. Owned by Pierre Cardin, it's a giant step from Barney's Uptown. A fashion coincidence? Perhaps. The "boite" is romantic in the evening, with live music, soft light and above average French food at manageable prices. **Closed: Tuesday & Saturday**

Top 10 $56+

Very Expensive

LE CIRQUE LD French

(F16) 58 E. 65th St. (Mad. & Park - Mayfair Hotel) 212/794-9292

F 8 / S 8 / A 8 / $65 MC V D AE

Still one of the most beloved places in town. "If only I could age as gracefully!" The decor is as stunning as the food. "Everything is exquisite." Owner Sirio Maccioni's legendary room made dining an event, and chef Sylvain Portray's cuisine is masterly prepared and beautifully presented. The clientele defines the NY power scene. "While they're still snooty, it's a marvelous experience."

SPEC: *Ravioli w/Swiss chard, arugula, artichokes & goat cheese $18; Black bass $31; Grilled salmon $28; Roasted stuffed saddle of rabbit $28*

LE PETIT SAIGON LD Vietnamese

(F17) 1164 1st Ave. (63rd & 64th) 212/207-4041 Fax: 207-4039

F 7 / S 4 / A 5 / $17 MC V AE **TO/D**

If the U.S. can normalize relations with Vietnam, and "Miss Saigon" can play on Broadway, then why not visit this authentic, truly petit, "healthy, fresh neophyte" Vietnamese restaurant next time you're in the neighborhood. It may not look like much, but the food is good and the prices compare favorably to its far more expensive cousins.

SPEC: *Vietnamese spring roll $3.95; Grilled shrimp wrapped in sugar cane $5.95; Bo Luc Lac (stir-fried marinated steak cubes) $10.95*

LE PISTOU   LD   French

(F16) 134 E. 61st St. (Park & Lex.) 212/838-7987 Fax: 758-3361

F 7 / S 7 / A 7 / $40   MC V D AE

A little sister to the famed La Cote Basque, Le Pistou attracts a sophisticated and knowledgeable uptown crowd, including many United Nations workers. Features the Provençal creations of an ambitious and highly-praised young chef, Xavier Mayonove. Yet, some believe, "It was better several years ago when Madame watched over everything."

SPEC: *Prix fixe dinner; Onion soup; Carpaccio of beef; Fillet of sole; Paupiettes of veal; Steak au poivre; Fruit tarts; Peach melba $34*

LE REFUGE   LD   French

(D17) 166 E. 82nd St. (3rd & Lex.) 212/861-4505 Fax: 737-0384

F 7 / S 7 / A 8 / $35   AE

A touch of France without attitude. "Still an oasis with tasty food," it's quiet, candle-lit and romantic. In fact, it's like "stepping through a door on 82nd street and winding up on the Normandy coast." Newly opened: Le Refuge's Bed and Breakfast, on City Island, where you can dine overlooking the Atlantic. **Closed: Sunday (summer)**

SPEC: *Duck liver pate $7.50; Snails in puff pastry $10.50; Poached salmon $22.50; Grilled chicken w/bacon $19.50*

LE REGENCE   LD   French

(F16) 37 E. 64th St. (Mad. & Park - Plaza Athenee) 212/606-4647

F 7 / S 7 / A 8 / $62   MC V D AE

A splendid dining experience in an incredibly lavish space. With its pearl blue walls and elaborate white scaffolding, the dining room seems appropriate for only the likes of Louis XIV. The waiters epitomize class and snobbery. Every aspect of the meal is perfect—the food, service, and overall ambiance. This marvel, however, is not without a hefty price tag. This classic French should not be missed, but try experiencing it on someone else's check.

SPEC: *Lunch: Crab meat & potato cake w/goat cheese $13; Fillet of red snapper $27.50; Sautéed calf's liver $19.50; Chocolate mousse cake $8*

LE RELAIS   LD   French

(F16) 712 Madison Ave. (63rd & 64th) 212/751-5108

F 6 / S 6 / A 7 / $34   MC V D AE

A bustling Madison Ave. crowd gathers here and gives order for traditional French food. Framed French cartoons, wine bottle labels and events from the Napoleonic era clutter the walls in this "simple setting..."

SPEC: *Medallions of mushrooms $23; Red snapper w/artichokes $23; Steak tartare $18.75*

LE TAXI   LD   French

(F17) 37 E. 60th St. (Park & Mad.) 212/832-5500

F 7 / S 7 / A 8 / $34   MC V D AE

Famed and framed Parisian movie, theater and magazine posters adorn the walls of this upscale French bistro. Here's where you'll find the South American classy and the foreign embassy dining crowd. Given its name and the ambassadorial clientele, there's sure to be a lot of double parking. But it's worth the wait. **Closed: Sunday**

SPEC: *Crab cake w/marinated tomatoes $9.75; Foie gras $14.75; Duck $19.75; Le tartare w/pommes frites $19.50*

0	1	2	3	4	5	6	7	8	9	10
disappointing		fair		good		very good		excellent		perfect

LE VEAU D'OR LD French

(F16) 129 E. 60th St. (Lex. & Park) 212/838-8133

F 7 / S 7 / A 7 / $42   MC V D AE DIS

They've been in business almost 60 years, so this French bistro must be doing something right. And Robert Treboux, the owner, has been in the restaurant business just as long. Relax in the elegance of "Old World charm" and, if you're lucky, Robert will be there. If he is, be sure to engage him in conversation. He's a remarkable story-teller, and he'll gladly offer himself up as the evening's entertainment. **Closed: Sunday**

SPEC: *Table d'Hote: Fillet of sole $24; Frog legs $25; Roast duck $26; Veal kidneys $24; Coq au vin $24 (includes appetizer & dessert)*

LENOX ROOM D American

(E17) 1278 3rd Ave. (73rd & 74th) 212/772-0404 772-3229

F 7 / S 8 / A 7 / $40   MC V D AE

Resplendent at its Upper East Side location as well as in its brown-beige, well-planted, interior environs, this "spirited, " "lively," and very fashionable restaurant is a toast to nouvelle American cuisine. Under the ever-present, accomodating auspices of co-owner Tony Fortuna, an "incredibly eclectic" crowd is served excellently prepared and "magnificently presented" dinners. Also open Saturday and Sunday from 12pm to 2pm for a chic, a la carte lunch.

SPEC: *Sesame glazed portobello mushrooms $8; Cumin glazed duck breast $20; Roasted lobster & ginger noodles $28*

Loui Loui

LOUI LOUI LD Italian

(E17) 1311 3rd Ave. (75th) 212/717-4500

F 7 / S 7 / A 7 / $30   AE

If we said, "Northern Italian with a Tuscan accent that loves to feed you," some might say, "My grandmother." Add cherrywood-paneled walls, tiled floors and a mural with an indisputably French slant and add, "Split personality?" Maybe. Split a few entrees. Definitely. Loui Loui...Baby, you can go...

SPEC: *Segato di carciofi (rucola, thin sliced baby artichokes, parmigiano) $7; Spaghetti w/clams $13; Risotto $14*

LUKE'S BAR & GRILL LD American

(D17) 1394 3rd Ave. (79th & 80th) 212/249-7070

F 6 / S 5 / A 5 / $18   Cash only   TO

A reasonably priced, All-American pub catering to the young Waspy and Yuppie 30-somethings, as well as neighborhood denizens. The bar scene has a big turnout on weekends and is a popular meeting place for couples as well as those on the prowl. The menu is pretty standard fare: burgers, fries and salads.

SPEC: *Chicken salad $8.50; Chicken stir fry $8.95; Decadent chocolate mud pie $3.95*

Lumi

LUMI — LD — Italian

(E17) 963 Lexington Ave. (70th) 212/570-2335 Fax: 288-6410

F 7 / S 6 / A 7 / $32 MC V D AE

Chef Hido Holli and wife Lumi Hadri are the dynamic duo behind this restaurant in an exquisite two-story townhouse. They have created a family-style atmosphere...fortunately, it's the side of the family you like to visit. Tastefully complete with fireplaces, chandeliers and a spiral staircase, it's a home away from home where you're likely to clean your plate.

SPEC: *Grilled quail $8; Salmon filet $21; Baby chicken $18; Veal shank $22*

LUSARDI'S — LD — Italian

(E17) 1494 2nd Ave. (78th) 212/249-2020

F 7 / S 7 / A 6 / $35 MC V D AE DIS

This upscale, uptown, grown up Northern Italian eatery doesn't lack for anything. It's sophisticated, well-established, "great neighborhood place," perfect for ladies and lawyers alike who love to lunch luminously at Lusardi's.

SPEC: *Beef carpaccio w/sautéed mushrooms $10.50; Risotto primavera $19; Sautéed swordfish $21*

MAD.61 — D — American

(F17) 10 E. 61st St. (Mad. Ave. – Barney's NY) 212/833-2200

F 6 / S 6 / A 6 / $34 MC V D

A Barney's eatery that aspires to posh, Mad.61 fails to be anything but a good place to be seen. It's a place to star gaze while eating innovatively-topped pizzas, or a funky risotto. The food is well-prepared, but pricey. And its basement location works against it. "Too much attitude," and "poor service," are common complaints.

SPEC: *Focaccia robiola $15; Asparagus salad $9; Basil cured salmon $23*

MADAME ROMAINE DE LYON — LD — French

(F16) 132 E. 61st St. (Lex. & Park) 212/758-2422

F 5 / S 4 / A 6 / $26 MC V D AE

Just moved to a new location, a few doors up the street, but it continues to be the place for one thing—omelettes. If you need to boost your cholesterol, or just give it a jump start, come here. The combinations seem never-ending. The rest of the menu is quite common. But it's "fine for a light lunch."

SPEC: *Omelettes made with any combination of ingredients: $12-$20*

0	1	2	3	4	5	6	7	8	9	10
disappointing		fair		good		very good		excellent		perfect

167

MAISON CARIBE   D   Caribbean

(D17) 343 E. 85th St. (1st & 2nd) 212/744-1227

F 5 / S 6 / A 6 / $28   MC V AE   **TO**

A neighborhood find. Cool jazz and hot, spicy Caribbean food with a European accent. Forget you're on the Upper East Side and picture yourself in a little place on, say St. Bart's or St. Lucia, only at half the price.

SPEC: *Potato crab cakes $7; Conch fritters $7; Shrimp al ajillo $16.50; Paella $16.50; Jerk chicken $13.50*

MALAGA   LD   Spanish

(E18) 406 E. 73rd St. (1st & York) 212/737-7659

F 7 / S 6 / A 6 / $28   MC V D AE   **TO/D**

Paella. Pollo. Gazpacho. Sangria. Any way you say it, you'll find it in this low-key family-run restaurant featuring the distinctive flavors of southern Espana. Reasonable prices. And a casual atmosphere that doesn't demand "attitude." All comers are welcome. Olé!

SPEC: *Shrimp ajillo $6.25; Spanish sausage $6.25; Lobster parrillada $18.95; Salmon steak $15.50; Guava $3.50*

MAMBO GRILL   LD   Latin

(D17) 174 E. 83rd St. (Lex. & 3rd) 212/879-5516

F 7 / S 6 / A 6 / $31   MC V D AE DIS   **TO/D**

A real Latin beat pulses at this happy, tropical spot. A definite surprise in this Upper East Side neighborhood. "Lively," with the "front room kind of rowdy." Arepitas are a specialty. And live music Saturday nights brings out the Carmen Miranda rhythm in us all.

SPEC: *Shrimp in garlic sauce $8; Avocado stuffed w/ceviche or shrimp $7; Tenderloin served w/yucca & guasacaca $20; Creme caramel $5.50*

MANANA   LD   Mexican

(F17) 1136 1st Ave. (62nd & 63rd) 212/223-9623

F 5 / S 6 / A 4 / $22   MC V D AE DIS   **TO**

It's been in the same spot for 30 years, so they must be doing something right. The interior is "schizophrenic." Walk past the bar toward the back of the restaurant, and it's south of the border, what with the Spanish style furniture—comfy padded chairs and couches. But hang a right and you're back north with your standard dull, wooden tables and straight-back chairs.

SPEC: *Shrimp & scallops marinated in lemon & lime juice $6.95; Chicken livers sautéed in sherry $5.95; Entrecot Manana $16.95*

MANHATTAN CAFE   LD   Amer/Continental

(F17) 1161 1st Ave. (63rd & 64th) 212/888-6556

F 8 / S 8 / A 7 / $38   MC V D AE DIS   **TO**

Done up in Victorian-French, with a hint of Oriental flair, this steakhouse is one of the most accommodating and comfortable restaurants in the area. The portions are generous, the atmosphere friendly, and the food, which will shoot your cholesterol off the scale, enormously satisfying.

SPEC: *Smoked trout $11.75; NY prime sirloin steak $29.75; Steak au poivre $29.75; Bolero cake (caramelized bananas, walnut, chocolate mousse, chocolate sponge, cream anglaise) $7.50*

MARK'S BLD French

(E16) 25 E. 77th St. (Mad. -The Mark) 212/744-4300

F 8 / S 7 / A 8 / $55   MC V D AE DIS

Called "the coziest, most comfortable restaurant in the city," this truly elegant space reminds us of the den we always wanted but couldn't afford. A harpist brings music to your ears and specially priced offers bring water to your mouth...only after you've seen dollar signs in your eyes. A super friendly and good humored host makes one forget that sometimes the bill of fare just isn't fair. On your Mark, get set, go.

SPEC: *Pacific Northwest oysters $14; Grilled loin of chicken $13; Sautéed Florida black grouper $28; Roasted Colorado rack of lamb $34; Chocolate pecan passion $8.50*

MARTI LD Turkish

(E17) 1269 1st Ave. 68th & 69th 212/737-5922

F 5 / S 6 / A 6 / $21   MC V D AE DIS   **TO/D**

Don't expect Topkapi Palace, but drop into this mini-grand bazaar of Turkish cuisine and culture for a comprehensive array of middle Eastern specialties. And if you wander in on a Friday or Saturday evening, don't be surprised to see a belly dancer performing while you dine.

SPEC: *Lamb kebab $11;95; Grilled swordfish fillet $12.95; Stuffed cabbage $10.95; Turkish coffee $1.75; Baklava $4.25*

MARY ANN'S LD Mexican

(E17) 1503 2nd Ave. (78th & 79th) 212/249-6165

See review on page 194.

MATCH LD American

(F17) 33. E. 60th St. (Park & Mad.) 212/906-9173

See review on page 52.

MATTHEW'S LD Mediterranean

(F17) 1030 3rd Ave. (61st) 212/838-4343 Fax: 593-2982

F 8 / S 7 / A 7 / $50   MC V D AE   **TO**

Young, in-vogue owner and chef Matthew Kenney has fashioned extremely palatable and handsomely presented dishes from "visits to Morocco and Egypt." This chic, Casablanca motif eatery is strewn with plants, upholstered rattan and proves airily romantic. From appetizers through desserts, expensive wines to grappas, Matthew's offers some of the best nouvelle cuisine to be found west or east of the Mediterranean.

SPEC: *Tunisian chili-rubbed lamb skewers $13; Peeky toe crab cakes $13; Crispy red snapper $25; Coriander crusted rabbit w/snap pea risotto $25*

MAZZEI D Italian

(D17) 1564 2nd Ave. (81st & 82nd) 212/628-3131

F 8 / S 7 / A 6 / $32   MC V D AE

This "sleeper," was named after an 18th century Italian-American patriot. It has a wood-burning oven, and serves primarily seafood in a style derived from the little known Puglia region of Italy. Divided into 3 rooms, the walls are beige stucco, offering a serene and attractive atmosphere.

SPEC: *Appetizers from the wood burning oven $8.50; Polenta $7; Veal chop $21.50; Monkfish in terracotta $20; Cream puffs $6*

0	1	2	3	4	5	6	7	8	9	10
disappointing		fair		good		very good		excellent		perfect

Mediterraneo

MEDITERRANEO   LD   Italian

(F17) 1260 2nd Ave. (66th) 212/734-7407

F 6 / S 5 / A 6 / $26   Cash only   **TO/D**

The big brother to Caffe Med up the street is light, airy, pleasant and affordable, an "elegant escape." Complete with marble top tables, brick oven and charcoal grill, it's a favorite with locals and a great spot to grab a bite after the movies. Diners are young and fun and the Florentine cuisine will welcome you again and again.
SPEC: *Carpaccio di pesce spada $12.50; Pizza arrabbiata $11; Risotto of the day P/A*

MEZZALUNA   LD   Italian

(E17) 1295 3rd Ave. (74th & 75th) 212/535-9600 Fax: 517-8045

F 7 / S 6 / A 6 / $32   Cash only   **TO**

Small and loud, this Italian trattoria is good for both the food and people watching. If a taste and feel of Italy is what you're looking for, then Mezzaluna is for you. Don't forget to bring your comfy and expensive Italian shoes, because there's almost always a wait. Diners suggest "more comfortable chairs."
SPEC: *Cuttlefish stew $10.50; Insalata Mezzaluna $10; Carpacci $13-$14; Black linguine in spicy sauce $14; Pizza $13-$14*

MOCCA HUNGARIAN RESTAURANT   LD   Hungarian

(D17) 1588 2nd Ave. (82nd & 83rd) 212/734-6470

F 6 / S 6 / A 4 / $19   Cash only   **TO**

An inexpensive restaurant offering authentic Hungarian food, served by waiters and waitresses in traditional black and white uniforms. "If you're Hungarian, German or Viennese, and you feel like being at your grandmother's, this is the place." With its comfortable and charmingly well-worn dining room, it is a throwback to another era.
SPEC: *Sautéed green peppers, onions & tomatoes w/smoked sausage $4.95; Marinated herring $4.95; Chicken Paprikas $9.95; Roast loin of pork $10.95; Palacsinta $4.25*

MULHOLLAND DRIVE   LD   American

(D17) 1059 3rd Ave. (62nd & 63rd) 212/319-7740

F 6 / S 5 / A 5 / $19   MC V D AE DIS

There's a certain pretentiousness about this place that makes it questionable as to whether it's worth the drive, even if it is across the street. "Huge portions of food served by zombies," says one diner. Others applaud the gestalt: "food is as sexy as the people." Overall, the bar scene is probably better than the food. Recently underwent a facelift, so we'll see if anything changes..
SPEC: *Fried zucchini $7.25; Garlic mashed potatoes $4.95; Chicken pot pie $13.75; Chicken roadhouse $15.25; Belgian chocolate bag $7*

MUSTANG GRILL   D   Southwestern

(D17) 1633 2nd Ave. (85th) 212/744-9194 Fax: 744-1411

F 6 / S 6 / A 5 / $21   MC V D AE DIS   **TO/D**

The Mexican masks, longhorn skulls, large cacti and palm trees are a dead giveaway that you're going to find a Southwestern inspired menu. Regulars rave about the mashed potatoes, but otherwise it's your normal, run-of-the-mill regional fare.

SPEC: *Chile rubbed chicken skewers w/grilled pineapple $5.75; Mashed Yukon potatoes $3.50; Pecan honey crusted chicken breast $12.50; Marinated Santa Fe flank w/tortillas; Key lime pie $5*

Napa

NAPA   D   American

(F17) 245 E. 84th St. (2nd & 3rd) 212/517-7068

F 6 / S 6 / A 6 / $27   MC V D AE DIS

Big Sur in the Big Apple. This California-style restaurant dishes up "fusion" cuisine, elegant and beautifully prepared mixes that yield dishes like grilled chicken with ancho glaze. Original mosaics and tile work add to the illusion that you're on the West Coast; but if you're homesick for the city, you can dine in the small sidewalk cafe. **Closed: Sunday**

SPEC: *Tuna roll $7.50; Scallion duck pizza $11; Grilled pork loin $15; BBQ mahi mahi $15; Ginger-spiked blood orange granita $7; Steamed risotto dumplings $7*

NAPA VALLEY GRILL   LD   American

(F17) 206 East 63rd St. (2nd & 3rd) 212/759-7772

F 7 / S 6 / A 7 / $37   V   **TO/D**

News flash: A slice of California has fallen off. Fortunately, it's landed on the Upper East Side. Owner Michael Toporek has combined his California pizza oven (Best in '94) with the genius of chef Greg Waters and his wife, Marina, the pastry chef. This creative couple and their product deserve an exhibit. Sit in the pastel surroundings, smell the hickory wood burning, and savor the spread.

SPEC: *Crab cakes $13.95; Pepper tuna $22.95; Lamb $26; Pizzas $8.50-$16.50; Molten chocolate cake w/sour cherries $7*

NICOLA'S   D   Italian

(D17) 146 East 84th St. (Lex & 3rd) 212/249-9850

F 8 / S 8 / A 6 / $34   AE   **TO**

Nicola's has long been known for its somewhat older and stylish crowd that keeps coming back—and for good reason. The food is good, the decor classy, and the staff treats regular patrons as if this was an extension of their own dining room. If there's a lull in the conversation, just look around and you're likely to see a celebrity or two, like regulars Dan Rather, Norman Mailer, or Mike Wallace.

SPEC: *Squid salad $10.50; Caesar salad $8; Filet of Boston sole $19; Veal scallopine $22; Cold zabaglione $5.50; Cream cheese cake $5.50*

0	1	2	3	4	5	6	7	8	9	10
disappointing		fair		good		very good		excellent		perfect

OLIO BL Italian

(F17) 788 Lexington Ave. (61st & 62nd) 212/3083552

F 5 / S 5 / A 4 / $23 D AE

What can you expect from this dimly lit pastel cafe that begins and ends with an O? Pastas, pizzas, veal and more...There's something in the middle for everyone. Water and oil may not mix, but the dishes at Olio gibe.

SPEC: *Marinated eggplant $5.95; Bresaola $5.95; Fettuccine al salmone $8.50; Risotto pescatore $14.95; Veal Milanese $13.95*

ORLEANS LD Cajun

(D17) 1438 3rd Ave. (81st & 82nd) 212/794-1509

F 5 / S 5 / A 5 / $24 MC V D DIS **TO/D**

After 5 years on the scene, Orleans has found a niche as a favorite meeting place for singles as well as neighborhood diners craving Cajun food at reasonable prices. The decor is simple and relaxed and the food portions are generous, which goes a long way in explaining its popularity.

SPEC: *Cajun popcorn $6.50; Jambalaya $10.95; Cajun kebabs $10.95; Bayou shrimp $13.95; Blackened catfish $11.95*

OTTOMANELLI'S CAFE LD Italian

(D17) 1518 1st Ave. (79th & 80th) 212/734-5544

(D18) 439 E. 82nd St. (1st & York) 212/737-1888

(D18) 1626 York Ave. (85th & 86th) 212/772-7722

(E18) 1370 York Ave. (72nd & 73rd) 212/794-9696

(F17) 1199 1st Ave. (65th) 212/249-7878

See review on page 41.

PAMIR LD Afghani

(E17) 1437 2nd Ave. (74th & 75th) 212/734-3791

F 6 / S 6 / A 6 / $20 MC V

The uniqueness of the Middle-Eastern dining experience is highlighted with a very nice room complete with soft Buddhist-style music and Oriental rugs. The portions are large and the prices are reasonable.

SPEC: *Aushak (scallion filled dumplings) $3.45; Korma-e-murgh (chicken) $12.95; Quabilli palaw (lamb) $12.95; Firnee (pudding) $3.25*

Top 10
$21-35
Moderate

PAOLA'S D Italian

(D17) 347 E. 85th St. (1st & 2nd) 212/794-1890

F 8 / S 7 / A 6 / $30 AE **TO**

A romantic setting reminiscent of those checkered-clothed Italian restaurants you remembered from your youth. . .or from old movies. All the food is prepared to order and, because Paola's is so small—only 13 tables— and popular, with repeat customers coming from all over the city, reservations are highly recommended.

SPEC: *Malfatti (spinach dumplings) $14.95; Trofie Genovesi (corkscrew pasta w/string beans, potatoes & pesto) $14.95; Pansotti)pasta stuffed w/spinach & swiss chard $14.95; Tiramisu $5.95*

PARIOLI ROMANISSIMO D Italian

(D16) 24 E. 81st St. (Mad. & 5th) 212/288-2391

F 8 / S 7 / A 8 / $53 MC V D DIS

Family owned and operated by the Rossis, this elegant and haute chic restaurant in a wonderful townhouse is simply one of New York's finest. Rich, classic Italian food, served in a sumptuously classic manner. Every touch is caring and personal. Seasonal game is a specialty. But remember, consistently high quality commands high prices.

SPEC: *Breast of guinea hen $28.50; Veal chop w/asparagus $34*

Park Avenue Cafe

PARK AVENUE CAFE LD French

(F16) 100 E. 63rd St. (Park Ave.) 212/644-1900

F 8 / S 7 / A 7 / $53 MC V D AE DIS

An unpretentious staff will make you feel like you're one of New York's most prominent citizens, as you experience your gastronomic orgasm, compliments of chef David Burke. It's got a Southern California feel to it: airy, comfortable and elegant without being stuffy. We have no reservations, but you certainly should if you want to dine here. "Unbelievable pastries." "Inventive kitchen."

SPEC: *Salad of mixed organic greens $8.50; Onion crusted roast organic chicken $24.50; Striped bass $27.50; Grilled rib steak $33.50; Crisp apple tart $8.50*

PARMA D Italian

(D17) 1404 3rd Ave. (79th & 80th) 212/535-3520

F 7 / S 5 / A 6 / $38 AE **TO**

A rarity among Upper East Side Italian eateries—a long time survivor. John Piscina's homemade, family style Northern Italian cuisine has been serving steady customers since 1977—"the best people come here" he says. The secret: reasonable prices and chef Frank Gulieri, who makes everything on the premises.

SPEC: *Antipasto Freddo $10.50; Parma ham $12; Zuppa di pesce $22; Saltimboca fiorentina $22; Lyonese potatoes $8*

PEPPERMINT PARK BLD American

(F17) 1225 1st Ave. (66th) 212/288-5054

F 6 / S 5 / A 5 / $12 MC V **TO/D**

This sometimes noisy ice cream-dessert parlor also provides cheap and unexceptional meals and, after 25 years, has become a neighborhood fixture. Eat in, take out, homemade ice cream in 30 flavors, as well as low-fat, low-calorie frozen yogurt, and the like. Bring the kids. They can keep busy watching a magician perform at posted times.

SPEC: *Belgian waffles $4-$5; Dessert crepes $4; Homemade ice cream in 30 flavors*

0	1	2	3	4	5	6	7	8	9	10
disappointing		fair		good		very good		excellent		perfect

PERSEPOLIS — LD — Middle Eastern

(E17) 1423 2nd Ave. (74th & 75th) 212/535-1100

F 6 / S 4 / A 4 / $23   MC V AE   **TO/D**

Named for the ancient city in Iran, this restaurant, with its contemporary decor—complete with Persian books, photos and artifacts—puts you in the executive dining room of the Persian Institute. It's by no means exotic, but it is nice, which explains why people come from near and far for the creative, interesting cuisine, including "Good kebabs."

SPEC: *Mashed eggplant & mixed kashk $4.25; Chicken kabab $12.95; Soltani kabab (filet mignon & chopped steak) $15.95; Persian cream puff $3.25*

PETALUMA — LD — Italian

(E17) 1356 1st Ave. (73rd) 212/772-8800

F 6 / S 6 / A 7 / $29   MC V D AE DIS   **TO/D**

With its light and airy setting, Petaluma is Italian with a California feel. It could melt the coldest of winter hearts because inside it's summer twelve months of the year. Look for the colorful banner that marks this sunny spot where the food has been consistent for the twelve years they've been in business.

SPEC: *Insalata di mare $9.50; Pizzas $12-$13; Salmone con verdure al vapore $19.50; Belgian chocolate cake $5.50*

PIG HEAVEN — LD — Chinese

(D17) 1540 2nd Ave. (80th) 212/744-4333 Fax: 744-4339

F 4 / S 5 / A 4 / $26   MC V D AE   **TO/D**

A good variety of foods and a loud decor with lots of pigs on the wall (if not in the seats) make this an "offbeat" Chinese food experience. Earning its name from the popular Cantonese-style pig and shredded pork with vegetables, the menu comes with subheadings like "Cold Pig," "Cold No Pig," and "Hot pig."

SPEC: *White cooked pork w/garlic sauce $6.95; Duck salad $5.95; Cantonese style suckling pig $13.95 (lg); Cantonese roast chicken $10.95 (lg)*

Post House

POLO, THE — LD — Continental

(E16) 840 Madison Ave. (69th-Westbury Hotel) 212/439-4835

F 6 / S 6 / A 6 / $40   MC V D AE

The Polo oozes ambiance and charm. It's a refined power scene with its dark wood accents, brass lamps and dark fabric trimmings. With its location on the ground floor of the Westbury Hotel, it's a favorite of the Hollywood set when they're in town, so it's no wonder you're likely to see celebrities breaking bread.

SPEC: *Smoked salmon w/eggplant caviar $13; Sashimi of yellowfin tuna $12; Herb basted Amish chicken $22; Roast bass $26*

POST HOUSE **LD** American

(F16) 28 E. 63rd St. (Mad. & Park) 212/935-2888

F 8 / S 7 / A 7 / $45 MC V D AE DIS

That smell in the air of this upscale steak house is… power. But…it's bright, attractive and bustling, with original contemporary art on the walls. "Generous portions" of surf and turf at generous prices. But what's with that portrait of a near-naked lady on the wall?

SPEC: *Maryland crab cocktail $12.75; Coconut shrimp $12.75; Filet tips w/vegetables in peppered crust $25.50; Filet mignon $19.75; Sirloin steak $29.75*

PRIMAVERA **D** Italian

(D17) 1578 1st Ave. (82nd) 212/861-8608

F 6 / S 6 / A 6 / $55 MC V D AE

This first-rate Northern Italian ristorante ranks high in every category. The cuisine is beautifully presented; the staff seems to know the clientele; and the place has a very clubby atmosphere. The dining room has beautiful carved woodwalls and decorative paneled glass.

SPEC: *Sturgeon w/baby shrimps $16.50; Grilled swordfish 28.50; Sautéed calf's liver $26.50*

Primola

PRIMOLA **D** Italian

(E17) 1226 2nd Ave. (64th & 65th) 212/758-1775

F 7 / S 7 / A 7 / $34 MC V D AE

Maturity has had a positive effect on this fine restaurant with tasty food, "creative dishes," and many specials. Take notes when your waiter reads them off. The ambiance is comfortable and understated. A paradise for power brokers.

SPEC: *Baby string beans w/mixed peppers & mushrooms $7.50; Smoked tuna & swordfish carpaccio $12.50; Quail w/rice $23.50; Rabbit cacciatora $18.50*

QUATORZE BIS **LD** French

(D17) 323 East 79th St. (1st & 2nd) 212/535-1414

F 7 / S 6 / A 6 / $34 MC V AE

Formerly found on 14th Street, this bistro relocated its ambiance to the Upper East Side to serve its large film and literary clientele. However, a precise menu and dining room with burgundy banquettes and a few original posters are deserving of a king. **Closed: Monday lunch**

SPEC: *Pate maison $7.25; Grilled sirloin & pommes frites $27.50; Half chicken, grilled w/herbs $19.95; Hot apple tart $7.50*

0	1	2	3	4	5	6	7	8	9	10
disappointing		fair		good		very good		excellent		perfect

Quatorze Bis

QUISISIANA   **LD**   **Italian**

(E17) 1319 3rd Ave. (75th & 76th) 212/879-5000 Fax: 772-0703

F 7 / S 7 / A 7 / $30   MC V D AE DIS   **TO/D**

This rustic Mediterranean eatery specializes in seafood from Capri. A brick oven is the center piece of the dining room and is Owner/chef Beppe Desiderio's pride and joy. You'll need reservations, but if you can't get in, he has six other branches in Florida, Switzerland and Italy.
SPEC: *Baby squid grilled w/lemon $9; Mixed fish w/aromatic herbs $21; Roasted scallops $18.50; Roasted baby chicken $16*

RAY BARI PIZZA   **LD**   **Pizzeria**

(E17) 1330 3rd Ave. (76th) 212/988-3337

F 7 / S 2 / A 4 / $7   MC V D AE DIS   **TO/D**

If New York City is still a melting pot, then Ray Bari is probably doing the cooking. Catering to pizza lovers who yearn for a pizzeria with the name Ray in them (there are scores of them, though who knows why), theirs is quick and good. And don't be surprised to see Mayor Giuliani and his son, Andrew, dining here on a Sunday.
SPEC: *Pizza starts at $1.75 a slice or $12.50 for a pie*

RED TULIP   **D**   **Hungarian**

(E18) 439 East 75th St. (1st & York) 212/734-4893

F 7 / S 7 / A 7 / $30   MC V D AE

Whomever coined the phrase, "Old World charm," must have had the Red Tulip in mind. Authentically Hungarian, food is served in a setting filled with red hearts and tulips, Hungarian arts and crafts, and furniture, including 150-year old tablecloths and three Gypsy folk musicians. **Closed: Mon & Tues**
SPEC: *Hortobagyi palascinta $5;Gulyas soup w/beef, vegetables & dumplings $4.75; Pheasant in tokay wine glaze w/roasted apples, red currants & oranges $21; Stuffed breast of veal $17*

RESTAURANT AT THE STANHOPE   **BLD**   **Amer/Contl**

(D16) 995 5th Ave. (81st) 212/288-5800 Fax: 517-0088

F 7 / S 8 / A 7 / $38   MC V D AE

Trekking through the Met and in need of a sit down? Cross the street and head for the Stanhope Terrace where the restaurant is elegant and "very continental." A people watcher's delight? Maybe. But the real story here, is the recently revamped main restaurant where chef Scott Cohen has transformed this Manhattan institution into a highly praised dining destination. In addition, the hotel boasts a tea salon that serves high tea all afternoon.
SPEC: *Roasted corn flan $9.50; Asparagus & Smithfield ham $7.50; Honey mustard roasted salmon $19.50; Sautéed veal chop $24*

Ronasi Ristorante

RONASI RISTORANTE   LD   Italian

(F17) 1160 1st Ave. (64th) 212/751-0360

F 6 / S 6 / A 4 / $28   MC V D AE DIS

Where do ROma, NApoli and SIcilia come together? RONASI, of course. An attractive newly refurbished ristorante where all the flavors of Italy reign. And where friendly service and affordable prices attract a crowd of neighborhood faithfuls.

SPEC: *Sword fish carpaccio $7.95; Bresaola con rugola $7.95; Pasta w/shrimps & rugola $13.95; Chicken stuffed w/radicchio & fontina cheese $13.95*

RUSSIAN CHEF, THE   LD   Russian

(D17) 340 E. 86th St. (1st & 2nd) 212/517-8717

F 6 / S 6 / A 6 / $17   AE   **TO/D**

Known also as "The Pie," because the pizzeria that preceded it left behind its sign. Bursting with personality, from the folk art on the wall, to the tea served in samovars and the poster of Lenin hanging in the bathroom. Even the "heavy" food has character.

SPEC: *Eggplant "caviar" $3.50; Russian pies available w/chicken, beef, fish, or vegetarian, priced from $8.75 to $14.95 (Czar pie made w/filet mignon); Russian-style tea service in samovar w/cookies and berry preserves $2 per person.*

SARABETH'S   American

(E16) 945 Madison Ave. (75th-Whitney Museum) 212/570-3670
See review on page 240.

SASSO   LD   Italian

(E17) 1315 2nd Ave. (69th & 70th) 212/472-6688 Fax: 472-8979

F 7 / S 7 / A 7 / $33   MC V D AE   **TO**

Show your passport at the door and hear soft Italian music and buon appetitos echo throughout this warm, spacious place.
Italian movie posters hover above, while generous portions linger below. "Wonderful beet gnocchi."

SPEC: *Beet gnocchi w/arugula & goat cheese $14.95; Veal chop alla griglia $23.95; Pasta w/lobster $17.95*

SEMOLINA   LD   Italian

(F17) 1149 1st Ave (63rd) 212/758-8703

F 5 / S 5 / A 4 / $15   MC V D AE   **TO/D**

This warm, wheat-colored Italian eatery is cheerful, stylish and extremely "accommodating." The prices are reasonable by anyone's standards and they deliver. Looks and feels expensive, but "surprisingly affordable." The service is quick and "amiable."

SPEC: *Ziti al forno $6.95; Linguine alla Vongole (fresh clams)$10.95; Pollo alla parmigiana $10.95; Budino di cioccolato (mousse) $2.95*

0	1	2	3	4	5	6	7	8	9	10
disappointing		fair		good		very good		excellent		perfect

SERENDIPITY 3   LD   American

(F17) 225 E. 60th St. (2nd & 3rd) 212/838-353

F 7 / S 6 / A 7 / $20   MC V D AE DIS

Serving their third generation of customers, Serendipity is, pardon the expression, an East Side institution. Foot long hotdogs are 2 feet in length, and the hot chocolate is served as a huge frozen dessert. Like the menu, everything is oversized and fun. A major must for any New Yorker or out of towner with or without kids. And while you're gorging on "fantastic desserts," remember it's not polite to stare. . .even if, sitting at the table next to yours, is…

SPEC: *Footlong hotdogs $5; Young chicken sandwich $12.50; Frozen mochaccino $6; Outrageous banana split $10.95*

SETTE MEZZO   LD   Italian

(E17) 969 Lexington Ave. (70th & 71st) 212/472-044

F 7 / S 7 / A 6 / $29   Cash only   **TO**

Busy. Noisy. Fun. And why not? Sette Mezzo (7 1/2) is the Italian version of black-jack. Imaginative, quality Italian fare.

SPEC: *Roast peppers & anchovies $5; Veal Milanese $22.50; Penne sette mezzo (radicchio, smoked provola & pancetta) $13.50; Chicken paillard w/rucola & tomato salad $12.50*

SHELBY   LD   American

(F17) 967 Lexington Ave. (70th & 71st) 212/988-4624 Fax: 988-4331

F 5 / S 4 / A 6 / $32   MC V D AE

Tucked away on a charming stretch of Lexington Avenue, Shelby offers casual country club elegance to an upper crust clientele. Catch the quiet murmer as it ascends Shelby's high ceilings and exits through sky lights. If you crave mahi-mahi (so good you could say it thrice), provocative soups or whatever, this is the place. No socks required.

SPEC: *Shelby salad $7; Grilled mahi-mahi $21; Grilled black angus sirloin & fries $24; Warm apple-pecan crisp w/Jack Daniels ice cream $6; Chunky peanut butter & chocolate cookie mousse $6*

The Sign of the Dove

SIGN OF THE DOVE, THE   LD   American

(F17) 1110 3rd Ave. (65th) 212/861-8080 Fax: 988-3703

F 7 / S 6 / A 8 / $65   MC V D AE DIS

Still one of the most elegant, exciting and romantic restaurants in the city. The rooms are airy and skylit, filled with antiques, and flowers. The lighting is soft and there's plenty of room between tables for that romantic tete a tete or private business meeting. Chef Andrew D'Amico creates wonderful meals and the desserts are original and tasty. Well worth breaking open the piggy bank. "The perfect anniversary restaurant." **Closed: Monday lunch**

SPEC: *Pre-fixe dinner (include app. & des.): Veal tenderloin $55; Rack of lamb w/couscous $55; "Pan Bagnat" of seared tuna $50*

SISTINA D Italian

(D17) 1555 2nd Ave. (80th & 81st) 212/861-7660

F 7 / S 7 / A 6 / $39   MC V D AE

You won't see the famed frescoes of the eponymous Vatican Chapel on this ceiling. But what you will find here is the delicately prepared and innovative cucina of owner/chef Joseph Bruno. This formal Italian ristorante is a bit off the beaten track, but well worth a detour. The flavors of Sistina would tickle Michaelangelo's palette.
Closed: Sunday
SPEC: *Grilled baby squids $10; Fish stew $23; Pounded veal chop $24; Rabbit w/garlic, white wine & fresh herbs $22*

SOFIA FABULOUS PIZZA LD Italian

(D16) 1022 Madison Ave. (79th) 212/734-2676

F 7 / S 7 / A 7 / $25   MC V AE   **TO/D**

This family-friendly upstart has quickly gained the support of the upscale neighborhood. Diners arrive in Armani suits and Polo loafers, yearning for fresh pizzas baked in wood-fired ovens. There's a 2nd floor Mediterranean dining room, or an open rooftop serving area. Food is remarkably well-turned out, much like the aesthetically pleasing and snooty dining crowd.
SPEC: *Calamari salad $14; Pizza w/fresh mushrooms & Italian sausage $12; Crema di polenta $6.50*

Soleil

SOLEIL LD Mediterranean

(E17) 1160 3rd. Ave. (67th & 68th) 212/717-1177

F 5 / S 5 / A 6 / $21   MC V D AE

For a sunny bit of pizza, pasta, or Sunday brunch, Soleil will put a smile on your face. Especially if you can't resist a pretty setting with a trendy twist minus the trendy baggage.
SPEC: *Margherita pizza $8; Pizza Soleil (marinated chicken, roasted peppers, tomatoes, onions & mozzarella) $8; Ossobucco $16; Spinach fettucine $11*

SOTTO CINQUE LD Italian

(D17) 1644 2nd Ave. (85th) 212/472-5563

F 4 / S 4 / A 4 / $13   Cash only   **TO/D**

"Pasta under $5," is the motto, making this the kind of restaurant Fred Mertz and Al Bundy would love. There are other things on the menu which cost slightly more, but you can't beat the deal on those $4.95 pastas. Your expectations shouldn't be too high, but then again, neither are the prices. "Waitresses seem to cater to men." "Okay cheap eats."
SPEC: *Grilled salsiccia $4; Broccoli sauté $4; Rigatoni cinque $4.95; Chicken parmigiana $8.95; Quad berry pie $3.25; Decadence cake $3.50*

0	1	2	3	4	5	6	7	8	9	10
disappointing		fair		good		very good		excellent		perfect

SUSHIHATSU D Japanese

(F17) 1143 1st. Ave. (62nd & 63rd) 212/371-0238

F 5 / S 5 / A 5 / $28 D AE **TO**

This lower than low key place is a little short on atmosphere, and lacking on location, but Mr. Miyachi's sushi bar is for connoisseurs. Seventy percent of the fish is flown in from Japan, and seats at the bar are reserved for your minimum $30 order (most customers spend closer to $100).For a regular meal, just sit at a table where you can expect to spend less. **Closed: Monday**

SPEC: *Small tempura $7.50; Small sushi $8; Yose-nabe (chicken, seafood & assorted vegetables) $15; Una-ju (broiled eel) $18*

TIRAMISU LD Italian

(D17) 1410 3rd Ave. (80th & 81st) 212/988-9780

F 6 / S 5 / A 6 / $28 Cash only

This northern Italian restaurant is still crazy after all these years...Crazy busy, that is. Consistency counts, and the extensive menu is just that. No gambling here. Wood burning oven pizza, antipasto, and pastas are the standouts.

SPEC: *Crostini al gamberi $6; Black linguine w/lobster $12; All'arrabbiata pizza $12; Fusilli alle verdure $12*

TONY'S DI NAPOLI D Italian

(D17) 1606 2nd. Ave. (83rd & 84th) 212/861-8686

F 4 / S 5 / A 5 / $36 MC V D AE DIS **TO/D**

Tony's is the East Side's answer to food family style, where the oversized portions feed 3 to 4 people (depending, of course, on how your family eats). Unfortunately, this informal and relaxed Carmine's wannabe, "just misses." The food is only mediocre, leaving the taste treat up to the company you keep. Still, if you like Italian food and lots of it, and you can't make it over to the West Side, Tony's will have to do.

SPEC: *Calamari Fritti $9; Shrimp & Calamari Fritti $12; Chicken Scarpiello $18; Tony's veal chop $22*

TRILOGY BAR & GRILL D American

(E17) 1403 2nd Ave. (73rd) 212/794-1870 Fax: 628-4792

F 5 / S 6 / A 5 / $17 MC V D AE

For years a mediocre neighborhood hangout under various names, Trilogy has a brand new owner who promises an "exciting new restaurant." Chef Sarah Jenkins from Boston's Figs and Olives Restaurant was brought in to prepare American-Italian fare. A live DJ from Thursday to Saturday, and added a Jazz Brunch on Sunday was added.

SPEC: *Grilled chicken strips w/teriyaki sauce $4.50; Fettuccini w/shrimp $9.95; Roasted half chicken w/caramelized shallot mashed potatoes $8.95*

TROIS JEAN LD French

(D17) 154 E. 79th St. (Lex. & 3rd) 212/988-4858 Fax: 988-4719

F 8 / S 7 / A 8 / $38 MC V D AE **TO**

What a delight! This "lovely, " "authentic," and often "favorite," Parisian bistro now imports an added French flair: Distinct "family dishes," traditionally prepared and changed daily. A befitting complement to "great food," "lovely atmosphere," and desserts that "rule." Trois Jean deserves to be proud of its "genuine pedigree" and continues to earn high ratings in all categories of excellence. "Three cheers" for chef and staff of this marvelous, eastside eatery.

SPEC: *Foie gras $18; Cassoulet $22; Warm chocolate cake $8.50;Creme brulee $7.50*

Trois Jean

USKUDAR   D   Turkish

(E17) 1405 2nd. Ave. (73rd & 74th) 212/988-2641

F 7 / S 8 / A 6 / $23   AE   **TO/D**

Easy to miss if you're not looking hard, but this little restaurant is worth a pause. Owner/chef Abdullah prepares a small, delectable range of Turkish dishes (lamb a specialty),and though tables are elbow-to-elbow, the decor is pleasant and the service warm.
SPEC: *Spinach pie $4.95; Eggplant salad $4.95; Lamb shish kebab $13.95; Chef's mixed grill $15.95; Shrimps w/mushroom sauce $14.95*

VA BENE   D   Italian

(D17) 1589 2nd Ave. (82nd & 83rd) 212/517-4448

F 6 / S 6 / A 6 / $35   AE

Upscale Italian cuisine with a twist: it's Kosher. Semi-elegant, attractive, intimate. The menu is obviously somewhat limited as a result of the dietary restrictions. But somehow, it still works. Choices run the gamut from pastas to fish. **Closed: Friday**
SPEC: *Tuna carpaccio $10.95; Gnocchi gratinati $16.95; Paglia & Fieno $16.95; Sole picata $23.95; Chocolate mousse $6.95*

VIA ORETO   D   Italian

(F17) 1121 1st. Ave. (61st & 62nd) 212/308-0828

F 8 / S 8 / A 6 / $25   Cash only   **TO**

Though Via Oreto has a well-rounded menu with all the essentials a Southern Italian restaurant should offer, the owners, a mother and son team, may want to rethink their strategy. The space is small, the decor lacking in appeal, and the reddish walls add to the claustrophobic feel one gets when eating there. Nevertheless, it seems to be a favorite of neighborhood patrons who, despite the ambiance, feel the food and service are worth it.
SPEC: *Peperoni ripieni (peppers filled w/rice, chopped meat, bread crumbs & garlic) $6.95; Grigliata mista (grilled racicchio, endive, w/garlic) $7.95; Bucatini chi sarde (fat spaghetti w/fresh sardines) $11.95; Pollo e salsiccia (chick sautéed w/sausage) $13.95; Napoleon $5.95; Zabaglione freddo $5.95*

VOULEZ-VOUS   LD   French

(E17) 1462 1st Ave. (76th) 212/249-1776

F 7 / S 7 / A 6 / $31   MC V AE DIS

First-rate French cuisine at 1st Avenue prices. Prepared by chef Claude Pasdeloup, listed in Maistres Cuisiners de France, 1994. He offers classic fare of the Loire Valley and traditional bistro food. Also, for a modest prix-fixe, the chef plans menus featuring regional cuisines of France with wine included. "Very good regional bistro cooking."
SPEC: *Fricasse of snails $7.95; Choucroute Alsacienne $20.50 Cassoulet Toulousain $20.50; Marquise au chocolat $6.50*

0	1	2	3	4	5	6	7	8	9	10
disappointing		fair		good		very good		excellent		perfect

181

WILLY'S | LD | American

(D17) 1538 2nd Ave. (80th) 212/734-1888

F 3 / S 3 / A 5 / $22   Cash only   **TO/D**

Nothing to rave about, yet there's always a wait for outside dining. Like most Upper East Side restaurants, this one caters to a younger, hipper crowd. The prices are reasonable—which may account for the crowds. But the food is only "so-so."

SPEC: *Chili con carne $5.50; Chicken stir fry $8.95; Ribeye steak $15.95; Polenta w/chorizo sausages $8.95; Mud pie $4.25*

YELLOWFINGERS DI NUOVO | LD | American

(F17) 200 E. 60th St. (3rd Ave.) 212/751-8615 Fax: 988-3703

F 6 / S 5 / A 6 / $24   MC V D AE DIS   **TO/D**

The name sounds like an Italian trattoria, but they refer to themselves as an American bistro. Beats us as to why, but what does it matter. It's convenient, the food is usually good and interesting—the fa'vecchia, for instance, a term they culled from "faccia vecchia," which was used for pizza like breads baked without toppings. Theirs, however, do have toppings. And they're good. "Roast chicken is great."

SPEC: *Focaccia $4; Caesar salad $5; Fa'vecchia $10-$13; Roasted marinated vegetable plate $12.50; Grilled mako shark salad $16; Cappuccino chocolate mousse cake $6*

YORKVILLE BREWERY& TAVERN | LD | American

(E17) 1359 1st Ave. (73rd) 212/517-2739

F 4 / S 5 / A 5 / $20   MC V D AE DIS   **TO/D**

This functional brew club with its old NY design, offers a sense of nostalgia for "the good ol' days." Big copper vats in the window welcome you to familiar place, where you expect "Norm" to stumble in any minute. The menu is obliging–not your typical pub grub–if only satisfactory. But with a host of beers to choose from, the true brew lover is sure to find "a pleaser."

SPEC: *NY steak w/ roasted potatoes $14.95; BBQ baby back ribs $12.95; Raspberry truffle $4.50*

ZUCCHERO | D | Italian

(E17) 1464 2nd Ave. (76th & 77th) 212/517-2541

F 6 / S 6 / A 6 / $19   Cash only   **TO/D**

"Sugar" is sweet and oh, so affordable. The walls of this attractive ristorante are yellow and there are plenty of tables. The nicest dining room for the least amount of money in the Italian restaurant-saturated bazaar of 2nd Ave.

SPEC: *Insalata Zucchero $4.95; Carpaccio parmigiano $5.95; Grilled chicken breast $9.95; Sautéed rabbit $10.95; Tiramisu $4.50*

ZUCCHINI | LD | Italian

(E17) 1336 1st Ave. (71st & 72nd) 212/249-0559

F 7 / S 7 / A 7 / $24   MC V D AE DIS   **TO/D**

The menu reflects the philosophy of the restaurant: healthy choices. And these choices are rather eclectic—"creative" pasta, vegetable kabobs, burrito melts, and curried chicken dishes. The one thing you won't find is red meat. The rustic atmosphere—with green the dominant color— puts us in mind of a country inn.

SPEC: *Puree of zucchini $3.50; Burrito melt $9.95; Basil chicken linguine $12.95; Chicken India w/mango chutney $11.95*

BARKING DOG LUNCHEONETTE   BLD   American

(C17) 1678 3rd Ave. (94th) 212/831-1800

F 8 / S 7 / A 7 / $17   Cash only   **TO/D**

This casual diner with-a-twist does burgers, deli dishes and continental fare, but with Cajun or Mediterranean influences.Breakfast served 8am to 4pm daily does not disappoint; nor does the eclectic doggie decor. College kids, yuppies, and other Carnegie Hillers know the Dog's bite is as good as his bark.

SPEC: *Grilled chicken & shrimp sate $5.95; Corn-meal crusted oysters $6.95; Grilled garlic sausage and crisp duck confit $12.95*

BISTRO DU NORD   LD   French

(C16) 1312 Madison Ave. (93rd) 212/289-0997

F 7 / S 7 / A 8 / $31   MC V AE   **TO/D**

A pleasant, intimate, low-key French bistro, with excellent service. The walls are decorated with famous vintage fashion photos, giving it a sophisticated feel, also reflected in the classic Gallic dishes offered on the menu. Try the chocolate soufflé, but remember to order a day in advance.

SPEC: *Pate maison $6.95; Prosciutto w/mango $9.25; Roasted breast of chicken $16.95; Cold poached salmon $16.75*

BURRITOVILLE   LD   Tex-Mex

(C17) 1606 3rd Ave. (90th & 91st) 212/410-2255

See review on page 77.

BUSBY'S   LD   American

(C16) 45 E. 92nd St. (Mad. & Park) 212/360-7373

F 7 / S 5 / A 6 / $27   MC V AE D

The buzz may have subsided at this American-style bistro with a turn of the century feel. But that's okay, because the Carnegie sophisticates care more about dependable meals than spotting soap stars. While some call it "pretentious," others applaud its "informality" and "good food."

SPEC: *Duck salad $9; Tuna $16.50*

CARNEGIE HILL CAFE   BLD   Mediterranean

(C16) 1308 Madison Ave. (92nd & 93rd) 212/534-7522

F 5 / S 6 / A 6 / $26   MC V   **TO**

This cozy, tri-level European style cafe offers an unusual variety of daily specials culled from cuisines chef/owner Sharleen Cowan encountered in her extensive Mediterranean travels. To quench your thirst, you can choose from a list of 41 wines by the glass. Some call it a "terrific, casual neighborhood spot," while others cite "horrid service."

SPEC: *Malaga salad $7; Paella valencina w/calamari, shrimp, scallops, chicken, chorizo $17; Shrimp curry w/almonds, sultanas & papadum $15*

Sylvia Woods
Owner of Sylvia's restaurant

"When I'm not in my restaurant, I prefer the warm-hearted atmosphere of **Emily's** and **Copeland's** of Harlem. These restaurants always feel like a home away from home. And for celebrating special occasions, I always choose the savory Caribbean cuisine of **La Detente**, in Queens."

0	1	2	3	4	5	6	7	8	9	10
disappointing		fair		good		very good		excellent		perfect

CHEF HO'S — LD — Chinese

(C17) 1720 2nd Ave. (89th & 90th) 212/348-9444

F 6 / S 6 / A 4 / $24   MC V AE   **TO/D**

Like dining inside a piece of Chinese porcelain, though some call it "too cramped." Specializing in traditional Hunan Chinese, it offers an inexpensive lunch to attract the neighborhood, but by evening the tablecloths come out for a more formal meal. Service can be spotty and sometimes it seems as though "waiters are doing you a favor."
SPEC: *Hot appetizers (for two) $7.95; Hunan dumplings w/red hot oil $3.95; Dragon & Phoenix (lobster & chicken) $15.95; Ho's beef $11.95*

DAKOTA BAR & GRILL — D — American

(C17) 1576 3rd Ave. (88th & 89th) 212/427-8889

F 5 / S 5 / A 7 / $30   MC V D AE DIS   **TO**

Contemporary American with a touch of Southwestern flair. This "fun, loud" and large bar/restaurant has a beautiful skylight and high ceilings that give it an airy, open feel. A hot singles scene, especially after work, when the "surprisingly good bar" area is jammed with business folk. A limited menu, but the "interesting" food, creatively prepared, is good.
SPEC: *Almond-fried squid w/two sauces $6.50; Grilled salmon w/basil mashed potatoes & asparagus $15.50; Herb-grilled chicken $14*

DEMI — LD — Continental

(C16) 1316 Madison Ave. (93rd & 94th) 212/534-3475

F 5 / S 7 / A 7 / $35   V D AE

There's nothing half-baked at Demi. This quintessential small, romantic restaurant has it all: from the ivy-covered exterior to intimate rooms, pink walls, a fireplace, roses, and plenty of good menu choices. Nevertheless, some call it "overpriced" and "over-rated," while others dub it "very sophisticated" and " a great find with the best brunch."
SPEC: *Seared tuna salad $12; Grilled veal chop w/asparagus & thyme risotto $25; Poached pear w/marscapone & fresh raspberries $7;*

ECCO-LA — LD — Italian

(C17) 1660 3rd Ave. (93rd) 212/860-5609

F 6 / S 6 / A 5 / $17   Cash only   **TO/D**

Budget Italian diner with colorful, clashing, eclectic decor. The room is small and tables crowded together to the point where diners beg for "elbow room." But the "big portions of great pasta" seem to please the Upper East Side clientele who fill the place every night.
SPEC: *Bocconcine Milanese $5.35; Bruschetta $4.75; Angel hair pasta w/chopped tomatoes, artichokes & mushrooms $8.95;Grilled salmon $11.75*

ELAINE'S — D — American

(C17) 1703 2nd Ave. (88th & 89th) 212/534-8103

F 6 / S 2 / A 8 / $34   MC V AE

Is it "P.T. Barnum lives!," as some diners suggest, or "the real thing in Big Apple saloons?" Service like a cab ride over potholes, but food often gets an undeserved Bronx cheer. Go for the excellent veal chop, or to sit among the wannabes, has-beens, and still-ares of journalism, literature and show biz. Like the city itself, feel free to visit…just don't expect anyone to be impressed. Weekends there's a piano player who's somewhere between kitsch and "too hokey."
SPEC: *Steamed mussels for 2 $10.75; Broiled veal chop $23.75; Broiled sirloin steak $21.75; Spaghetti squash $13*

EMILY'S BLD Southern

(A16) 1325 5th Ave. (111th) 212/996-1212 Fax: 996-5844

F 6 / S 6 / A 4 / $21   MC V AE

This down-home Harlem diner serves southern food to a family crowd with some neighborhood influences like sides of fried plantains. Some find the "portions small," and "overly seasoned." The wait staff is pleasant, but the "price adds up."

SPEC: *Fried plantains $3; Baby back ribs $14.95; Chopped barbecue sandwich $5.95; Fried pork chops $11.95*

FUDDRUCKERS LD American

(C17) 1619 3rd Ave. (90th & 91st) 212/876-3833

F 4 / S 4 / A 2 / $16   MC V AE   **TO**

The mall-like ambiance won't knock you out, but you can get a quick, dependable bite here and you don't have to worry about anything except eating inexpensively. This chain provides the kind of food your mother told you not to eat, but hey, we can't always listen to what mom says, can we?

SPEC: *Grilled country chicken salad $6.75; Oriental 1/2 lb. hamburger $5.75; Bayou chicken fingers $8.25; South of the border sundae $2.25*

GABRIEL'S D Continental

(C17) 1370 Lexington Ave. (90th & 91st) 212/369-9374

F 6 / S 6 / A 4 / $29   MC V D AE   **TO/D**

92nd Street Y patrons regularly fill all seats for dinner and Sunday brunch here, proving their good taste in cultural events extends to the culinary area. Its decor is nothing special, but it does manage to project charm and warmth. Choice of 12 wines by the glass complements a broad array of menu favorites.

SPEC: *Grilled portobello mushroom salad $7.50; Grilled jumbo shrimp w/fresh tomato caper butter $17.50; Paella $12*

ISLAND LD Amer/Continental

(C16) 1305 Madison Ave. (92nd & 93rd) 212/996-1200

F 7 / S 8 / A 9 / $29   MC V AE

This Carnegie Hill "good, local hangout," serves up a nautical Van Gogh atmosphere to preppy Park Avenue diners who come for grilled fish dishes or pasta. Bellini, an Italian champagne drink, is available, and an unusual assortment of Long Island wines add novelty to the wine list.

SPEC: *Tomato & grilled fennel soup $6; Oven roasted shrimp w/black bean salad $8.75; Penne w/mozzarella & fresh tomato $13.50; Veal & spinach loaf $15.50*

JACKSON HOLE BLD American

(C16) 1270 Madison Ave. (91st) 212/427-2820

See review on page 231.

ONE FISH TWO FISH LD Continental

(C16) 1399 Madison Ave. (97th) 212/369-5677

F 6 / S 6 / A 6 / $20   MC V D AE DIS   **TO/D**

This family fish house has late bar hours, dozens of varieties of broiled and fried seafoods, as well as typical turf dishes. Most entrees come in big portions, the side orders are inexpensive, and the fresh salads are unlimited. Nevertheless, diners warn that it's "best if hungry."

SPEC: *Steamed clams $6.95; Fried calamari $5.95; Crab legs $18.95; Cajun catfish $10.95*

0	1	2	3	4	5	6	7	8	9	10
disappointing		fair		good		very good		excellent		perfect

RUPPERT'S LD Amer/Continental

(C17) 1662 3rd. Ave. (93rd) 212/831-1900
See review on page 239.

SARABETH'S BLD American

(C16) 1295 Madison Ave. (92nd) 212/410-7335
See review on page 240.

SARANAC LD Continental

(C16) 1350 Madison Ave. (94th & 95th) 212/289-9600
F 7 / S 8 / A 8 / $18 MC V AE D TO

Scott Fitzgerald or any Park Avenue family would feel at home dining here on meatloaf with garlic mashed potatoes. Part Ivy League tap room, part hunt club, part country club, Saranac is named for a region in the Adirondacks. This is hearty Yankee fare to be enjoyed after a day of trapping or mail-ordering from L.L. Bean. And if you're lucky, like one diner, you might run into "Paul Newman here."
SPEC: *New England clam chowder $5; Spicy popcorn shrimp $6.95; Meat loaf $9.95; Fried chicken $9.95; Banana bread pudding w/cinnamon ice cream $5.25*

SYLVIA'S BLD Southern

(E22) 328 Lenox Ave. (126th) 212/996-0660 Fax: 427-6389
F 8 / S 8 / A 8 / $17 AE TO

South Carolina soul food—and lots of it—has been Sylvia Woods' specialty for 30 years. This Harlem institution dishes up fried chicken, barbecued ribs, oxtail, and other southern favorites. Live music—including a Sunday gospel brunch—makes the wait worthwhile. No garlic, wasabi, mahi-mahi, vegetarians or dieters come within miles of the place. Some find it "closest to authentic southern in the city," while others find it "disappointing," and crack that it's a "good thing Japanese tourists don't know what soul food is supposed to taste like."
SPEC: *Sylvia's World Famous Bar-B-Que ribs $10.95; Oxtail $8.95; Pork chitterlings $11.95; Short ribs of beef in brown gravy $11.95*

TABLE D'HOTE LD French

(C16) 44 E. 92nd St. (Mad. & Park) 212/348-8125
F 8 / S 8 / A 8 / $38 MC V D AE

Set up to resemble a French country dining room, and almost as "small" (only 9 tables), this "pleasant," charming and romantic restaurant is relaxed, cordial and intimate. But perhaps even more important, the food is both adventurous and consistently reaches a level of excellence.
SPEC: *Baby artichokes w/parmesan shaving $8; Hangar steak w/garlic mashed potatoes $19; Loin of lamb shank w/wild mushrooms $21*

TWINS D American

(C17) 1712 2nd Ave. (88th & 89th) 212/987-1111
F 6 / S 6 / A 6 / $26 MC V D AE DIS

Double the fun! They're all twins here, from the waiters to the bartenders, to the owners, one of whom is actor, Tom Berenger. If you can't beat 'em, join 'em—order two of the same dish. And when you're finished eating, top off your pleasure with the complimentary stick of, you guessed it, Doublemint gum.
SPEC: *Paté Duke platter $10.95; Screaming oysters $10.95; Southwestern pizza $9.95; Grilled chicken breast $14.95*

AJA | LD | Asian

(E10) 937 Broadway (22nd) 212/473-8388

F 7 / S 6 / A 7 / $27 MC V D AE

Pronounced "Asia," both its menu and its space is packed with quirky tropical eclecticism. "Great food, ugly room." The menu should entice a palate for anyone who yearns for the exotic flavorings of Southeast Asia. "Imaginative, intelligent cooking," say some. Others think "food has too many ingredients–not fusion, but confusion cuisine." "Crowded," and "good for people watching."
Closed: Sunday
SPEC: *Tuna tartare $9.50; Seared scallops $12.50; Red snapper $15.50; Grilled leg of lamb $14.50; Pear & almond strudel $7.50; Mango sundae $7.50*

ALLEY'S END | D | American

(F8) 311 W. 17th St. (8th & 9th) 212/627-8899

F 7 / S 6 / A 7 / $25 MC V DIS

A great place to take a date, hang out with old friends, or make new ones. The atmosphere is relaxed– "surprising waterfalls and greenery"–and the food good and "in large portions," is reasonably priced. Just keep this a secret–we want to avoid a yuppie and bridge and tunnel invasion.
SPEC: *Grilled sausage $7.50; Blue corn dusted soft shell crabs $8; Atlantic halibut $12; Pork tenderloin $11; Pear crumble $6*

BENDIX DINER | BLD | American

(F9) 219 8th Ave. (21st) 212/366-0560 Fax: 929-1362

F 5 / S 4 / A 4 / $16 MC V **TO**

A bright, neon sign in the window orders you to "Get Fat," while another at the entrance warns you'll only be seated if you "behave yourself." The food at this eccentric, "unique" diner, is mostly home-cooking with a touch of Asia thrown in. While some wonder, "how does this dump stay open and packed?" others, call it "fun," "cheap," "a scene" and "good."
SPEC: *Chicken satay $4.50; Pork chops $7.95; Pad see noodles $6.45; Quad berry pie $3.25; Chocolate layer mousse $3.25*

BIRICCHINO RESTAURANT | LD | Italian

(E9) 260 W. 29th St. (7th & 8th) 212/695-6690

F 6 / S 6 / A 7 / $30 MC V D AE

This "reliable" Italian restaurant serves a small but tasteful stable of Italian dishes to a discriminating Chelsea crowd. The appetizers are homemade and antipasto prepared daily. Grilled chicken and veal dishes are quite popular.
SPEC: *Grilled shrimp & mushrooms $8.25; Ravioli filled w/veal, prosciutto and parmesan $12.95; Veal piccata w/wild mushrooms $17.50*

BLU RESTAURANT | LD | American

(E9) 254 W. 23rd St. (7th & 8th) 212/989-6300

F 6 / S 6 / A 7 / $29 MC V D AE DIS

"A great interior," with an indigo theme, like the night sky. Folks rave about "the wonderful garden" and "terrific atmosphere." Perfect if you're catching a movie in Chelsea, or want to have a summertime garden meal. It's a sapphire oasis on bustling 23rd street, complete with live jazz brunch on Sunday.
SPEC: *Mushroom soup $5; Carpaccio $6.50; Pan roast chicken $14; Grilled breast of duck $17; Bourbon spiked Run for the Roses pie $6*

0	1	2	3	4	5	6	7	8	9	10
disappointing		fair		good		very good		excellent		perfect

BLUE MOON MEXICAN CAFE   LD   Mexican

(F9) 150 8th Ave. (17th & 18th) 212/463-0560
See review on page 149.

BOOK-FRIENDS CAFE   LD   American

(F10) 16 W. 18th St. (5th & 6th) 212/255-7407

F 5 / S 6 / A 8 / $17   MC V AE

For the romantic bibliophile longing for Paris in the '20s. Book-lined walls, a small cafe, and great music conjure the ghost of Henry Miller— "I promise myself to return to Paris every time I'm in this place." Afternoon tea is not to be missed. Reasonably priced, and a great place for soaking up the delectably dusty atmosphere. **Closed: Sunday June, July, August**
SPEC: *Roast chicken sandwich $10.25 Chicken pot pie $9.95; Smoked salmon sandwich on sourdough $10.75; Chocolate velvet $4.50*

BRIGHT FOOD SHOP   LD   Southwestern

(F9) 216 8th Ave. (21st) 212/243-4433

F 6 / S 5 / A 4 / $17   Cash only   TO/D

NYC diner gone hip. This bright little restaurant, formerly a coffee shop, serves an "eclectic" health conscious menu of Mexican, Southwestern and Asian food. Seated at the counter or at one of the small tables, you look into the kitchen, and can peruse the artwork created by Taylor Marshall 3 years ago when he was 8. If you're in the mood for takeout, try their shop two doors down. **Closed: Sunday night & Monday**
SPEC: *Pacific rim salmon cakes $5.75; Gulf shrimp wontons $5.75; Moo Shu Mex $11.50*

BRYANT PARK GRILL   LD   American

(C10) 25 W. 40th St. (5th & 6th) 212/840-6500 Fax: 840-8122

F 6 / S 5 / A 7 / $30   MC V D AE   TO

Private business in public space feels very American. But once inside, Bryant Park Grill captures old European atmosphere in a New American restaurant. A spacious, light room. The prettiness of the Grill extends past the glass and wood structure and into Bryant Park. Comments range from "a great addition," to "interesting, but needs more time." But the service gets "thumbs down."
SPEC: *Black & blue yellowfin tuna carpaccio $9.95; Grilled free range chicken $15.95; Marinated pork tenderloin $16.95*

CAJUN   LD   Cajun

(F9) 129 8th Ave. (16th) 212/691-6174 Fax: 691-4578

F 6 / S 6 / A 7 / $21   MC V D AE DIS

A Chelsea mainstay for almost 20 years, serving everything from oyster Bienville to gumbo to crawfish etouffee, all guaranteed to scorch your hot spot. The menu offers a wide range of authentic Cajun and Creole cuisine. And "even Dixieland sounds okay here."
SPEC: *Jambalaya $3.95; Andouille-tasso-black-eyed peas $9.95; Gumbo-crock $11.95; Red beans & rice $9.50; Fried catfish $13.95*

CAL'S   LD   American

(F10) 55 W. 21st St. (5th & 6th) 212/929-0740

F 7 / S 7 / A 7 / $32   MC V AE DIS

With its high ceiling, friendly staff, and original artwork by Cal himself, this place is quite irresistible. "A lovely surprise," in fact. The food is American but with a Moroccan influence. And some people swear that they have the "best burger" in town. **Closed: Sunday**
SPEC: *Crayfish & snail-filled ravioli $8.75; Roast stuffed quail $8.50; Mixed grill of beef, pork, chicken, quail, sausage & sweetbreads $21*

CHELSEA COMMONS   LD   American

(E8) 242 10th Ave. (24th)   212/929-9424

F 6 / S 6 / A 7 / $17   MC V D AE DIS   **TO/D**

A homey pub with surprisingly good food. The "great garden" in the spring/summer//fall is an added plus while the fireplace in winter gives it a cozy charm. The bar is "ambitious," and there's free, live jazz on Wednesday and Saturday nights.
SPEC: *Blackened steak tidbits $5.25; Andouille sausage $5.50; Sirloin steak, blackened $11.75; Fish and chips $9.95; Chocolate cake $3.50*

CHEYENNE DINER   BLD   Diner

(D8) 411 9th Ave. (33rd)   212/465-8750

F 4 / S 5 / A 5 / $13   MC V D AE DIS   **TO/D**

One of Hell's Kitchen's 24-hr joints, a haven among the desolate concrete backdrop of warehouses, garages, and the grayest slab of the West Side highway. A genuine diner housed in an aqua-blue, aluminum sided megatrailer. Offers home-cooked meals to young dramatists, cabbies, and anyone who ventures west of 8th Avenue.
SPEC: *Grilled chicken breast on a bun $4.95; 1/2 lb. burger specials $5.25-$6.85; 3-egg combination omelettes $5.45-$8.95*

CHEZ JOSEPHINE   D   French

(C8) 414 W. 42nd St. (9th & 10th)   212/594-1925

F 6 / S 7 / A 7 / $33   MC V AE

Legendary actress Josephine Baker is the inspiration for this "charming," "romantic," darkly-lit theater district night spot. Her son, Jean Claude, oversees the menu of French food with some southern touches. It's a "nice surprise, especially for the theater district." Nightly jazz. **Closed: Sunday**
SPEC: *Risotto w/scallops, shrimp, pancetta & collard greens $19.50; Lobster cassoulet w/shrimp, scallops, seafood sausage & black beans $22*

CLAIRE   LD   Seafood

(F9) 156 7th Ave. (19th)   212/255-1955

F 6 / S 6 / A 6 / $20   MC V D AE DIS

With the under-the-sea theme, aquamarine and pink decor, this seafood place has every color of the rainbow, if you get our drift. Some call it "the best seafood in town." The menu changes regularly, according to fresh fish availability, but the basics remain the same. And "the conch chowder is incredible."
SPEC: *Talmade oyster $7.95; Bayou crawfish patty $4.95; Sautéed "Drunk & Crazy" chicken breast medallions $9.95; Game hen $12.95; Key lime pie $4.50*

DA UMBERTO   D   Italian

(F9) 107 W. 17th St. (6th & 7th)   212/989-0303

F 7 / S 7 / A 7 / $50   MC V D AE

The "fabulous," airy, unpretentious decor makes this place seem so authentic you'll imagine an accordion in the background. Great place to go with the family or good friends for a celebration. The Tuscan cuisine is "exquisite," but it can be noisy, even raucous, so it's not quite right for that romantic evening you might have in mind.
Closed: Sunday
SPEC: *Carpaccio con parmigiano $9; Veal chop con cognac $26; Spiedini di scampi $20; Paillard di pollo con erbe $16*

0	1	2	3	4	5	6	7	8	9	10
disappointing		fair		good		very good		excellent		perfect

EL CID TAPAS BAR & RESTAURANT   LD   Spanish

(F8) 322 W. 15th St. (8th & 9th) 212/929-9332

F 8 / S 7 / A 6 / $21   D AE

This Chelsea tapas bar is intimate enough for anyone to imbibe plenty of good sangria (try the El Cid special blend),and fill up on grilled shrimp in not fancy, but fairly festive comfort. One diner asks us, "Don't mention it. We want to keep it to ourselves."
Closed: Monday
SPEC: *Hot and cold tapas $3.95 to $9.75; Pollo al pisto $9.95;Lobster in green sauce) P/A; Poached pears in wine w/raspberry sauce $3.95*

EL QUIJOTE   LD   Spanish

(E9) 226 W. 23rd St. (7th & 8th) 212/929-1855

F 5 / S 6 / A 5 / $28   MC V D AE DIS

At 65, the oldest Spanish restaurant in NY shows no indication of retirement. Festive patrons consume 3,000 lbs. of lobster weekly, guaranteed fresh, harvested by owner Manny Ramirez's own Maine fleet. And if you've recently won the lottery, you might try the $369 bottle of Vega Sicilia 1960, served nowhere else in the world.
SPEC: *Paella Valenciana w/lobster $17.95; Lobster (1 1/4 lbs) $12.95-$39.95; Guava w/cream cheese $2.95*

Empire Diner

EMPIRE DINER   BLD   Diner

(F8) 210 10th Ave. (22nd & 23rd) 212/243-2736

F 5 / S 5 / A 6 / $18   MC V D AE DIS

Opened in 1929 and still going strong 24 hours a day, 7 days a week, this is the ultimate in diners. "Sustains you after clubbing." The crowd is local, artistic, hip and fun. "Blue Plate specials often a treat." Live piano weekends from 12-3 pm, and week nights from 7-11 pm. Late night jazz only makes this place even more ideal for winding down when the party's over but the night's still young.
SPEC: *Chicken or tofu fajita $5.50; Pigs in blankets $4.95; Open hot turkey sandwich $8.95; Brownie all the way $5.95*

FLOWERS   LD   American

(F10) 21 W. 17th St. (5th & 6th) 212/691-8888 Fax: 647-9698

F 6 / S 5 / A 6 / $35   MC V D AE

"It's hip again." Come here for a one-stop entertainment experience. The restaurant has aged nicely since opening 2 years ago and still serves good, innovative American cuisine with international touches. The huge bouquets of fresh flowers are magnificent.On the 2nd floor is a dimly-lit lounge where hipsters in fake eyelashes and platform shoes sway to the throbbing music. Up one more flight, you'll find yourself in the pretty rooftop garden, where a more casual atmosphere prevails.
SPEC: *Spicy tuna tartare w/avocado $9; Japanese barbecued sturgeon $21; Rack of lamb $23*

FOLLONICO   LD   Italian

(E10) 6 W. 24th St. (5th & 6th)   212/691-6359

F 7 / S 7 / A 7 / $39   MC V D AE

With wood-paneled bar and wood-burning oven in the dining room, this is a *Gourmet Magazine* photo come to life. "Wonderful place to gather with friends." At lunch, it's a favorite for publishing folk, while at night the crowd is more formal. A good spot to take someone you're trying to impress, since the service, atmosphere and food make you feel like you sound clever and look good.
SPEC: *Herb-printed fassoletto $12); Deep-fried oysters $12; Grilled rack of lamb $24; Chocolate-hazelnut mousse cake $6.50*

FOOD BAR   LD   American

(F9) 149 8th Ave. (17th & 18th)   212/243-2020

F 7 / S 7 / A 8 / $22   MC V   **TO**

Mussels may not be on the menu, but they're sure to be found at this "hip" Chelsea hangout. With patrons mostly men, high on music, food "low in cost," and an emphasis on shaking one's groove thing (either sitting under colorful hand-made lamp shades, or leaning against the slick aluminum bar,) you'll find that hindsight's 20/20.
SPEC: *Risotto w/sundried tomatoes and asparagus $8.95; Meatloaf, mashed potatoes & vegetables $8.50; Seared tuna au poivre $11.50*

FRANK'S RESTAURANT   LD   Italian

(F8) 85 10th Ave. (15th)   212/243-1349

F 7 / S 7 / A 6 / $35   MC V D AE DIS

No longer on the charming and historic meat-packing block of west 14th, Frank's has now moved to the less historic, but also less gritty block of west 15th. "A little gussied up, but still great," this bigger, sunnier, shinier Frank's is no bargain. But chances are, if you're a regular customer to this Italian steakhouse, you already drive a Cadillac. **Closed: Sunday**
SPEC: *Tripe $7.50; Sweetbreads vin blanc $7.50; Broiled shell steak $26.50; Filet mignon $26; Cheesecake $5.50*

FRESCO TORTILLA GRILL   LD   Mexican

(C9) 125 W. 42nd St. (6th & B'way)   212/221-5849
(E9) 253 8th Ave. (22nd & 23rd)   212/463-8877
See review on page 106.

GASCOGNE   LD   French

(F9) 158 8th Ave. (18th)   212/675-6564

F 7 / S 7 / A 7 / $36   MC V AE

This rustic, romantic French hideaway in Chelsea is lovely in every way. The garden may be one of the better kept secrets in New York, but Gascogne is beautiful all year round. The menu is simple, but not in a basic way, and the food "memorable." Several people comment on the "great prix-fixe value." **Closed: Saturday**
SPEC: *Pastry crust filled w/duck confit, sautéed onions $8; Assortment de foie gras maison a la'Ancienne $18*

GOOD DINER, THE   BLD   Diner

(C7) 554 11th Ave. (42nd)   212/967-2661

F 5 / S 6 / A 5 / $13   MC V AE   **TO/D**

Just blocks away from the real McCoys–Market Diner and Munson's– this newcomer serves up "nouveau diner" food to late night clubbers and theater-goers. Decor is eclectic with the nouveau diner theme of neon seats with chrome touches here and there.
SPEC: *Buffalo wings $4.50; Greek salad $5.65; Good burger $5.55*

0	1	2	3	4	5	6	7	8	9	10
disappointing		fair		good		very good		excellent		perfect

HOULIHAN'S   LD   Amer/Continental

(D9) 2 Penn Plaza Penn Station (7th & 8th) 212/630-0348
See review on page 230.

KAFFEEHAUS   LD   Austrian

(F9) 131 8th Ave. (16th & 17th) 212/229-9702 Fax: 321-9182
F 6 / S 5 / A 6 / $19   MC V D DIS   **TO**

With its large selection of desserts and Viennese coffees, this
"homey and comfortable" restaurant functions nicely as a candle-
lit coffee bar, making it the perfect spot for blind dates." But don't
miss its full menu of contemporary Austrian and American food,
"especially the schnitzel."
SPEC: *Frisee, endive & watercress salad $5.95; Citrus cured salmon
charlotte $7.25; Austrian-style espressos & cappuccinos $1.95-$4.50*

Keen's Chophouse

KEEN'S CHOPHOUSE   LD   American

(D10) 72 W. 36th St. (5th & 6th) 212/947-3636
F 7 / S 7 / A 7 / $39   MC V D AE

This 110 year-old historical landmark boasts the world's largest
clay pipe collection and the wandering ghost of Lily Langtry, for
whom a room is named. Keens is nothing less than a time machine
whisking you back to the past where red meat was the preferred
entree. "A private club for those without the necessary pedigree."
"The best mutton chop!" **Closed: Sunday**
SPEC: *Tomato & basil soup $6; Mutton chop $27.50; Aged prime sirloin strip steak $29.75; Warm pear cinnamon frangipane $6*

L'ACAJOU   LD   French

(F10) 53 W. 19th St. (5th & 6th) 212/645-1706
F 7 / S 6 / A 6 / $32   MC V D AE DIS

L'Acajou or "Mahogany" (for English readers) is a lively French
bistro that's sure to put the notion that the French are snobs to
rest...at least for the night. "Fun and funky" it's a spacious cafete-
ria-like dining room with seasonal hand-painted art work is
accommodating to both the sweet 16 and 80th birthday. Meals
served briskly by the "tattooed staff."
SPEC: *Onion tart $7; Escargots a l'Alsacienne $8.50; Steak au poivre
$24; Roasted breast of duck $18.50*

LA LUNCHONETTE   LD   French

(F8) 130 10th Ave. (18th) 212/675-0342
F 8 / S 7 / A 7 / $27   MC V

This petite bistro aims to recreate a visit to Grand mere's maison,
not only with the authentic home cooked French food, but the dis-
tance you have to travel to get there. Many say, it's well worth the
voyage. But others say, "it's not as perfect as it used to be."
SPEC: *Escargot au cognac $6.50; Veal sweetbreads vinaigrette $6;
Whole trout w/shrimp, lemongrass & wild mushrooms $15.50*

LE MADRI   LD   Italian

(F9) 168 W. 18th St. (7th Ave.) 212/727-8022

F 8 / S 7 / A 7 / $38   MC V D AE

This romantic, Tuscan room is both lovely and romantic. If things are happening in New York, they are probably happening at Le Madri. "Sometimes snooty, sometimes nice–always good food." Perfect for the Barney's shopper seeking refreshment. After the kitchen closes at 11:30, you can still get pizza until 12:30.

SPEC: *Shrimp & asparagus salad $9.50; Carpaccio di filetto pepato $9; Ossobuco $24; Grilled tuna $25*

Luma

LUMA   D   American

(E9) 200 9th Ave. (22nd & 23rd) 212/633-8033

F 8 / S 7 / A 6 / $33   MC V D AE DIS

Formerly vegetarian, it's now a chic, intimate Chelsea eatery that manages to be hip and welcoming, not an easy combination to pull off. But this must be why it has so many celebrity fans, from Sam Waterston to Lenny Kravitz, who come for the wholly organic "eclectic" American, French influenced menu. "Great food, good value."

SPEC: *Luma salad $8; Seared peppered tuna $9.50; Roasted Maine codfish $18; Crisped skate $18*

MAN RAY   LD   Amer/Continental

(F9) 169 8th Ave. (18th & 19th) 212/627-4220

F 6 / S 6 / A 6 / $21   MC V D AE   **TO/D**

The spare, deco design obviously influenced by the photographic work of Man Ray, contrasts nicely with the long bar. Good mix of basics: pasta, burgers, pizza and grilled chicken. You'll find yourself dining alongside a celebrity or two. Some suggest "it's dropped a notch or two" lately.

SPEC: *Fried calamari $5.50; Grilled chicken breast w/sun dried tomatoes, spinach & goat cheese $12.95; Maryland crab cakes $14.95*

MARKET CAFE, THE   LD   Continental

(C8) 496 9th Ave. (37th and 38th) 212/967-3892 Fax: 967-4092

F 6 / S 4 / A 5 / $17   MC V D DIS AE   **TO/D**

Fashion district and business clients flock to this industrial bistro for grilled meat salads at lunch, ignoring the more creative offerings which tend toward the game-y. Evenings, the crowd broadens in the "funky" diner as theater-goers and neighbors and arrive. The "red room" in back hosts poetry readings and a variety of musical acts. **Closed: Sunday**

SPEC: *Corn chowder $4.50; Grilled flatbread w/potato, anchovy & parmesan topping $5.25; Garlic-crusted free range chicken $12.50; Nectarine pie $4*

0	1	2	3	4	5	6	7	8	9	10
disappointing	fair		good			very good		excellent		perfect

193

MARY ANN'S — LD — Mexican

(F9) 116 8th Ave. (16th St.) 212/633-0877

F 6 / S 5 / A 4 / $16   Cash only

It may not look like much, but Mary Ann's offers good, reasonably priced Mexican food. which may explain why it's always hard to find a table. Some diners claim "they're getting a little sloppy" and that lately "it's gone down hill," while others complain about the "rotten" service.

SPEC: *Ceviche $7.95; Purée of black beans w/shrimp & fresh cilantro $4.95; Pollo Yucatan $7.95; Mole poblano $7.95*

MERCHANT'S — LD — Continental

(F9) 112 7th Ave. (17th) 212/366-7267
See review on page 234.

NEGRIL — LD — Jamaican

(E8) 362 W. 23rd (8th & 9th) 212/807-6411

F 7 / S 8 / A 7 / $25   MC V AE   TO/D

This cheerful spot is like an instant vacation, straight to the Caribbean. Jerk chicken and Thursday night calypso music are a sure cure for any kind of urban ennui. Sit at the bar, have a frozen drink, and watch the aquarium full of tropical fish for a quick fix.
SPEC: *Escovitch fish filet w/Bammie $6.50; Jerk chicken $7.50; Bajan fish $8.50; Mom's bread pudding $3.50*

NGONE — LD — African

(E10) 823 6th Ave. (28th & 29th) 212/967-7899

F 7 / S 8 / A 4 / $15   Cash only   TO/D

Recently upgraded from a cafeteria-style coffee shop to an African/ tropical motif. Ousmane, the owner, is a cheery host who'll instruct you on your food choices. Attracts an eclectic mix ranging from cab drivers to fashion models who come not only for the authentic Senegalese cuisine, but for the genuine "African experience."
SPEC: *Black-eyed peas $3.95; Fish stewed in tomato sauce w/eggplant, yucca & white cabbage $11.95; Chicken mafe $10.95*

Top 10 $36-55
Expensive

PERIYALI — LD — Greek

(F10) 35 W. 20th St. (5th & 6th) 212/463-7890

F 8 / S 8 / A 8 / $38   MC V D AE

Since 1987, this quaint Flatiron district bistro has offered the "best Greek food" in Manhattan. Owners Nicola Kotsoni and Steve Tzolis have brought class back into the world of Greek cuisine. The main dining room features white stucco walls, long wooden bar, and loads of fresh flower arrangements. As an added lure, there's an intimate outdoor garden. "Almost as refreshing as a trip to the isles."
SPEC: *Octopus in red wine $10.50; Chicken & fennel brochette $9.50; Charcoal grilled filet mignon $23*

PORTFOLIO RESTAURANT — LD — Italian

(F10) 4 W. 19th St. (5th) 212/691-3845 Fax: 691-4307

F 5 / S 6 / A 6 / $20   MC V D AE   TO/D

Diners enjoy a variety of moderately priced Italian dishes, while they study the photography on the wall by guest artists, which management rotates each month. "Great food, service, prices, atmosphere. Waiters can be gossipy..." And service can be "pushy–"Another beer? Are you sure?— but homemade pasta dishes make it worth the bother.
SPEC: *Tortellini in brodo (soup) $2.50; Fried calamari $4.95; Fettuccine Alfredo $8.95; Salmon w/brandied pesto sauce $10.95*

ROCKING HORSE MEXICAN CAFE, THE LD Mexican

(F9) 182 8th Ave. (19th and 20th) 212/463-9511 Fax: 243-3245

F 6 / S 5 / A 5 / $20   MC V AE

This small Mexican cafe spices up the decor with drawings done by customers. The emphasis is on authentic, healthy and fresh cooked south of the border fare. "Always fun," it's a good place to celebrate Cinco de Mayo, El Dia de los Muertos (All Saints) and Posada (a Christmastime celebration).

SPEC: *Quesadillas w/mushrooms & house-made chorizo $5.95; Chiles poblanos rellenos $10.95; Warm Mexican chocolate tortaw/cinnamon ice cream*

TRAMPS CAFE   LD   Cajun

(F10) 45 W. 21st St. (5th & 6th) 212/633-9570

F 5 / S 5 / A 6 / $24   MC V D AE   **TO**

Tramps Cafe provides sustenance to fans of Southern Louisiana cooking, and Tramps Club, next door, to music fans. "Fantastic and authentic New Orleans-style cooking." The atmosphere is relaxed, the tables well-spaced. The open kitchen is nice to look at, but makes the restaurant stifling in summer in spite of air conditioning. An unnecessary annoyance: unshielded ceiling lights hurt the eyes.

Closed: Sunday & Monday

SPEC: *Crawfish boiled in spicy broth w/seasonal vegetables $5; Red beans & rice w/turkey tasso $6; Crabcakes $12; Fried chicken $10*

TWIGS   D   Mediterranean

(F9) 196 8th Ave. (20th) 212/633-6735

F 6 / S 6 / A 6 / $21   MC V AE

A "comfortable," neighborhood restaurant offering your basic Italian/Mediterranean cuisine. Twigs prides itself on its pizzas, which you can create yourself from a long list appearing on the menu, as well as its seafood. Monday night's a good time to visit, since the second entree you purchase is 1/2 price. "Always good. Wonderful people."

SPEC: *Grilled mozzarella $6; Grilled salmon $13.75; Pizzas $8.50-$10; Spaghettini fra diavolo $13; Grilled yellowtail tuna $13.75*

VERNON'S   LD   Jamaican

(E9) 252 W. 29th St. (7th & 8th) 212/268-7020

F 5 / S 5 / A 6 / $22   MC V AE   **TO**

If you hear the word "jerk" and think of the Steve Martin movie, it's time to get yourself re-signified. Vernon's can do the trick, dishing up flavorful plates of meats and fish smoked and fruit-sauced in the Caribbean barbecue style. Mellow reggae, incense burning, and exotic drinks with or without alcohol spice up the meal, like the "Knock-Down" which, says the menu, will "nice up your sex life."

Closed: Sunday

SPEC: *Cod fish cakes $1.50; Vernon's paradise dip $3; Jerk pork $12; Jerk chicken $12; Fish "Eccovitch" style P/A; Rum raisin cake $3*

WEST BANK CAFE   LD   American

(C8) 407 W. 42nd St. (9th) 212/695-6909

F 4 / S 4 / A 5 / $21   MC V AE   **TO/D**

Wendy Wasserstein, Dustin Hoffman and up and coming theater wannabes all hang out at this Italian restaurant/bar/theater space. It's known among insiders as the place to find everyone who's anyone in theater town. The downstairs theater has been known to put on good shows.

SPEC: *Corn chowder w/shrimp $4.50; Blackened tuna roll $7; Stuffed chicken breast $11; Penne Siciliana $9; Key lime tart $5*

0	1	2	3	4	5	6	7	8	9	10
disappointing		fair		good		very good		excellent		perfect

ZIG ZAG BAR & GRILL LD American

(E9) 206 W. 23rd St. (7th & 8th) 212/645-5060

F 4 / S 2 / A 6 / $20 MC V AE

At press time, this ultra-hip B & G was undergoing renovations. But if it lives up to its former life, it might serve as a fine oasis in a neighborhood that struts the line between sleazy and upscale.

ZIP CITY BREWING CO. LD American

(F10) 3 W. 18th St. (5th & 6th) 212/366-6333

F 6 / S 6 / A 6 / $26 MC V D AE DIS

This newly opened microbrewery is cool as it is comfortable. Choose wooden nooks to while away the day; or sit at the bar and contemplate the large copper vats. Reasonable prices and German-style beer attract a loyal after work crowd.
SPEC: *Pan fried breast of chicken $6.25; Yellowfin tuna chili $9.75; Zip City meat loaf $12.50; Sour cream apple pie $5.25*

ZUCCA LD Mediterranean

(E8) 227 10th Ave. (23rd & 24th) 212/741-1970

F 7 / S 7 / A 7 / $29 MC V D AE **TO**

Meticulously prepared, innovative dishes are served proudly by a knowledgeable staff who actually love their chef. And after eating here, so will you. Cited by some for "the best appetizers." The location may be odd, but you'll pay more elsewhere for meals of this quality.
SPEC: *Maine sea scallops $7; Hudson Valley foie gras $10; Rack of Australian lamb $17; Chatham cod $16*

WEST 43RD – 59TH STREET

AFGHAN KEBAB HOUSE LD Afghani

(B8) 764 9th Ave. (51st & 52nd) 212/307-1629

F 5 / S 4 / A 3 / $12 Cash only **TO/D**

Of the three Afghani restaurants in a two block strip of Ninth Avenue, this is the best and most popular. The mouth-watering smell is an attack on the senses, and the kebabs, especially the chicken, do not disappoint. Forget the atmosphere–a small, narrow dining room, with photos of crowded mosques and "Read the Qu'ran" bumper stickers on the wall. But there's "excellent value" and "real food." **Closed: Sunday**
SPEC: *Bolanee pumpkin #2; Bolanee potato $2; Chicken breast kebob $7.50; Lamb kebob $7.50; Fish kebob $8; Firnee (pudding) $2.50; Baklava $2*

ALGONQUIN HOTEL LD Amer/Continental

(C10) 59 W. 44th St. (5th & 6th) 212/840-6800

F 6 / S 6 / A 7 / $38 MC V D AE DIS

Dorothy Parker and her "theatre ghosts" made the hotel a note-worthy spot with their literary highjinks. Though her crowd ordered the cheapest items from the menu–like scrambled eggs–today's chef Robert Funicelli's kitchen turns out hearty con-tinental fare amid "old world elegance." The ornate lobby, wood-paneled with chandeliers, fancy sofas and wingchairs strategically tucked in nooks and crannies, doubles as a bar and proves both intimate as well as social.
SPEC: *Roasted baby eggplants w/seared chicken filets & gazpacho sauce $9; Prime rib of beef $22; Chicken pot pie $16*

AMERICAN FESTIVAL CAFE · BLD · American

(B10) 20 W. 50th St. (5th & 6th-Rockefeller) 212/246-6699

F 6 / S 6 / A 7 / $40 · MC V D AE

Nestled amid the towers of Rockefeller Center, AFC offers an unexpected "good quality" and "very friendly service." The menu features a nice array of American cuisine, including a "great burger," "very good gazpacho and penne." A bit touristy to a New Yorker, its central location, "great view," and "relaxed atmosphere," makes it a good place to take out of town guests. During the summer you'll enjoy the lovely fountain and flowers "under the umbrellas."
SPEC: *Crab cake $9.95; Angus steak $24.95; Swordfish $17.95; Granny Smith deep dish apple pie w/vanilla bean ice cream $6.50*

APERITIVO · LD · Italian

(A10) 29 W. 56th St. (5th & 6th) 212/765-5155

F 7 / S 6 / A 6 / $24 · MC V D AE

With renaissance decor, this is the perfect spot to take your parents for a pre-theater dinner. There's the charm of Little Italy in the 1960s (without the low prices alas.) and the food and service rates a consistent "very good." Not to be overlooked for a midtown business lunch or a midday, Fifth Avenue shopping spree respite.
Closed: Sunday
SPEC: *Peperone alle brace con alici (roast peppers w/anchovies) $8.50; Veal chop $27.50; Sogliola "Aperitivo" (filet of sole w/garlic & oregano) $22.50; Tiramisu $6; Macedonia di Frutta Fresca $7*

AQUAVIT · LD · Scandinavian

(A10) 13 W. 54th St. (5th & 6th) 212/307-7311

F 6 / S 6 / A 7 / $66 · MC V D AE

Formerly the residence of John D. Rockefeller, the midtown townhouse is now home to one of the city's "outstanding" Scandinavian restaurants. Aquavit offers a delicate selection of "lovely food" in an atmosphere of sleek, "really beautiful," "Scandinavian grandeur." Divided into two sections, there is first an upper level cafe and bar where you can sample 8 varieties of Aquavit, as well as graze on light meals and snacks. Full meals are served in an 8-story, glass-walled dining room atrium, adorned with fanciful mobiles and a magnificent gray-tile waterfall.
SPEC: *Pre-fixe: Smoked venison salad; Gravlax; phyllo-wrapped baked salmon; Hot sweet mustard-glazed arctic char; Pan roasted arctic venison, Swedish cheesecake; Ginger bread "Lockelse;" $55*

ARGENTINE PAVILION · LD · Argentinian

(B10) 32 W. 46th St. (5th & 6th) 212/921-0835

F 5 / S 5 / A 4 / $27 · MC V D AE DIS

Boasting the largest open grill in New York City, this "carnivores only" palace won't leave you asking "where's the beef?" With a diverse Argentinian fare served plentifully, the restaurant is also famous for steaks, so, "Be ready to eat red meat!"
SPEC: *Chorizos $5.75; Steak, Argentinian-style $16.50; Queso con dulce (cheese w/quince) $4.25; Flan con crema $4.25*

ARRIBA ARRIBA! · LD · Mexican

(B8) 762 9th Ave. (51st) 212/489-0810 Fax: 249-1429

F 6 / S 6 / A 6 / $19 · MC V D AE · TO/D

In a neighborhood where the ethnic food choices are unlimited, this inexpensive eatery delivers a stand-out Mexican menu. With the "best margaritas in N.Y.," and "best guacamole and chips," it's become a popular hangout for local actors and artists.
SPEC: *Chicken quesadilla $6.75; Chalupas $4.75; Fajitas $10.95; Crepa di camarones $10.95; Helados fritos (fried ice cream) $4.75*

0	1	2	3	4	5	6	7	8	9	10
disappointing		fair		good		very good		excellent		perfect

B. Smith's

B. SMITH'S LD Continental

(B9) 771 8th Ave. (47th) 212/247-2222 Fax: 502-1308

F 6 / S 6 / A 7 / $29 MC V D AE

Owned by former model, Barbara Smith, this restaurant/bar has long been a magnet for successful singles. "Elegant," "tasteful," and "sophisticated," this westside "oasis" is a "great choice for theatre goers." Its sleek, stylish interior reflects the equally sleek and often stylish theatrical clientele.

SPEC: *Gulf shrimp steeped in Chardonnay w/garlic & herbs $8.95; Cassoulet of duck confit, sausage & white beans $9.95; Tuna w/ pigeon peas & rice $17.95; Pork chops w/fried green apples $13.95*

BANGKOK CUISINE LD Thai

(B9) 885 8th Ave. (52nd & 53rd) 212/581-6370

F 7 / S 6 / A 5 / $18 MC V AE TO

One of the first Thai restaurants in the city. And though they have lowered the heat of many of their dishes to suit popular tastes, they still serve some of the city's best and still "inexpensive" Thai food.
SPEC: *Sate $8.95; Tod mun pla (minced king fish w/Thai curry) $4.95; Masaman curried shrimp $17.95; Pa-Nang beef $14.95;*

BANJARA LD Indian

(B8) 741 9th Ave. (50th & 51st) 757- 25-77

F 5 / S 6 / A 5 / $18 MC V D AE DIS TO/D

The $7.95 lunch buffet draws huge crowds. But, if you're in the ethnic laden neighborhood in the evening and you have a hankering for good, inexpensive Indian food, Banjara, proud owner of its own tandoori oven, is a decent choice. The interior is festive, complete with Indian murals all the way down to year-round Christmas lights.
SPEC: *Assorted vegetarian appetizers $4.95; Chicken tandoori $6.95; Chicken tikka masala $7.95; Tandoori mixed grill $13.95*

BARBETTA RESTAURANT LD Italian

(B8) 321 W. 46th St. (8th & 9th) 212/246-9171

F 7 / S 7 / A 8 / $42 MC V D AE DIS

One of the most "beautiful" restaurants in N.Y. There's a lovely outdoor, centerpiece garden with a pool and sculptured figures surrounding. Located in a sumptuous 19th century, Astor townhouse, the private dining room on the second floor bespeaks, "romance in a castle and food to match." The main dining room can be used as a ballroom, so be prepared for a "truly romantic evening," where "love is in the air." **Closed: Sunday**
SPEC: *Rollatine of Piemontese robiola in grilled zucchini $9.75; Agnolotti $15; Risotto w/porcini mushrooms $16; Raw filet of veal $28; Monte bianco $8*

BECCO · LD · Italian

(B8) 355 W. 46th St. (8th & 9th) 212/397-7597

F 6 / S 6 / A 8 / $26   MC V D AE DIS

This Northern Italian restaurant in the heart of the theater district offers a choice of two extensive and reasonably priced, prix-fixe dinner menus: one for $19.95 (two courses), and the other ranging from $23.95 to $29.95. If meat isn't on your diet, then try the pastas: they're all homemade.

SPEC: *Homemade pastas $14; Osso buco $18.95; Beefsteak Fiorentina alla Becco $20.95*

Ben Benson's Steak House

BEN BENSON'S STEAKHOUSE · LD · American

(B9) 123 W. 52nd St. (6th & 7th) 212/581-8888 Fax: 581-1170

F 7 / S 6 / A 8 / $50   MC V D AE DIS   **TO**

Ben Benson's ranks as one of the best steakhouses in the city. With a rustic yet elegant interior, there is a separate eating area by the bar for more informal dining and the upstairs boasts an additional large room suitable for private parties. Ben Benson also takes his wine service seriously, with an incredible selection and many bottles handsomely housed, in antique wooden cabinets.

SPEC: *Lump crab meat cocktail $13.50; Lemon peppered shrimp $14*

BENIHANA OF TOKYO · LD · Japanese

(A10) 47 W. 56th St. (5th & 6th) 212/581-0930

F 6 / S 7 / A 6 / $34   MC V D AE DIS

Once it had "it," now it doesn't. But this Japanese-style steak house is "fun for a group" and a "place to go with a crowd." It offers entertainment to kids and a display for out-of-towners as chefs continue to put on a table-side show of legerdemain, slicing, and creative dicing. "Nice for lunch." Karaoke at the East Side location.

SPEC: *Sushi roll $5; Calamari tempura $6; Steak & chicken $20.25; Tenderloin & ocean scallops $24; Panna-cotta $3.50*

BROADWAY DINER · BLD · Diner

(B9) 1726 Broadway (52nd) 212/765-0909
See review on page 121.

BROADWAY GRILL · LD · Continental

(B9) 1605 Broadway (Holiday Inn 48th) 212/315-6161

F 4 / S 3 / A 5 / $23   MC V D AE

The decor of this "uncommon" second-floor "grill," which is really nothing more than a glorified diner, is "unpretentious" and subdued. Actually, it's little more than a large room with well-spaced tables but a satisfying respite from the neon-fest peep shows a couple of floors below. For a "low-key, Midtown lunch," "this place tries." **Closed: Sunday**

SPEC: *Grilled chicken paillard $11.95; Fettucine w/chicken $12.95*

0	1	2	3	4	5	6	7	8	9	10
disappointing		fair		good		very good		excellent		perfect

BROADWAY JOE   LD   American

(B8) 315 W. 46th St. (8th & 9th) 212/246-6513

F 5 / S 5 / A 4 / $40   MC V D AE DIS

A great place if you love lawn jockey statues and a fairly expensive menu. With "good steaks" but "big prices" the restaurant garnishes overall mixed reviews. And, why go all the way to Broadway just to feel like you're eating on Staten Island?

SPEC: *Stuffed avocado $6.75; Onion soup $6.75; Prime sirloin steak $24.75; Surf & turf $28.75; Chocolate Grand Marnier cake $5.75; Country Epicure Chocolate layer cake $4.75*

Top 10 $0-20

Inexpensive

BROOKLYN DINER   BLD   American

(A9) 212 W. 57th St. (B'way & 7th Ave.) 212/977-1957

F 7 / S 6 / A 7 / $20   MC V D AE   TO/D

One of the newest entries on restaurant theme row, this one, a recreation of a 1950s Brooklyn snack shop, comes complete with Dodger memorabilia and an authentic soda fountain. It also features hot dogs, egg creams and Reuben sandwiches. Check your cholesterol at the door.

SPEC: *Unbread Reuben sandwich $10.75; 15-bite Brooklyn hot dog $9.75; Coney Island cobb salad $11.75*

CABANA CARIOCA   LD   Brazilian

(B9) 123 W. 45th St. (6th & 7th) 212/581-8088

F 6 / S 6 / A 5 / $18   MC V D AE DIS   TO

Don't expect to eat light at this Brazilian/Portuguese restaurant, celebrating its 25th anniversary. "Lumberjack portions," and "dependable, hearty food," await on 3 restaurant levels. The higher you go, the less formal the atmosphere. Those in the know eat on the second level. The "all you can eat" lunch is one of N.Y.'s best bargains. But the a la carte menu with "bargain South American steaks" offers "great value" and better fare.

SPEC: *Clams bulhao pato $5.75; Portuguese sausage $5.95; Rib steak gaucho style $13.95; Feiojada (Brazilian national dish)$10.95; Codfish carioca $9.95*

CAFE BOTANICA   LD   French

(A9) 160 C.P.S. (6th & 7th-Essex House) 212/777-9700

F 7 / S 6 / A 8 / $38   MC V D AE

Tucked away in the lobby of the posh Essex Hotel, this "charming" spot offers a nice selection of food and drink, in a "very pretty," floral, garden setting. The meals are light in terms of preparation, yet incredibly satisfying. The waitstaff is friendly and sincere which makes this not only a "nice lunch place," but also a "good place for business dinner." And yes, it's, "a great place to take your mom."

SPEC: *Sauteed artichoke & wild mushrooms $9; Grilled sea scallops $21.50; Seared tuna loin $21.50; Grilled chicken breast $19.50*

CAFE UN DEUX TROIS   LD   French

(C9) 123 W. 44th St. (B'way & 6th) 212/354-4418 Fax: 840-2169

F 5 / S 5 / A 5 / $28   MC V D AE

"Old reliable, pre-theatre French." Bring your beret and contemplative expression but unfortunately, due to New York's no smoking laws, you'll have to leave the Galouises at home (unless you're willing to light up at the bar). It's "quaint," though sometimes "crowded," "noisy," and a bit "expensive." However, it remains, "convenient for theater," and boasts an "interesting crowd."

SPEC: *Soup a l'oignon gratine $5.50; Pate de campagne $5.75; Steak tartare $14.75; Calf's liver $15.25; Cous cous $19.95*

CARMINE'S — LD — Italian

(C9) 200 W. 44th St. (B'way & 8th) 212/221-3800
See review on page 244.

CARNEGIE DELI — BLD — Deli

(C9) 854 7th Ave. (55th) 212/757-2245

F 6 / S 5 / A 4 / $22 — Cash only — **TO/D**

This New York classic is a lovable zoo, taking you back to a time when it was okay to eat home-cured pastrami and "the best corned beef sandwich in the city." Save your appetite for those other "great" skyscraper sandwiches and the best cheesecake in town. "Expensive," "overrated," and "campy," it might be. Be sure to study the celebrity photos on the walls–and remember: "This is what N.Y. is all about!"

SPEC: *Pickled herring $7.95; Chopped liver $9.45; The Woody Allen (corned beef & pastrami) $12.95; Long John sandwich (gooseneck liverwurst & Bermuda onion w/sliced egg & tomato) $10.45*

CENTURY CAFE — LD — American

(C9) 132 W. 43rd St. (6th and B'way) 212/398-1988

F 7 / S 7 / A 7 / $24 — MC V D AE

An attractive crowd gathers here for business lunches and "good pre-theater" meals. There's "solid, reliable," food at this "consistently good winner." With movie posters and memorabilia of Hollywood scattered throughout, this was a theme restaurant before these kinds of places ever had a chance to become big. **Closed: Sunday**

SPEC: *Crab & fish soup $3.95; Asparagus risotto $6.50; Seared peppered tuna $15.95*

CHARLOTTE — LD — American

(C9) 145 W. 44th St. (6th & B'way) 212/789-7508

F 6 / S 6 / A 6 / $34 — MC V D AE

This spacious, sleek bistro offers innovative cuisine, nicely presented. "Great chef, poor service" is one refrain. But it is a good place for business meetings, or for pre-theater dining, as it has an air of elegance not found in most of the area's other restaurants.

SPEC: *Rock shrimp & white bean soup $7; Caesar salad $8.50; BBQ braised short ribs $19; Grilled salmon $22; Gulf coast snapper $20*

CHEZ NAPOLEON — LD — French

(B8) 365 W. 50th St. (9th Ave.) 212/265-6980

F 6 / S 6 / A 5 / $27 — MC V D AE DIS

Dwarfed by the gleaming Worldwide Plaza, the "classic" and "lovely" Chez Napoleon has endured for almost 40 years under the watchful eye of Marguerite Bruno, who oversees the kitchen. Her daughter, Elayne, runs the restaurant. It's French food the way it ought to be, and still is: "One of the last of a special breed. The truly traditional French bistro." **Closed: Sunday**

SPEC: *Escargots de Bourgogne $5.75; Bouillabaisse $25; Duck a l'orange $15; Rabbit in mustard sauce $14.75; Frog's legs $15*

CHINA GRILL — LD — Asian

(A10) 52 W. 53rd St. (6th -CBS Building) 212/333-7788

F 7 / S 5 / A 6 / $41 — MC V D AE DIS

A favorite hangout for entertainment execs, this "boisterous," "scene restaurant," offers "creative" Asian fusion cuisine. The bar scene "hops," and diners seem to have one eye on their plates and the other on the lookout for celebrities dropping by, perhaps after having "taken" a meeting upstairs at CBS' "Black Rock."

SPEC: *Duck pancakes $12.50; Sizzling whole fish $22; Spice rubbed pork loin $23.50; Grilled garlic shrimp $22.50*

0	1	2	3	4	5	6	7	8	9	10
disappointing		fair		good		very good		excellent		perfect

CHRISTER'S   LD   Scandinavian

(A9) 145 W. 55th St. (6th & 7th) 212/974-7729

F 7 / S 7 / A 7 / $41   **TO**

This upscale restaurant emphasizes seafood with "inventive ideas about fish" and particularly loving attention paid to "very delicious salmon." "Don't go if you dislike salmon," and it's all "very creative." With "nice atmosphere and service,.." the restaurant offers a smattering of veal and chicken dishes to help round out the menu. It's where business executives meet theatrical clientele.

SPEC: *Smorgasbord bar $12.50; Swedish gravlax $10.50; Swordfish $23.50; Rack of N.Z. lamb $27; Sautéed red snapper $24*

CIAO EUROPA   LD   Italian

(A10) 63 W. 54th St. (5th & 6th) 212/247-1200

F 7 / S 7 / A 6 / $35   MC V D AE DIS

This noisy ristorante offers "great service, fine food (and) good value." Tasty pasta dishes are served with a relaxed European ambiance and a sincere, attentive wait staff. Ciao Europa has a solid reputation for offering good food at reasonable prices. "Handy for Carnegie Hall," just don't expect the best of romantically-inclined acoustics.

SPEC: *Basil crepe w/sauteéd radicchio & endive $9.75; Spaghetti with Alaskan Crab meat & tomato $16.75; Risotto of the day P/A*

Cité

CITÉ AND CITÉ GRILL   LD   French

(B9) 120 W. 51st St. (6th & 7th) 212/956-7100

F 6 / S 6 / A 6 / $42   MC V D AE

This French steakhouse with high ceilings and closely aligned tables, has also been called "a wine lover's paradise." Diners applaud the "best filet mignon in the city," and give high marks for having a "swinging bar," that's "filled with beautiful people."

SPEC: *Grilled corn chowder $6.75; Crab cake $10.75; Sliced steak $25.50; Veal chop $25.50; Baby rack of lamb $25.50; Creme brulee rice pudding $7.75*

CORRADO RESTAURANT   LD   Italian

(A10) 1373 6th Ave. (55th & 56th) 212/333-3133

F 7 / S 6 / A 6 / $35   MC V D AE   **TO/D**

Northern Italian, "robust" fare is served at this "friendly," midtown trattoria. The "food's delicious but the din at lunch is deafening." It's sophisticated, "worth the money," and a popular midtown business gathering spot. There's a bit of an outdoor feel and ample portions of pasta are served at very palatable prices. Don't miss the snappy take-out alternative–Corrado Kitchen, next door.

SPEC: *Tuna tartare $9.50; Veal oscheritana $7.95; Seared sea scallops $19.50; Herbed chicken paillard $17.50;Grilled salmon $19.95*

DA VALENTINO · BLD · Italian

(A9) 1701 Broadway (54th)   212/765-3160

F 6 / S 5 / A 3 / $17   MC V AE   **TO/D**

A hop, skip and a jump away from the Ed Sullivan Theater, this nondescript Italian spot resembles any other in Manhattan. But on closer inspection, diners may notice this is the place David Letterman makes the subjects of jokes and snacks on his late-night show. (The near life-size wooden image of Dave outside the door is a dead giveaway.) The prices are reasonable and diners can always hope to be caught by one of the roving Letterman-cams.

SPEC: *Stuffed mushrooms $5; Pizza all aglio $7; Grilled chicken breast $8.50; Strawberry shortcake $3.25*

DARBAR · LD · Indian

(A10) 44 W. 54th St. (5th & 6th)   212/432-7227

F 7 / S 7 / A 7 / $35   MC V D AE

A find among the city's wealth of "good" Indian restaurants. Fine food and excellent service amid a lavish setting of orange fabric covered walls and tapestries. The majority of the entrees are northern Indian and some spiced "hot beyond belief." The two-level bistro features a bar downstairs decorated with elaborate hammered-copper hangings. The main dining room features these same brass decorations, as well as beautiful hanging tapestries.

SPEC: *Mulligatawny $5.95; Vegetable pakoras $8.95; Shahi lamb chops $23.95; Fish darbari (red snapper) $23.95*

DISH OF SALT · LD · Chinese

(B9) 133 W. 47th St. (6th & 7th)   212/921-4242

F 7 / S 7 / A 7 / $31   MC V D AE

The decor of this upscale "very Cantonese" restaurant is a bit cold and modern. But a business lunch or quiet meal among intimate theater-going couples would be an impressionable experience. The dishes from the region are tastily accentuated with garlic, ginger, honey and fruit flavors. Even the fortune cookies are interestingly "chocolate-laced." **Closed: Sunday**

SPEC: *Beef sate $6.25; Scallops stuffed w/shrimp $6.75; Fillet of sole $22; Marinated steak $17.50; Roast plum duckling $19.50*

EAST · LD · Japanese

(A9) 251 W. 55th St. (B'way & 8th Ave.)   212/581-2240

See review on page 105.

ELLEN'S STARDUST DINER · BLD · American

(B9) 1650 Broadway (51st)   212/956-5151
(A10) 1377 6th Ave. (56th)   212/307-7575   Fax: 489-5656

F 5 / S 5 / A 7 / $19   MC V D AE DIS   **TO/D**

Sha-boom! Sha-boom! Pull up a stool and sit down at this "hip" and "nostalgic" American Graffiti-type theme diner, where American grub is served on glistening formica. Former Miss New York Subways are pin-ups from the past, including founder-owner Ellen Hart. It's all "very entertaining" and a hoot for parties, special events, or just a "good lunch." And while you eat, Doo-woppers will serenade you (like it or not).

SPEC: *Ethyl's potato skins $4.50; Fred Mertz-arella sticks $4.50; Burgers $6-$8.25; Cowboy steak $11.95; Chubby Checker sundae $4.25; Brownie mudslide sundae $3.95*

0	1	2	3	4	5	6	7	8	9	10
disappointing	fair			good		very good		excellent		perfect

Ellen's Stardust Diner

FANTINO   D   Italian

(A9) 112 W. 59th St.   (6th & 7th–Ritz Carlton Hotel)   212/664-7700

F 7 / S 7 / A 8 / $42   MC V D AE DIS

Entering this Italian palace is like stepping into the Marchesa's salon for tea. Venetian charm with Versace touches offers "first rate," "gracious Italian dining." Fantino means jockey and Norman, the bar man, holds forth for a decidedly upscale clientele. The food is "magnifico." The service discreet. And the ambiance is, they say, "simply superb." **Closed: Sunday**

SPEC: *Smoked sea bass & eggplant $13; Monkfish $23; Braised Long Island duck $24; Grilled Angus beef filet $29*

FASHION CAFE   LD   American

(B10) 51 Rockefeller Plaza   (5th & 6th)   212/765-3131

F 5 / S 5 / A 5 / $25   MC V D AE

Just what New York City needed: another "copy-cat," theme restaurant. Frankly, this one baffles us. The menu is packed with all kinds of treats we know no self-respecting model would dare approach. The music is loud and the place designed like a fashion show: flashing lights and all. But if you think you're going to find Naomi, Elle, or Claudia dining, well, good luck. More likely, they're down in Soho.

SPEC: *Fashion burger $7.95; Grilled ahi $11.95; Claudia's N.Y. strip $15.95; Naomi's fish & chips $9.95; Fashion tarte $5.95*

FILM CENTER CAFE   LD   American

(C8) 635 9th Ave.   (44th & 45th)   212/262-2525

F 5 / S 5 / A 5 / $21   AE V MC   **TO**

Wanna be in pictures? Well, you might want to hang out at the Film Center Cafe. It's a hip precursor to Planet Hollywood, second-rate movie memorabilia (mostly posters) and all. The crowd is "casual" but interesting and the service friendly and personal. "Good for lunch," great after theatre." The food is better than the newer "real theme" restaurants ... and a lot less pretentious.

SPEC: *Fried calamari $4.95; Grilled chicken salad $8.95; Meatloaf $10.95; Philly cheesesteak $8.95; Cajun chicken $11.95*

44/ROYALTON HOTEL   LD   American

(C10) 44 W. 43rd St.   (5th & 6th)   212/944-8844

F 7 / S 7 / A 8 / $44   MC V AE D

This "very sexy design," post-modern dining experience is where editors schmooze on white couches as Robert Palmer video waitrons sachet down the sleek long hall in little black outfits. But snacking with the paparazzi isn't cheap. Lobby tidbits, like an organic turkey sandwich, run $16. And most entrees are $25 before you tack on $7 for sides like sautéed spinach or yellow potato puree. But the view, and the room, are worth it.

SPEC: *Mackerel $9; Terrine of pheasant & goose liver $15; Ahi tuna $26; Veal chop $28; Caramelized lemon tart $8.75*

FRANKIE & JOHNNIE'S   LD   American

(B9) 269 W. 45th St. (7th & 8th) 212/997-9494

F 8 / S 8 / A 7 / $41   MC V D AE   **TO**

A bit "dated, and very proud to be so," and slightly "over-rated," this West Side steakhouse offers traditional fare, "great pizza," and "the best steak in the theatre district." The ceilings are low, the tables crammed together and the wait staff unfortunately inflexible. It's good "before theater" dining with sizable portions, but the prices, like the feel, can be a little stiff.

SPEC: Chopped chicken livers $3.95; Sirloin steak $24.95; Double loin lamb chops $24.95; Surf & turf $29.50; Marble cheesecake $5

GALLAGHER'S STEAK HOUSE   LD   American

(B9) 228 W. 52nd St. (B'way & 8th) 212/245-5336

F 7 / S 6 / A 6 / $44   MC V D AE DIS

The "granddaddy" of NY steakhouses serves hefty portions of good, old-fashioned red meat. A "real man's restaurant," the room is huge, with brass railings, an enormous bar, checked tablecloths and pictures of sports figures adorning the walls. The only thing missing is sawdust. "The steaks are terrific!"

SPEC: Dungeness crabmeat cocktail $10.75; Sirloin steak $29.75; Filet mignon steak $28.75; Chocolate mousse cake $5.50

HALCYON   LD   American

(A9) 151 W. 54th St. (6th & 7th-Rihga Hotel) 212/468-8888

F 7 / S 7 / A 7 / $38   MC V D AE

This "steady," "quiet place," offers an eclectic selection of foods, beautifully presented in a lavish space. The main room is high ceilinged and bedecked with fresh flowers and white sculptures. The waiters are attentive, accommodating and serve tastily garnished meals that can be specially prepared to meet diners' needs. With a "great buffet," the restaurant receives acclaim as being "always wonderful," and "one of the better hotel eateries."

SPEC: Lobster bisque $7.50; Tuna carpacccio $9.50; Roasted sea scallops $23; Vegetable bateau $21.50; Pepper roasted salmon $21.50

HAMBURGER HARRY'S   LD   American

(B9) 145 W. 45th St. (6th & B'way) 212/840-0566 Fax: 302-5126

F 5 / S 5 / A 5 / $15   MC V AE   **TO/D**

If you "really want a burger and fries adult style," this is the place to go. It's "quick and inexpensive," and it attracts a big business lunch crowd as well as touristy types. "Excellent," for the family "before matinee." The prices are also significantly palatable. But don't expect much more from this, what-you-see-is-what-you-get, down home, "hamburger joint." **Closed: Sunday**

SPEC: Burgers $6.50 Fajitas $9.95; BBQ Chicken breast $10.95; Chocolate forever (Mississippi Mud Cake) $3.95; Key lime pie $3.95

HARD ROCK CAFE   LD   American

(A9) 221 W. 57th St. (B'way & 7th) 212/459-9320

F 3 / S 5 / A 4 / $25   MC V D AE DIS

Save your money and buy your T-shirt from a street vendor; and save your time by avoiding the long lines: your ears and stomach will thank you. This "grandfather of theme restaurants," is "bad, bad and oh yes, bad," "too loud," "overrated," and "best left to the tourists." If you really want to see some cool Rock 'N Roll memorabilia, go to the Hall of Fame in Cleveland.

0	1	2	3	4	5	6	7	8	9	10
disappointing		fair		good		very good		excellent		perfect

HARLEY DAVIDSON CAFE   LD   American

(A10) 1370 6th Ave. (56th) 212/245- 60-00

F 5 / S 5 / A 6 / $22   MC V D AE

For pseudo-biker types, babes, and bona fide theme restaurant enthusiasts, this is "where it's at!" "Hearty" portions of "decent" roadhouse grub, coupled with "cool" Harley memorabilia puts you in HOG heaven and makes for "fun!" "High cholesterol" food, like Elvis, is still alive and so is a "best meatloaf" and other familiar, "O.K. food" choices. But come prepared: It's "loud," "touristy," and some ask "Where are the real bikers?"

SPEC: *Roadhouse chicken wings $6.50; Pot stickers $4.95; Homestyle meatloaf $9.75; Grilled hamburger $7.50; Tank full of sundae $7.95; Reeses chocolate peanut butter pie $5.95*

HOULIHAN'S   LD   Amer/Continental

(B9) 729 7th Ave. (49th) 212/626-7312

See review on page 230.

HOURGLASS TAVERN   LD   American

(B8) 373 W. 46th St. (8th & 9th) 212/265- 2060

F 6 / S 6 / A 6 / $15   Cash only

This "tiny," wood-paneled restaurant, wedged into a crowded block on Restaurant Row, serves simple, prix-fixe menus . "Here's a way to enjoy a $35 dinner for only $15. And good!" Never mind that you can look directly into the kitchen from most tables–the effect is "warm" and intimate. And if the hourglass on each table runs out, you know it's time to leave.

SPEC: *Pre-fixe dinners $12.75: Pan fried blacked Atlantic coast redfish; Grilled summer vegetables w/chipolte vinaigrette; Penne w/hot sausage, chicken & spinach*

Hurley's

HURLEY'S   LD   Continental

(B10) 1240 6th Ave. (49th) 212/765-8981 Fax: 956-3469

F 5 / S 4 / A 5 / $26   MC V D AE   **TO**

When Rockefeller was ready to build his center, Hurley wouldn't sell, and the famous attraction was redesigned to be built around his small pub. Hurley's has served fine meals and spirits since 1892, and stands as a tribute to the little man. Daylight brings suits in abundance; nighttime empties the neighborhood and turns Hurley's into an eclectic after hours spot, for journalists, politicians, musicians and off-duty restaurant folk. Rumor has it that Henry Kissinger was once tossed out of here for being too rowdy. Do we dare believe it?

SPEC: *Crisp Long Island duck w/fruit sauce & pineapple fritter $15.75; Hot poached salmon steak, w/dill hollandaise $19.75*

IPANEMA RESTAURANT   LD   **Brazilian**

(B10) 13 W. 46th St. (5th & 6th) 212/730-5848

F 7 / S 6 / A 5 / $30   MC V D AE DIS

Caramba! (Wow!) Esta picante! (This is hot!) Well, it's the self-application of home grown pimenta malaqueta, crushed, fiery, Brazilian peppers. Entrees are also robust and strikingly authentic. And if Jorge is your waiter, he might proudly reveal their multicultural history (but you have to ask). Desserts, like the super rich quindao, are deliciously homemade. Even the 3-dimensional "taiha" (woodcuts) on the walls are Portuguese inspired, and genuine.
SPEC: *Feijouda (black bean stew) $17; Zapata (fish & shrimp) $17*

JEAN LAFITTE   LD   **French**

(A10) 68 W. 58th St. (6th Ave.) 212/751-2323

F 7 / S 7 / A 8 / $36   MC V D AE

They celebrate Bastille Day at this tres francaise, very left bankish spot in the heart of N.Y.'s midtown fashion hub. Yes, it's "just like being in France." And, don't be surprised to spot famous faces from stage and screen, as well as some important publishing people, who frequent this "homage" to classic French cuisine and style.
SPEC: *Cold oysters $9.95; Seafood jambalaya $8.50; Grilled catfish, Cajun style $18.25; Duck w/paprika sauce $19.25*

JEKYLL & HYDE CLUB   LD   **American**

(A10) 1409 6th Ave. (57th & 58th) 212/541-9517

F 5 / S 6 / A 7 / $23   AE

This interactive "social club for eccentric explorers and mad scientists" has five floors, its own "entertaining" fictional history, and is "great for adolescent thrills." Watch for leering portraits and many other bizarre and wonderful oddities. It's "goofy," "corny," good for "lots of laughs," "fun for parties," "great for birthdays," and "great to bring out-of-towners." Does anybody actually eat here?
SPEC: *Dr. Jekyll pizza $7.95; New York steak sandwich $8.95; BBQ chicken & rib combo $12.95*

JEZEBEL   D   **Southern**

(B8) 630 9th Ave. (45th) 212/582-1045

F 8 / S 8 / A 9 / $38   AE

The feeling of sinful New Orleans begins when you realize how hard-to-find this restaurant really is. Tucked away behind a subtle door with drawn curtains it rests on an obsequious theater district corner. Inside, the "romantic," flowers-in-the-attic, Victorian decor is as overwhelming as the "delicious," and rich "Southern food" offerings. True southerners may never have eaten grits with dinner. But it's "fun," has "good food," and there's "theatre dining at a reasonable price." **Closed: Sunday**
SPEC: *Pork chops w/grits & okra $21.75; Shrimp creole $23.75; Salmon w/black-eyed peas & macaroni & cheese $23.75*

JIMMY ARMSTRONG'S SALOON   LD   **Amer/Cont'l**

(A8) 875 10th Ave. (57th) 212/581-0606

F 7 / S 6 / A 4 / $19   MC V D AE   **TO/D**

Yes, this is the same Armstrong's frequented by Matt Scudder, the fictional P.I. in the popular mystery series written by Lawrence Block...before he gave up drinking. The menu is incredibly eclectic–from Caribbean specialties, to burgers. Armstrong's draws a loyal crowd: a mix of CBS employees, local residents, and tourists. Well worth the trip west.
SPEC: *Chorizo appetizer $4.50; Burritos $6; Peruvian ceviche $10; Marinated pork chops $11; Arroz con pollo $8.50*

0	1	2	3	4	5	6	7	8	9	10
disappointing		fair		good		very good		excellent		perfect

JIMMY'S NEUTRAL CORNER   LD   American

(C9) 125 W. 43rd St. (6th & B'way) 212/764-2366

F 6 / S 8 / A 7 / $21   MC V D AE   **TO**

Former corner man, Jimmy Glenn, has recreated an old-time "tough-guys" joint minus the cigar smoke and with the welcome addition of solid, diverse entrees. On any given night you're likely to rub shoulders with fight fans and sports personalities. **Closed: Sunday**

SPEC: *Pan seared soy & ginger tuna steak $13.95; Meatloaf w/mashed potatoes $8.95; Double chocolate layer cake $3.50; Strawberry shortcake $4.50*

Judson Grill

Top 10 $36-55

Expensive

JUDSON GRILL   LD   Amer/Continental

(B9) 152 W. 52nd St. (6th & 7th) 212/582-5252

F 8 / S 8 / A 8 / $39   MC V AE

The decor is sophisticated and classy, as is the menu, which features imaginative entrees, impeccably prepared. Separate bar area, which hops at night, and a balcony where you can look down on some of New York's best: especially notables from the publishing and entertainment industry. And be nice to your waiter – he might just turn out to be the next William Goldman!

SPEC: *BBQ quail salad $10; Seared venison flank steak $24; Provencale roasted tuna loin $24; Hot fudge dim sum for 2 $10.50; Toasted pistachio-butterscotch semifreddo dome $8*

JULIAN'S   LD   Mediterranean

(A8) 802 9th Ave. (53rd & 54th) 212/262-4800

F 6 / S 6 / A 7 / $22   MC V D AE   **TO/D**

A lovely, "amazingly Mediterranean" addition to the ethnic "Hell's Kitchen" restaurant scene. Outdoor dining in the alley garden is especially charming. Esthetically, a standout, in an area usually associated with less than attractive ambiance.

SPEC: *Fried mixed fish Vesuvio $6.50; Penne w/ smoked salmon $9.50; Tuna with white beans $14.95; Grilled calamari $12.95*

KOYOTE KATES   LD   Southwestern

(B8) 307 W. 47th St. (8th & 9th) 212/956-1091

F 6 / S 5 / A 4 / $26   MC V D AE   **TO**

If you like Western flavor with a Blues twist, this is definitely your haven. With its wood floors, long dark wood bar and high ceilings, there's a distinct saloon feeling. Surprisingly enough, the menu features an interesting blend of both grease and health, with sweet potato fries that are awesome. There's a boisterous bar scene which makes it a fun place to hang out for a drink or quick bite, and the perfect place for a party.

SPEC: *Tortilla tenders $5.95; Herb lime chicken $14.95; Cattleman steak $16.95; Sizzling fajitas $12.95-$14.95*

LA BONNE SOUP LD French

(A9) 48 W. 55th St. (5th & 6th) 212/586-7650

F 6 / S 6 / A 7 / $19 MC V AE

An informal "French bistro" that serves up "reliable," hearty country dishes including "the onion soup that made Les Halles famous." Opened in 1973, "after all these years, it's still a classic!" The Red gingham wallpaper and matching tablecloths would be too much anywhere else, but here they're quaint. "Excellent" for post-work, pre-theatre and most definitely a less expensive "shopping lunch."
SPEC: *Soupe Paysanne a l'Orge $10.95; Creme Andalouse $10.95; Quiche Lorraine $7.95; Croque Monsier $7.95; Les escargots de Bougogne $7.75; Creme caramel $3.75; Mousse au chocolat $3.75*

LA CARAVELLE LD French

(A10) 33 W. 55th St. (5th & 6th) 212/586-4252

F 8 / S 8 / A 8 / $60 MC V D AE

Top 10 $56+

Very Expensive

This 33-year old "very steady," "classic" staple of the NY dining scene has "kept up with the times" and continues to produce lavish meals amid a "delightful setting." The menu features French food with Japanese influences as well as "wonderful technique," and "attentive," traditional tableside service. The wine list is extensive.
SPEC: *7 Course tasting menu $75; Marinated fluke, crabmeat +$6.50; Grilled salmon; truffeled pike; roast chicken, crispy duck, rabbit stew; carpaccio of angus beef*

LA RESERVE LD French

(B10) 41 W. 49th St. (5th & 6th) 212/247-2993

F 7 / S 7 / A 7 / $58 MC V AE

There are few experiences as "excellent" in New York dining as a "gracious," meal at La Reserve. "Always dependable and good," the food, service and decor complement each other perfectly. Delicate murals adorn the walls and a "formal" dining room buzzes with an army of tuxedoed waiters and servers attempting to anticipate every need. With a nice selection of delicate poultry and meats, the seafood is still among the best prepared in the city.
SPEC: *Prix-fixe dinner $51; Duck foie gras , Smoked duck breast salad; Poached Dover sole; Red snapper; Salmon steak; Veal medallion; Rack of lamb +$10; Hot souffles +$7*

LA VERANDA LD Italian

(B9) 185 W. 47th St. (6th & 7th) 212/391-0905

F 7 / S 7 / A 6 / $28 MC V D AE

La Veranda has been around for more than two decades, yet has failed to make a name for itself among the other long time city establishments. The menu features traditional Italian cuisine, without innovative flair. Since it has longevity, there must be something special about it, yet for the life of us, the reason remains a mystery.
SPEC: *Baked clams $7.95; Linguine portobello $13.95; Scampi parmigiana $19.95; Scaloppine Biffi Scala $14.95*

LANDMARK TAVERN LD Irish-American

(B7) 626 11th Ave. (46th) 212/757-8595

F 7 / S 7 / A 8 / $27 MC V D AE DIS

Formerly on the waterfront, this 1868 "classic New York pub" is brimming with history, antiques (like a working pot-bellied stove) and a couple of friendly ghosts. It's off the beaten path but convenient to the Javits Center. "Excellent on a cold night," and "a great place for a rainy Sunday," it can be worth the trip crosstown for its colorful past and friendly service.
SPEC: *Grilled English bangers $6.50; Duck & cherry pate $5.50; Shepherd's pie $10.50; Corned beef & cabbage $14.50*

0	1	2	3	4	5	6	7	8	9	10
disappointing		fair		good		very good		excellent		perfect

LANGAN'S   LD   American

(B9) 150 W. 47th St. (6th & 7th) 212/869-5482

F 4 / S 5 / A 5 / $30   V D AE

A theater district pub offering a good prix fixe dinner for $17.95, and a theater brunch for $12.95. There's a variety of seafood and pasta dishes. The bar in front is usually crowded, but the dining room in back is less hectic.

SPEC: *Shredded Long Island duck $8.95; Maryland crab cakes $21.95; Garlic crusted tuna over ratatouille $20.95*

Lattanzi Ristorante

LATTANZI RISTORANTE   LD   Italian

(B8) 361 W. 46th St. (8th & 9th) 212/315-0980

F 7 / S 7 / A 7 / $42   AE

A "red brick," and "comfortably upscale" Lattanzi offers a fine selection of family-style Italian fare. Unlike many of its counter-parts, they feature a complete Jewish-style menu, available both at lunch and after 8 pm for dinner. The dining room is "charming" and has an intimate feel with cloth-draped hanging lamps and decorous paintings of ancient Pompeii.

SPEC: *Dry beef w/marinated zucchini $11.95; Veal scaloppine w/arti-chokes $18.95; Red snapper $21.95; Tiramisu $6.95*

LE BAR BAT   LD   American

(A8) 311 W. 57th St. (8th & 9th) 212/307-7228

F 6 / S 5 / A 6 / $32   MC V D AE DIS

This former recording studio and church manages to combine ele-ments of both to create a "fun" and "unusual" multi-level experi-ence. With gold and platinum albums decorating the walls, be prepared for "very dim" and "dark" spaces with "lot's going on." There's live music, a dance club downstairs and nostalgia, too: This is where Barbra Streisand recorded the "Guilty" album with Barry Gibb. **Closed: Sunday**

SPEC: *Dungeness crabmeat quesadilla $9; Swordfish $19; Black pep-per & chili crusted leg of lamb $17; Peanut brittle brownie parfait $6*

Top 10 $56+

Very Expensive

LE BERNARDIN   LD   French

(B9) 155 W. 51st St. (6th & 7th) 212/489-1515

F 8 / S 8 / A 8 / $68   MC V D AE

Despite a new head chef and a new pastry chef, both within the past 2 years, the "splendid," "very ritzy" Le Bernardin has maintained its "top notch" reputation and comes close to being: "the most profes-sional restaurant in America." The dining room soars to teak ceiling heights with gray-blue walls and oversized oil paintings depicting fishermen at sea. With "Perfect, imaginative seafood," and "snob-bish good food," it is "without qualification," "one of the best."

SPEC: *Prix fixe lunch $42; Loin of mackerel; Roast bay lobster tail on asparagus & crepe risotto + $10; Crusted cod; Roast skate; Black bass; Atlantic salmon; Red snapper.*

LE MADELEINE   LD   French

(C8) 403 W. 43rd St. (9th Ave.) 212/246-2993 Fax: 586-7631

F 7 / S 7 / A 7 / $27   MC V AE DIS   **TO**

Come here for the "charming" enclosed garden room, dimly lit, with a skylight, for an intimate experience. Le Madeleine, named perhaps for the cookie that made Proust trip on memory for five straight books, is not as intense as the name suggests. It's a "good" theater district restaurant with "solid bistro" food that emphasizes grilled fish dishes. The staff is friendly, professional, and the atmosphere is warm. A classical guitarist accompanies Sunday night dinner.

SPEC: *Pistou (French vegetable soup w/garlic & basil) $5.50; Pate maison $7; Sautéed grouper $15; Duck a l'orange $17; Creme brulee $5; Tarte Tatin $5.50*

LE QUERCY   LD   French

(A10) 52 W. 55th St. (5th & 6th) 212/265-8141

F 7 / S 7 / A 6 / $24   MC V D AE DIS

In the same spot since 1977, "old reliable," Le Quercy is easy to miss in the midst of midtown's crush. Step inside and find "a nice surprise:" "Cozy," and "pleasant," this unpretentious bistro serves "very French" fare without classic French fare prices. Exposed brick walls flanking a narrowed space still can't detract from the homey, comfortable and casual atmosphere. **Closed: Sunday**

SPEC: *Chilled leeks vinaigrette $4.25; Gravlax de saumon a L'Aneth $6.25; Hangar steak w/pommes frites $15; Roast monkfish $14 ; Peach melba $4.50*

LE RIVAGE   D   French

(B8) 340 W. 46th St. (8th & 9th) 212/765-7374

F 6 / S 6 / A 6 / $35   MC V D AE

This staple of the midtown dining scene provides huge portions of traditional French food with a bit of a nouvelle flair. The main dining room has a warm and cozy atmosphere, perfect for either a romantic evening, "before theatre" meal, or a business dinner.

LES CÉLÉBRITÉS   D   French

Top 10 $56+

(A9) 155 W. 58th St. (6th & 7th-Essex House) 212/484-5113

F 8 / S 8 / A 9 / $75   MC V

Very Expensive

Newly renovated and located in the lobby of the posh Essex House, Les Célébrités is "regal in service and decor." The intimate restaurant has only 14 tables set apart by columns in a lavish dining room. Ceiling moldings, crescent-shaped banquettes and dark mahogany walls are accented by rich red carpets. Paintings by show biz celebs like Phyllis Diller, Gene Hackman and James Dean complement the decor. And Chef Delouvrier creates "outstanding" culinary delights from a blend of both Eastern and Western cuisines.

SPEC: *Raw tuna tart $18; Lobster w/asparagus & snow peas $42; Rack of lamb $33; Red snapper $32; Hot apple gratin $12*

LES SANS CULOTTES SPORTS   LD   French

(B8) 329 W. 51st St. (8th & 9th) 212/581-1283 Fax: 581-1283

F 5 / S 6 / A 5 / $25   MC V D AE

A French sports bar? Yes, that seems to be the peculiar anomaly here, where soccer trophies stand side by side with cuisine Francaise in a casual bistro. This ever-popular theater district spot is festooned with the tricolors of the French flag. "Convivial" and decidedly non-stuffy.

SPEC: *Escargots $6; Veal picatta $11.95; Minute steak w/shallots $15.95; Surprise du Sans Culottes $5*

0	1	2	3	4	5	6	7	8	9	10
disappointing		fair		good		very good		excellent		perfect

LOTFI'S MOROCCAN RESTAURANT LD Moroccan

(B8) 358 W. 46th St. (8th & 9th) 212/582-5850

F 7 / S 7 / A 7 / $28 MC V AE DIS **TO**

A father and son establishment born in Brooklyn Heights has taken its star cuisine all the way to a delicious Broadway run. The Moroccan decor, with pretty dishes gracing the walls, offers the perfect setting to enjoy the "highly authentic" North African cuisine. "As good as Moroccan gets in New York." **Closed: Monday**

SPEC: *Breewhats $2.75; Couscous $12.95-$14.95; Lamb, chicken or kefta kabab $12.95; Almond snake $2.75; Cornes de gazelle $2.75*

LUCKY'S BAR & GRILL LD American

(A10) 60 W. 57th St. (6th Ave.) 212/582-4004

F 6 / S 7 / A 6 / $30 MC V D AE

We doubt there's really a "Lucky," but that doesn't detract from this mid-town, all American bistro. With light and airy checkerboard tablecloths, the menu also beckons with subtle dishes for the more health conscious. Apart from the civilized menu, there's also a sophisticated "adult" bar scene – a nice departure from the neighboring "theme park city" establishments.

SPEC: *Goat cheese bruschetta $7.95; Pan roasted osso bucco of monkfish $16.95; Warm fusilli pasta salad $13.95*

Manhattan Ocean Club

MANHATTAN OCEAN CLUB LD Seafood

(A10) 57 W. 58th St. (5th & 6th) 212/371-7777

F 7 / S 7 / A 7 / $47 MC V D AE

Having won nearly every award in the culinary world, this is regarded as one of the city's finest "smart dining" seafood establishments. "Expensive, but good," it's worth the treat to sample "good seafood," and "good service," complete with a handsome wine selection. "Great for entertaining," this two-level restaurant features fish so fresh it tastes like it just leaped out of the water. There's also a large but pleasant downstairs bar, perfect for a casual drink.

SPEC: *Fish soup $6.75; Lobster salad $13.50; Salmon w/shitake mushrooms $26.75; Swordfish $29.75*

MARKET DINER, THE BLD Diner

(C7) 572 11th Ave. (43rd) 212/695-0415

F 6 / S 6 / A 5 / $16 MC V D AE **TO/D**

Come marvel at the Star Trekkian lighting, or the booth-backs shaped like pianos and the "good simple food." This 30-year old former drive-in is on a block somewhere between a Harley dealership and a desolate stretch of "Hell's Kitchen." But the jello is jiggling, breakfast pastries sit freshly plastic wrapped and the 24-hour menu offers the standard all-day breakfast, grilled and cold sandwiches and other Mom food.

SPEC: *Mozzarella sticks $4.95; Chili jackets $5.75; Philly steak sandwich $6.25; Fried clams $6.25; Cheesecake $2.25; Banana split $4.75*

MICHAEL'S — BLD — American

(A10) 24 W. 55th St. 212/767-0555

F 8 / S 7 / A 7 / $40   MC V D AE

A business man's paradise. Tables in this "elegant" restaurant, are spaced wide apart, making for quiet, private conversation. Art on the walls, including works by David Hockney, adds nicely to the overall sense that you're dining somewhere special. The cuisine is California inspired, and there's a glass-enclosed garden room. And, for those voyeurs among us, there are always plenty of celebrities to gawk at.

SPEC: *Pre-theater dinner 5:30-6:30pm $29.50*

MICKEY MANTLE'S — LD — American

(A10) 42 Central Park South (5th & 6th) 212/688-7777

F 5 / S 6 / A 6 / $27   MC V AE D DIS

Now that the beloved Mick's gone, you can still bathe in the warmth of his memory while you munch on his favorites, like hickory smoked baby back ribs and chicken fried steak. This is an all-purpose upscale sports bar with the usual plethora of TVs, a sports art gallery (lithographs are for sale), and a representative number of sports figures who hangout here. It won't be the same without old #7, but heroic memories really do live on.

SPEC: *Southern fried chicken fingers $7.50; Chicken pot pie $12.95; Chicken fried steak $16.95; Chocolate chunk rice pudding $4.95*

MIKE'S BAR & GRILL — LD — American

(B8) 650 10th Ave. (45th & 46th) 212/246-4115

F 6 / S 6 / A 7 / $19   AE   **TO/D**

Service attitude is somewhat over-the-top, as is the decor, but this pre-theater spot is known for dishing out large portions of American eclectic dishes and for changing its sets quarterly. Music industry types have been known to frequent this "great funky atmosphere," "solid good" place for pork chops, lamb sausages and fajitas. Mary Tyler Moore themes have been attempted and even a jungle safari theme complete with monkeys, nets and bananas, swung slightly below the ceiling.

SPEC: *Vegetable taco $5.75; Seafood cakes $7.25; Penne w/chicken $11.25; Pork chops $13.75; Panfried catfish $13.25*

MOTOWN CAFE, THE — LD — American

(A10) 104 W. 57th St. (6th & 7th) 212/581-8030

– / – / – /

Yet another, and certainly not the last, theme restaurant to open in the 57th street area. From the name and the statues of Motown greats like Marvin Gaye, Martha Reeves and a young Michael Jackson that greet you, you'll get the idea.

MUNSON DINER, THE — BLD — Diner

(B7) 600 W. 49th St. (11th Ave.) 212/246-0964

F 5 / S 5 / A 4 / $9   Cash only   **TO/D**

Truckers, cabbies and auto mechanics patronize the Munson's short, 24-hour menu.. The fading neon sign, pulsing into the night, is evidence that not much has changed since the place opened in 1908. The blue wall paneling, orange counter and table tops, and red seating create the genuine shoddy effect that trendier '90s diners attempt. HBO likes to shoot here, and you can see why.

SPEC: *Roast prime beef $6; Virginia ham $6; Meat loaf $6; Apple pie $1.50*

0	1	2	3	4	5	6	7	8	9	10
disappointing		fair		good		very good		excellent		perfect

NEW WORLD GRILL   LD   American

(B8) 329 W. 49th St. (8th & 9th) 212/957-4745 Fax: 957-4758

F 5 / S 5 / A 4 / $22   MC V D AE DIS

Robin Leach and John F. Kennedy, Jr., are a couple of the celebrities known to drop in for a quick bite. Located in the midst of the sprawling World-Wide Plaza (home of the two-buck flick), the interior of this cafe is "nothing special." But it does have a great view of the fountain and statue of the plaza and, surrounded by windows, you'll have the perfect vantage point to do some "serious people watching."

SPEC: *Chicken quesadilla $6.75; Grilled salmon $14*

NIRVANA   LD   Indian

(A10) 30 Central Park South (5th & 6th) 212/486-5700

F 6 / S 7 / A 8 / $32   MC V D AE

"You can't reach for more with less," as you take this "nice detour to India" and enjoy the spectacular panorama afforded by a roof-top restaurant at the foot of Central Park. The interior is familiarly New York-style Indian and the food is traditional but the result is surprisingly good. The wait staff is huge–at times there are too many waiters at the table. But you "can't beat the view," so, bring along your sojourners and be prepared to enjoy the stay.

SPEC: *Vegetable samosa $4.95; Beef saagwala $17.95; Chicken masala $16.95; Tandoori platter $21.95*

OLLIE'S NOODLE SHOP & GRILLE   LD   Chinese

(C9) 200 W. 44th St. (B'way) 212/921-5988

See review on page 236.

ORSO   LD   Italian

(B9) 322 W. 46th St. (8th & 9th) 212/489-7212

F 7 / S 7 / A 7 / $26   MC V   **TO**

A favorite of the literary and theater set, especially those who work at the New York Times. "Always satisfactory and fun," "always reliable with lots of celebrities, there's "great star gazing," at this "excellent restaurant row choice." The menu is bilingual–Italian and English, and the wine list is extensive. You'll find "good Italian," food, an "informal light menu before theatre," and all at a moderate price.

SPEC: *Pizza con olio e rosmarino $6; Carpaccio con crescione e parmigiano $8; Grilled tuna w/orzo pasta salad & mint butter $21; Strawberry gelato $4.50; Chocolate granita $4.50*

PALIO   LD   Italian

(B9) 151 W. 51st St (6th & 7th) 212/245-4850

F 7 / S 7 / A 8 / $44   MC V D AE

The name comes from an old horse race held in Siena, Italy and the theme is reiterated throughout. The ground level bar is adorned with a wraparound mural depicting the event. "Superb cuisine in an elegant setting," is served in the "pretty" second-floor dining space. There are high coffered ceilings, walls covered with flags from the Palio competition, ornate woodwork and large sunflower bouquets to add life. With both tasting menus and a la carte selections. **Closed: Sunday**

SPEC: *Polenta courton w/wild mushroom ragout $15; Baked lobster $23; Filet of rabbit $29.50; Orange creme brulee tart $10*

PATSY'S   LD   Italian

(A9) 236 W. 56th St. (B'way & 8th) 212/247-3491

F 2 / S 1 / A 2 / $40   MC V D AE

This Neapolitan Italian offers little more than large, hearty portions. Patsy's has been around a long time and maybe that's the problem. Service is slow and the wait staff not overly friendly. Mystifying enough, it's a popular place for old-time New Yorkers. Still considered a see-and-be-seen place, it's good for people watching, just don't expect a 4-star meal.

SPEC: *Minestrone Milanese $4.75; Chicken cardinal $16.75; Beef scallopine marsala $24.75; Ricotta cheesecake $4.50*

PERUVIAN RESTAURANT   BLD   Latin

(B8) 688 10th Ave. (48th & 49th) 212/581-5814

F 5 / S 5 / A 5 / $18   Cash only   TO/D

As one of the few Peruvian restaurants in the city, this one is a hotspot for South American immigrants seeking genuine cuisine of their homeland. They are not disappointed. The varied menu offers many traditional South American delights. The dining room is small and narrow, but the food is what counts here.

SPEC: *Ceviche $9.50; Bistec encebollado (steak Peruvian style) $8.50; Pescado a lo macho (fried white fish w/shrimps, squid & octopus) $11*

PETROSSIAN   LD   Russian

(A9) 182 W. 58th St. (7th Ave.) 212/245-2214

F 8 / S 7 / A 8 / $65   MC V D AE   TO

"The place for caviar and salmon." Petrossian offers "caviar galore!" and serves a handsome selection of "fabulous" Russian cuisine. The "delightful caviar bar" boasts nearly a dozen varieties of precious sea eggs. The casual dining area, quietly nestled beside a handsome take-out stand, serves "extraordinary" food with dignity. The waitstaff is a bit stiff but knowledgeable and the location makes this a very fine, pre-Carnegie Hall choice.

SPEC: *Teasers (French & Russian Zakouski) $19 or $25; Prince Gourmet (15 grams ea. of Sevruga, Ossetra & Beluga caviar $58; Salmon sampling $19 or $25*

PIERRE AU TUNNEL   LD   French

(B9) 215 W. 47th St. (B'way & 8th) 212/575-1220

F 7 / S 5 / A 7 / $38   MC V D AE

At this "charming, old fashioned French bistro," diners can expect to find a "dependable," "good, inexpensive" French meal. Portions aren't overwhelming and the service isn't spectacular, but the crowd can be "interestingly eclectic," especially on weekends. It offers "good value in the theater district," where many restaurants remain very pricey in comparison.

PIETRASANTA   LD   Italian

(B8) 683 9th Ave. (47th) 212/265-9471

F 6 / S 6 / A 5 / $24   MC V AE

A bit off the beaten track, but a do-able walk to the theater district, Pietrasanta offers reliable, quality fare at a reasonable tariff. The pasta here gets raves, but don't overtax the kitchen. A great place for lunch when the prices are an even better bargain than dinner.

SPEC: *Smoked salmon w/goat cheese $6.95; Risotto w/roasted peppers, spinach & parmesan $11.95; Penne con vitello $12.95; Tiramisu $5.50*

0	1	2	3	4	5	6	7	8	9	10
disappointing		fair		good		very good		excellent		perfect

PLANET HOLLYWOOD — LD — American

(A9) 140 W. 57th St. (6th & 7th) 212/333-7827

F 5 / S 6 / A 7 / $24   MC V D AE

Where else can you gawk at Rocky's red silk robe or Tom Jones's melton coat and still chow down on burgers, fries and mud pie! This is another "great adventure," theme restaurant so please, "bring the kids," "Good for grandchildren," "fun for young teens," and "O.K. for tourists." Planet Hollywood also provides a shop that hawks over-priced geegaws. It all gets "noisy," even boisterous, and there are long lines waiting to further try an adult's patience.

SPEC: *Pot stickers $4.95; Blackened shrimp $9.25; St. Louis ribs $14.95; BBQ pizza $9.95; Hollywood mousse pie $5.95*

POMAIRE — LD — Latin

(B8) 371 W. 46th St. (8th & 9th) 212/956-3055

F 6 / S 4 / A 5 / $20   MC V AE DIS   **TO**

"Visit Chile without leaving New York," says the small prix-fixe menu. At $14.95 for dinner and $7.95 for lunch, this cozy, family-oriented restaurant offers "good specials" and remains "economical." Actually, a steal because as a bonus, there's live music every night!

SPEC: *Prix-fixe dinner, $14.95; Beef w/onions, olive, egg & chicken; 1/2 marinated chicken; Fish steak (catch of the day)*

PREGO — LD — Italian

(A10) 1365 6th Ave. (55th & 56th) 212/307-5775

F 6 / S 6 / A 6 / $21   MC V D AE DIS   **TO**

Prego is a descendant of the original opened in Naples in 1902 by Grandma Anna. "A great dining experience," this trattoria offers authentic dishes, freshly prepared with generous portions in true Neapolitan tradition. The atmosphere is convivial, the location convenient and the prices very reasonable.

SPEC: *Spedini alla Romano $4.95; Caesar salad $4.50; Ziti al forno $9.75; Pollo alla primavera $14.75; Salsicci e peperoni $9.50*

Rainbow Room

RAINBOW ROOM — D — American

(B10) 30 Rockefeller Plaza (49th & 50th 65th Fl.) 212/632-5100

F 6 / S 7 / A 8 / $58   MC V D AE

Synonymous with "real, old, New York style," the "beautiful" Rainbow Room is a place that "everyone should go to at least once." Diners have extensive skyscraper views from most tables in this "grand," "art deco design" room. "Aubergine" silk walls, crystal chandeliers and a tiered bandstand with a '40s style 10-piece band and revolving dance floor all highlight a romantic evening. With executive chef Arnauld Briand at the helm, the kitchen prepares tasty lavish meals "as close to paradise as possible." **Closed: Monday**

SPEC: *Oysters Rockefeller $15; Lobster thermidor (main course) $35; Tournedos Rossini, truffle sauce $35; Roasted rack of lamb $31*

RALPH'S RESTAURANT   LD   Italian

(A8) 862 9th Ave. (56th)   212/581-2283

F 6 / S 6 / A 4 / $17   MC V D AE DIS   **TO/D**

Not much has changed here since Ralph's opened in 1957. "Old world" Italian both in decor and ambiance, the food is "nothing fancy" but "good," "hearty" and served "abondanza." Great for families and not far from the "Broadway Theatre" circuit.

SPEC: *Zuppa de clams posillipo $8.50; Veal parmagiana $11; Calamari marinara $9; Chicken francese $10; Steak pizzaiola $10; Broiled swordfish $14; Pasta calabrese $8; Homemade Italian cheesecake $2.50*

RAPHAEL   LD   French

(A10) 33 W. 54th St. (5th & 6th) 212/582-8993

F 8 / S 8 / A 9 / $42   MC V D AE

Top 10 $36-55
Expensive

Some call this the most romantic restaurant in New York. This elegant spot is lovingly tended by owner-hosts Raphael and Mira Edery. With a vest-pocket rear garden and an intimate feel, this find has a coterie of devoted regulars, many of New York's power-brokers, and numerous awards for food and wine. A charming spot to hold hands. Or close that big deal. **Closed: Sunday, Saturday lunch**

SPEC: *Octopus salad w/string beans $10.50; Duck pate w/foie gras & pistachios $10.50; Red snapper $24; Duck meat confit $25*

Remi

REMI   LD   Italian

(A9) 145 W. 53rd St. (6th & 7th) 212/581-4242 Fax: 581-7182

F 7 / S 7 / A 7 / $38   MC V D AE

Bellissima! Chef Francesco Antonucci deftly prepares his renowned Venetian recipes. "Beautiful Murano glass" renditions of the Canale Grande grace an elegant decor. The "wonderful" covered atrium provides a "nice business," midday power scene for in season, outdoor dining. The William Morris Agency is in the building, so be prepared to catch a few falling stars.

SPEC: *Sardines w/sweet & sour red onions, pignoli & white raisins $10; Risotto of the day P/A; Tuna w/spinach & capers in a shallot sauce $25*

RENE PUJOL   LD   French

(B8) 321 W. 51st St. (8th & 9th) 212/246-3023 Fax:245- 5206

F 6 / S 7 / A 7 / $33   MC V D AE

A "lovely, old world" spot offering "good, solid, country French" fare and prix fixe dinner until 8 pm, after which you may also order a la carte. Situated in two joined brownstones, it's decorated in pinks and floral porcelains, giving it the decided air of a French country inn. The food is consistently good with a "great rack of lamb," and "an excellent wine list." **Closed: Sunday**

SPEC: *Lobster salad $11; Roasted capon breast $14; Rack of lamb for 2 $75; Creme caramelisee a l'orange $4; Marquise au chocolat $6*

0	1	2	3	4	5	6	7	8	9	10
disappointing		fair		good		very good		excellent		perfect

217

REVOLUTION   LD   American

(C8) 611 9th Ave. (43rd & 44th)   212/489-8451   Fax:489-8045

F 7 / S 7 / A 6 / $20   MC V D AE DIS   **TO**

The decor peppered with "Peace" signs, lounge chairs and couches is a dead giveaway that the owners of this trendy hangout, are out to bring back the '60s and '70s. It works. The "cool, quick," retro look attracts a young crowd looking for '60s "hip" style. If you want "good food, reasonably priced," come early or for lunch, since the late night crowd makes it almost impossible to get a table.
SPEC: *Crab cakes $7;Poached shrimp and vegetable cocktail $7; Grilled salmon $13; Mushroom ravioli $10*

RICE 'N' BEANS   LD   Brazilian

(B8) 744 9th Ave. (50th & 51st) 212/265-4444

F 7 / S 6 / A 4 / $18   MC V   **TO/D**

This tiny, 18-seat eatery offers "the best South American food" and packs them in at all hours. All meals are cooked to order and the service can be slow, but the food is definitely worth the wait. An "excellent value, if short on ambiance," the $6.50 lunch special is an unusual bargain.
SPEC: *Creamy black bean soup $3.50; Rice & beans $5; Fish Amazon style $11.25; Chicken Leblon style $9.50; Fried sweet plantains $2*

RUMPELMAYER'S   LD   Continental

(A10) 50 Central Park So.   (6th-St. Moritz Hotel)   212/755-5800

F 5 / S 5 / A 5 / $24   MC V D AE DIS

Although the recent, "nice renovation" has taken away some of the storybook magic for adults, Rumpelmayer's is still "cute "with toys and stuffed animals and yes, wonderful ice cream and ice cream concoctions. Grandparents, aunts, uncles, and godparents will make friends of their young guests for life. The restaurant also serves continental food but that's not the reason to come.
SPEC: *Warm herb & goat cheese tart $8.50; Chicken pot pie $13.75; Chocolate decadence torte $5.75; Banana split $8.50*

RUSSIAN TEA ROOM, THE   LD   Russian

(A9) 150 W. 57th St. (6th & 7th) 212/265-0947

F 6 / S 6 / A 7 / $38   MC V D AE DIS

Now that the Russian Tea Room has changed ownership, (it remains open until renovation begins in January), we await the return to "excellent food" it was once known for. Still heralded as a "fantastic place to dine," patrons also continue to find it, "mood lifting," with "good food." Yes it's a "restaurant for celebrities," and to some, "strictly for business," but New Yorkers will recognize the temporary loss and soon miss the loving care of the grand Faith Gordon.
SPEC: *Hot or cold borscht $7.50; Caucasian shashlik $19.75; Cotelette a la Kiev $24.50; Blinchiki (3 crepes w/cheese, apple and cherry fillings) $17.50*

RUTH'S CHRIS STEAK HOUSE   LD   American

(B9) 148 W. 51st St. (6th & 7th) 212/245-9600

F 7 / S 7 / A 8 / $40   MC V D AE   **TO**

"It's better than the average steak house, Boo Boo," as that unabashed carnivore, Yogi Bear, might say. And he'd be right. Ruth Chris's only Manhattan location offers "the best steak," "consistent in NYC as everywhere else" (there are about 50 across the United States). With "nice atmosphere," and a great "steak for 2," standards remain high. So do the prices.
SPEC: *Mushrooms stuffed w/crabmeat $9.95; Homemade potato chips $3.50; Filet $26.50; Rib-eye $26; Porterhouse steak $27*

SAMPLINGS   D   American

(B9) 1605 B'way (48th & 49th-Holiday Inn Crowne) 212/315-6000

F 4 / S 4 / A 4 / $37   MC V D AE

Samplings offers basic American food at basic prices. Though nothing on the menu is spectacular and the service is ordinary, it's still a good place to get a quick bite before or after the theater. There's also a good selection of beers and nice wines by the glass.
SPEC: *Mozzarella & tomato tart $7.95; Pan roasted red snapper filet $17.95; Grilled tuna mignon $18.95; Grilled double chicken breast $15.95*

SAN DOMENICO   LD   Italian

(A9) 240 Central Park South (B'way & 7th) 212/265-5959

F 8 / S 7 / A 7 / $56   MC V D AE

With terra-cotta floors, low-level lighting, ocher-tinted windows, scalloped glass sconces, and luxurious leather chairs, the dining room oozes a significant "classy" elegance. Because of this "smooth and flawless" ambiance, you will "feel very special dining here." Chef Schoenegger serves "superb food," and especially innovative appetizers. The wine list contains more than 600 selections, many of which are matched to particular entree choices.
SPEC: *Medallions of crispy sweetbreads $13.95; Risotto w/butter, parmigiano & beef glaze $19.50; Sautéed goose liver $42.50*

Sardi's

SARDI'S   LD   Italian

(C9) 234 W. 44th St. (B'way & 8th) 212/221-8444

F 5 / S 6 / A 6 / $38   MC V D AE DIS

This world famous, old-time theater district restaurant still serves classic food to Shubert Alley diners. "You could spend all day with the caricatures" of the actors and actresses lining the walls and partitions. The upstairs bar still serves great cocktails and (at a same fixed time) the delicious, antipasti pizza. There are also the familiar, well-prepared Italian and continental dishes, like Baked Alaska, that have kept Sardi's in the limelight throughout
SPEC: *Caesar salad (lunch) $6; Sardi's burger (lunch) $14; Grilled filet mignon $26; Chocolate mousse layer cake $6*

SEAGRILL, THE   LD   Seafood

(B10) 19 W. 49th St. (5th & 6th-Rockefeller) 212/246-9201

F 6 / S 7 / A 8 / $42   MC V D AE

The SeaGrill offers "one of the best meals in Manhattan" along with an excellent view for a reasonable price. The dining room overlooks the skating rink and is decorated with bubbling marble pools, well-spaced tables, and wine racks on one wall. Executive chef Seppiu Renggli, formerly of the Four Seasons, cooks up sumptuous seafood dishes with an innovative approach. Closed: Sunday
SPEC: *Chicken & vegetable curry soup $6.50; Seafood gazpacho $12.50; Halibut T-bone steak $22; Yellowfin tuna $26*

0	1	2	3	4	5	6	7	8	9	10
disappointing		fair		good		very good		excellent		perfect

SETTE MOMA — LD — Italian

(A10) 11 W. 53rd/12 W. 54th MOMA (5th & 6th) 212/708-9710

F 4 / S 4 / A 3 / $35   MC V D AE

A young sibling to Setto Mezzo, but with a truly arty twist. MoMA, the world-famed repository of contemporary art, felt the need for a first-rate restaurant and this filled the void. Featuring light, contemporary, "pricey" Italian fare in a most civilized style. With movable art, a courtyard balcony–where a Julliard Chamber ensemble plays in summer. **Closed: Sunday and Wednesday**

SPEC: *Warm goat cheese wrapped in phyllo dough $9; "Straccetti" in a veal, beef & lamb sauce $15; Roasted banana w/caramel ice cream $6*

SIAM INN — LD — Thai

(A9) 916 8th Ave. (54th & 55th) 212/489-5237

F 6 / S 6 / A 4 / $19   MC V D AE   **TO/D**

One of the standouts in an area populated by Thai restaurants. "Flavorful food" such as the curries, seafood and especially the Thai dumplings are spectacular even at "very reasonable prices."

SPEC: *Steamed Thai dumplings $ 4.25; Bangkok duck $14.95; Thai bouillabaisse $14.95*

SIAM INN II — LD — Thai

(B9) 854 8th Ave. (51st & 52nd) 212/757-4006

See review above.

SOUTHWEST — LD — Italian

(C8) 621 9th Ave. (W. 44th) 212/315-4582

F 8 / S 7 / A 5 / $19   MC V AE DIS   **TO/D**

This brightly painted, family owned, pre-theater spot offers Southern Italian dishes as well as lighter offerings like grilled chicken salads, grilled sandwiches and pizza. The servings are generous and the menu is broad enough for everyone to find a dish they like, including the kids.

SPEC: *Focaccia $4.95; Eggplant rollatini $6.95; Pasta del giorno $9.95; Salmon 44 $13.95*

STAGE DELI — BLD — Deli

(A9) 834 7th Ave. (53rd & 54th) 212/245-7850

F 7 / S 6 / A 6 / $20   MC V AE   **TO**

Everything here is big–sandwiches, crowds, prices, wait-staff attitude. Tourists come in droves to the 58-year-old deli for the "outrageous variety" of celebrity-named "sandwiches to die for." Locals know this ain't Zabar's. "Not hungry, tough!"

SPEC: *Marv Albert (corned beef, Swiss cheese) $13.95; Liz Smith (turkey, ham, Swiss cheese) $14.95; Rudy Giuliani (salami w/sauerkraut & melted Swiss cheese) $13.95*

TRATTORIA DELL'ARTE — LD — Italian

(A9) 900 7th Ave. (56th & 57th) 212/245-9800 Fax: 265-3296

F 7 / S 6 / A 7 / 34   MC V D AE

"Handy for Carnegie Hall" with its glistening antipasto bar, famous artwork of giant body parts, including the giant nose displayed in the window above the entrance, and a celebrity clientele, this "chatty" restaurant turns eating into theater. Fortunately, " the food lives up to its presentation" and Milton Glaser's funky design look.

SPEC: *Vegetable antipasto (selection of 7) $12.95; Seafood antipasto (selection of 6) $15.95; Filet mignon of tuna $24.95; Double veal chop $33.95*

Trattoria Dell'Arte

TRATTORIA TRECOLORI — LD — Italian

(A9) 133 W. 45th St. (6th & 7th) 212/997-4540

F 5 / S 5 / A 5 / $23   MC V D AE DIS   **TO/D**

While low on atmosphere, this Italian eatery does serve hearty, homestyle veal and chicken dishes with homemade pasta. A daily lunch special at $9.75 is a favorite among weekday business folk or Saturday brunchers. **Closed: Sunday**

SPEC: *Gnocchi alla baba (potato dumplings) $8.50; Pollo fantasia $9.95; Pollo saltimbocca a la Fiorentina $10.25*

"21" CLUB, THE — LD — American

(B10) 21 W. 52nd St. (5th & 6th) 212/582-7200 Fax: 581-7138

F 7 / S 7 / A 7 / $60   MC V D AE

The "21" Club is "consistent" and still among the most exclusive restaurants in the world. In this posh midtown townhouse, everything remains famous: the bar area, where the rich and powerful drink; the old, framed newspaper clippings; and the 100s of toys dangling from the ceiling. Chef Michael Lomonaco's menu features a blend of "21" classic as well as contemporary dishes, and there's a fabulous assortment of domestic and international wines.

SPEC: *Grilled rabbit loin salad $17; "21" burger $24; "Speakeasy" steak tartare $30; "21" Sunset salad $26*

UNCLE NICK'S — LD — Greek

(B8) 747 9th Ave. (50th & 51st) 212/245-7992 Fax: 399-7027

F 7 / S 5 / A 5 / $25   MC V AE   **TO/D**

"Huge portions at very reasonable prices" along with quality grilled meats and seafood make Uncle Nick's "the best Greek restaurant outside Astoria". The large, taverna-style dining room with photographs of Greek family life alongside autographed photos of celebrities like Anthony Quinn and that other famous Greek entertainer, James Brown, remind us that in NY, anything goes.

SPEC: *Three combo spread (tzatziki, tarama, melitzanosalata) $6.95; Spinach pie $7.95; Gyro plate $9.95; Swordfish $12.95; Uncle Nick's famous rice pudding $2*

VICTOR'S CAFE 52 — LD — Cuban

(B9) 236 W. 52nd St. (B'way & 8th) 212/586-7714

F 7 / S 7 / A 7 / $35   MC V D AE DIS

Hardly a cafe, this full-blown "Cuban paradise" serves family-style and regular entrees. At the bar, grilled sandwiches and mixed drinks like the "Ernest Hemingway," foreshadow bigger stuff to come. Give them 24 hours and you've got yourself some suckling pig.

SPEC: *Frijoles negros (black bean soup) $4.95; Crispy cassava fingers $5.95; Florida red snapper $25.95; Red snapper filet "Miralda" $24*

0	1	2	3	4	5	6	7	8	9	10
disappointing		fair		good		very good		excellent		perfect

Matthew Kenney
Owner/chef of Matthew's

"**Elio's** is an owner-operated restaurant that conveys the charm and personality of its owner. It has an upscale, energetic, neighborhood clientele. The food is consistent, accessible and creative."

VIRGIL'S BBQ   LD   Southern

(C9) 152 W. 44th St. (6th & 7th) 212/921-9494

F 7 / S 6 / A 6 / $28   MC V AE   **TO**

Even if you don't eat barbecue, at least sniff the woodsmoke here. The "down home uptown" aroma might just turn you around. Exhaustive beer list, "reasonable prices", and a clean, woodsy interior make for a surprising repast just yards from the Broadway limelight. This is "not a place to go when on a diet."
SPEC: *Brunswick stew $4.95; Texas red chili w/cornbread $7.50; Memphis pork ribs (wet or dry) $14.95; Peanut butter pie $4.50*

WOLF'S DELICATESSEN   BLD   Deli

(A10) 101 W. 57th St. (6th) 212/586-1110

F 6 / S 6 / A 5 / $23   MC V AE   **TO**

With Carnegie and the Stage, this is the last of an uptown dying breed–overstuffed sandwiches at overstuffed prices. The service is as cold as the pastrami's hot, but if you're in a pickle and must get your deli fix here–go for it!
SPEC: *Stuffed derma $5.95; Pastrami sandwich $8.25; Hungarian beef goulash $12.95; Chicken in the pot $12.95*

ZEN PALATE   BLD   Asian

(B8) 663 9th Ave. (46th) 212/582-1669
See review on page 118.

ZUNI   LD   Southwestern

(C8) 598 9th Ave. (43rd) 212/765-7626

F 6 / S 6 / A 6 / $19   MC V AE DIS   **TO/D**

The Zuni are a Native American Indian tribe, and this restaurant serves up Southwestern dishes with flavorful and exotic twists. Decorated in bright colors and wooden touches, a neighborhood artist supplies bright modern paintings which imbue a Mediterranean feel. Dishes are often grilled with an emphasis on fruit, onion, and chile flavors to bring out the essence of seafood and chicken.
SPEC: *Quesadilla of the day $6.95; Grilled tuna tostada w/red & green chile vinaigrettes $7.75; Roasted loin of pork $13.95*

WEST 60TH – 86TH STREET

AEGEAN   LD   Greek

(E14) 221 Columbus Ave. (70th) 212/873-5057

– / – / – /   MC V   **TO**

The latest entry on Columbus Avenue is a welcome relief from the plethora of other ethnic eateries that line the street. Taking the place of the late, unlamented Cantina, Aegean offers the cool, clean, blue feel of the ocean, and if you get a table by the large glass floor to ceiling windows, there's still good people-watching.
SPEC: *Assorted Greek spreads (for 2) $10.95; Stuffed vine leaves $5.95; Spit roasted baby lamb $14.95; Lamb shish kebob $12.95*

ALL STATE CAFE | LD | American

(E13) 250 W. 72nd St. (B'way & WEA) 212/874-1883

F 6 / S 5 / A 6 / $21   Cash only

An intimate, homey spot notorious as the real-life "Looking For Mr. Goodbar" murder pick-up joint. Today soap stars, writers, and musicians, as well as neighborhood diners, gather here not out of morbid fascination, but for first-rate home-cooked meals offered from a surprisingly sophisticated and diverse menu that changes daily.
SPEC: *Sautéed boneless breast of chicken w/lemon & capers $11.50; South Carolina low country stew w/shrimp, chicken & garlic sauce $11.50; Homemade angel hair pasta w/sautéed shrimp, scallops, sundried tomatoes & string beans $11.50; Cappuccino cake $3.25*

ARTEPASTA | LD | Italian

(E14) 106 W. 73rd St. (Col. & Amst.) 212/501-7014

See review on page 74.

BACI | LD | Italian

(D14) 412 Amsterdam Ave. (79th & 80th) 212/496-1550

F 6 / S 6 / A 5 / $25   Cash only   **TO**

Once the rage of Amsterdam Ave, Baci has seen better days, but the pasta con le sarde, caponata and other Sicilian specialties are still first rate. "Crowded, but worth the squeeze." "The best pasta on the westside."
SPEC: *Fried artichokes $6.95; Caponata $6.50; Pasta con le Sarde $10.95; Anelletti $12*

BARNEY GREENGRASS | BL | Seafood

(D14) 541 Amsterdam Ave. (86th & 87th) 212/724-4707

F 7 / S 5 / A 4 / $20   Cash only   **TO/D**

The same location since 1929 and not much has changed since then. Not inexpensive, but the best smoked fish in the city. The Sturgeon King's reputation is world-wide. As Groucho once opined, "Barney Greengrass may not have ruled any kingdom, or written a great symphony, but he did a monumental job with sturgeon." **Closed: Monday**
SPEC: *Homemade borscht $2.25; Nova Scotia, scrambled eggs, onions $11; Sturgeon sandwich $11.50; Whitefish platter $14.75*

BERTHA'S BURRITOS | LD | Mexican

(E13) 2160 Broadway (76th) 212/362-4955

F 6 / S 6 / A 5 / $14   Cash only   **TO/D**

A popular Upper West Side hangout for those looking for a fix of California/Mexican food. The prices are cheap, the food pretty good, and the western saloon style bar gives New York tenderfeet the illusion that they're south-of-the-border. "Great frozen margaritas."
SPEC: *Burritos $5.75-$8.50; Frozen grande (23oz margarita) $8.75; Flan $2.75; Key lime pie $3.50*

BIG NICK'S BURGER JOINT | BLD | Coffee Shop

(D14) 2175 Broadway (77th) 212/724-2010

F 5 / S 6 / A 3 / $12   Cash only   **TO/D**

This unpretentious "dive" is a favorite among starving actors, writers, artists and local celebrities whose photos, along with hundreds of items not on the already extensive menu, clutter the walls. Be careful of the sizzling deep fryer located perilously close to the front door. "Don't miss trying the spinach pie."
SPEC: *Burger platter $4.75; Big Nick's moussaka $6.60; Spinach pie $4.40; Homemade Baklava $2.15; Sweet stick a la mode (combo of Kataifi & Baldava) $2.95*

0	1	2	3	4	5	6	7	8	9	10
disappointing		fair		good		very good		excellent		perfect

Blue Nile

BLUE NILE D Ethiopian

(E14) 103 W. 77th St. (Col.) 212/580-3232

F 7 / S 6 / A 7 / $21   MC V D DIS   **TO/D**

Ethiopian cuisine may not be for every day tastes, but for an authentic, off-beat experience, and spicy, flavorful food, Blue Nile is worth a visit. Sit on surprisingly comfortable three-legged stools, listen to African music and experience the exotic sensuality of dining without utensils. "Great fun to eat with your fingers."
SPEC: *Kulalit (beef kidneys) $4.95; Kitfo (steak tartare) $15.95; Ye'assa tibs (red snapper) $21.95; Yekik wot (red lentils) $9.95*

BOATHOUSE CAFE BLD American

(E15) Central Park (East Park—73rd) 212/517-2233

F 5 / S 6 / A 8 / $37   MC V AE

If you're taking a break from a jog, walk, rollerblade or returning your bike rental, stop by the cafe for a fast snack. For a special event, use the porch for a large party or take an out-of-town friend for a romantic meal at the sit-down restaurant which serves from 5:30. But don't bother during the winter months, as the Cafe is closed between mid-November and a mid-April re-opening (still open for special events.) "Location yes, food no."
SPEC: *Goat cheese parfait $11; Grilled Louisiana prawns $12; Grilled seafood risotto $20; Loin veal chop $28*

BOW THAI D Thai

(E14) 329 Columbus Ave. (75th & 76th) 212/496-1840

F 5 / S 5 / A 6 / $25   MC V D AE

An odd mix of Thai and Italian. Where else could you find grilled Thai chicken and Cioppino on the same menu? A long attractive bar is where most of the nightly action takes place. "Thai+Italian=inedible," say some. "Good diverse menu," say others. **Closed: Sunday**
SPEC: *Satays $1.50 ea.;Spicy vegetable noodle $8.75; Crispy fish $17.95; Thai fried chicken $11.75; Primavera bow tie $9.75*

BURRITOVILLE LD Tex-Mex

(D14) 451 Amsterdam Ave. (81st & 82nd) 212/787-8181
See review on page 77.

CAFE CON LECHE BLD Cuban

(E14) 424 Amsterdam Ave (80th & 81st) 212/595-7000

F 6 / S 6 / A 5 / $16   MC V AE   **TO/D**

A step above the Chinese/Cuban restaurants in the area. The ambiance is that of a tropical cafe. There's a $5.95 lunch special which can't be beat. Developing such a big following that they recently expanded. "Coffee worthy of their name." "Succulent arroz con calamares."
SPEC: *Arepas de Yuca patties $2.95; Arroz con pollo $7.25; Pescado con limon $9.50; Batidos (tropical milkshakes) $2.95*

CAFE DES ARTISTES   D   Amer/Continental

(F14) 1 W. 67th St. (CPW & Col.) 212/877-3500

F 7 / S 7 / A 8 / $50   MC V D AE

Unless you're from outer space, you don't need to be told much about Cafe Des Artistes, which just celebrated its 70th anniversary. Okay, we'll state the obvious: it's one of the prettiest, most romantic spots in the city. Surrounded by Howard Chandler Christy's naked nymphs who dance their way into your heart, you will be served superb food which will dance down your throat, all the way to your stomach. It doesn't get much better than this. "Where else to get a sweetheart to say 'yes?'" But service can be "snotty."

SPEC: *Gravlax salmon $10; Mussels $9; Smoked chicken $19.50; Duck confit $27.50; Salmon $25*

CAFE LA FORTUNA   LD   Pastry

(E14) 69 W. 71st St. (CPW & Columbus) 212/724-5846

F 6 / S 5 / A 6 / $7   Cash only   **TO**

Long before the Seattle coffee craze, this neighborhood fixture flourished as a little bit of Italy on the Upper West Side, complete with photos of Caruso and other operatic legends gracing the wall. Though the desserts and coffee are the reason this small cafe is such a popular after-dinner spot, they also serve tasty sandwiches. In warm weather, try the garden in back. **Closed: Monday**

SPEC: *Iced cappuccino w/ Italian ice $3.50; Italian cheesecake $3.25; La Fortuna Supreme $3.75*

Boathouse Cafe

CAFE LALO   BLD   Pastry

(D14) 201 W. 83rd St. (Amst. & Col.) 212/496-6031 Fax: 874-1578

F 5 / S 4 / A 4 / $10   MC V   **TO/D**

For a change of pace, skip the fast food coffee bars like Starbucks and Coopers and relax with a cappuccino and cannoli at this charming, dynamic and soulful cafe. "Reminds me of a Viennese cafe." Besides coffee and pastry, they also feature a wide selection of wine and beer and a variety of mixed drinks and cordials.

SPEC: *Fruit tart $4.95; Cannolis $1.25; Tiramisu $4.25*

CAFE LUXEMBOURG   LD   French

(E14) 200 W. 70th St. (Amst. & Col.) 212/873-7411 Fax: 721-6854

F 7 / S 6 / A 7 / $32   MC V D AE

Since opening in 1982, this French bistro, despite its out of the way location has attracted a loyal downtown, fashionable following. The room is "cavernous," and sometimes there's a "cold" feel to it. The prices are no bargain, but the food is "excellent."

SPEC: *Crisp baby artichokes $9.50; Country salad $7.75; Steak frites $25; Cassoulet $21; Crispy duck $24; Bananas foster $7.50; Creme brulee $6.75*

0	1	2	3	4	5	6	7	8	9	10
disappointing		fair		good		very good		excellent		perfect

Cafe Mozart

CAFE MOZART LD Pastry

(E14) 154 W. 70th St. (B'way) 212/595-9797 Fax: 873-3428

F 6 / S 5 / A 7 / $13 MC V D AE DIS **TO/D**

While literary and after-theater latte swillers ogle tiramisu and peanut butter fudge pie in the Viennese cafe's dessert case, a musician plays live classical piano and back-table dieters debate sugarless pies, lowfat cheesecakes, and skim milk coffee drinks. All 12 varieties of coffee are fresh-ground for each order and served in a mini-pot. Light fare—pasta, croissant sandwiches, salads, and an $8.95 weekend brunch—make this a neighborhood favorite.

SPEC: *Salieri's revenge (espresso fudge brownie a la mode) $5.75; Caffe Viennechino (espresso w/whipped cream) $2.75*

CAFFE BUON GUSTO LD Italian

(E14) 71 W. 71st St. (Col.) 212/875-1512
See review on page 151.

CAPRICE CAFE LD Mediterranean

(F14) 199 Columbus Ave. (68th & 69th) 212/580-6948

F 5 / S 6 / A 5 / $19 MC V AE **TO/D**

Yet another outdoor/indoor cafe lining Columbus Avenue. The difference here is that it doesn't pretend to be anything it isn't, which means it doesn't have the attitude others of its ilk flaunt. Seating inside is multi-level; there is a small smoking section at the bar, and as soon as the weather turns acceptable, the outdoor cafe becomes a popular attraction.

SPEC: *Grilled portobello mushroom napoleon $6.50; Mediterranean tasting plate $10.95; Bucatini w/portobello mushrooms $10.95*

CARNEVALE LD Italian

(D14) 410 Amsterdam Ave. (79th & 80th) 212/595-7100

F 6 / S 6 / A 4 / $25 MC V D AE DIS **TO/D**

Offering Italian taste at decent pricing, Carnevale fits itself into a college environment. But don't be fooled, the clientele is diverse. Seafood is on the menu, as well as in a 55-gallon fish tank provided for viewing during your dining experience.

SPEC: *Homemade mozzarella $5.95; Lasagna primavera $9.95; Grilled breast of chicken $10.95*

Sarabeth Levine
Owner of Sarabeth's

"**Mesa Grill** is big, noisy fun, and the food is simply excellent. **Arcadia** is where I go with guests because it's an ideal place to impress out-of-town visitors. Drew Nieporent is a jovial host who balances **Montrachet's** extraordinary food with open-hearted hospitality."

CHAZ & WILSON GRILL AND BAR — D — American

(D14) 201 W. 79th St. (Amst) 212/769-0100 Fax: 769-0102

F 5 / S 5 / A 5 / $21   MC V D AE   **TO/D**

Go more for the sights and the bar scene, than for the food. A favorite spot for big-time athletes and celebrities. With live jazz and rhythm and blues every night, C & W brings a little bit of sophistication to the Upper West Side. Also, keep an eye out for special meal deals during the week.
SPEC: *Mae's creamed spinach $5.95; Potato parmesan $5.95; Steak $19.95; Chicken Caribbean $17.95; Chicken shepherd's pie $11.95*

CHINA FUN — LD — Chinese

(E14) 246 Columbus Ave. (72nd) 212/580-1516
See review on page 154.

CICCIO & TONY'S — D — Italian

(E14) 320 Amsterdam Ave. (75th) 212/595-0500

F 6 / S 6 / A 6 / $22   MC V D AE   **TO/D**

Attractive prices and attractive people help make this a hot spot for Italian dining. The room is romantic and airy, and there's a nifty outdoor cafe. On Mondays check out the Pasta Festival. For the price of $13.75, every ten minutes a different pasta can be sampled. Salad and dessert included. "Noisier than the IRT."
SPEC: *Risotto fritelle $4.75-$5.75; Osso buco $15.75; Veal Milanese $15.75; Chicken marsala pizza $9.75; Penne con carciofini $11.75*

CONSERVATORY — BLD — Continental

(F14) 15 CPW (60th & 61st-Mayflower) 212/265-0060

F 5 / S 5 / A 6 / $28   MC V D AE

One of N.Y.'s nicest hotels has a restaurant where the staff tries hard, but the prices make you think you're on top of a skyscraper instead of admiring the nice view of lower Central Park from ground level. The sedate, even stodgy atmosphere is best for a breakfast meeting.
SPEC: *Bruschetta $6; Caesar salad $6; Pan roasted striped bass $18; Grilled baby chicken $15*

DALLAS BBQ — LD — American

(E14) 27 W. 72nd St. (CPW & Col.) 212/873-2004 Fax: 787-6367

F 4 / S 4 / A 5 / $10   MC V D AE DIS   **TO/D**

You're hungry and all you've got is 10 bucks in your pocket. So, partner, what do you do? Come here, where for a sawbuck you can stuff yourself with chicken, ribs, cornbread, and giant-sized Texas drinks. It's huge, "noisy," filled with families and guaranteed you won't leave with an empty spot in your belly. Best summed up by one diner as "Grease!"
SPEC: *Early Bird Special (2 meals) $7.95: chicken vegetable soup, half chicken served w/cornbread & potatoes; Baby back ribs $8.95*

DINISTIA CHINA — LD — Chino/Latino

(E14) 145 W. 72nd St. (B'way & Col.) 212/362-3801

F 7 / S 6 / A 4 / $14   MC V AE   **TO/D**

While you wait to be served immense portions of comidas Chinas Criollas, try not to lose your appetite as you peruse the walls covered with autographed photos of "celebrities" like Ming the Bodybuilder and porn talk show hostess Robin Byrd.
SPEC: *Fried boneless chicken, Spanish style $8.75; Ropa Vieja $8.85; Cuban pot roast $7.85; Cafe con leche $1.35*

0	1	2	3	4	5	6	7	8	9	10
disappointing		fair		good		very good		excellent		perfect

E.J.'S LUNCHEONETTE BLD Diner

(D14) 447 Amsterdam Ave. (81st & 82nd) 212/873-3444

F 6 / S 5 / A 5 / $15 Cash only **TO/D**

This upscale neighborhood luncheonette, a favorite with "slumming" Westsiders, has been so successful it's spawned branches on the Upper East Side and in the Village. Above average diner food has them flocking in, especially on the weekend when there's a mob scene for breakfast and brunch. "What's the deal here? The food is nothing special," say some. "Particularly child friendly."

SPEC: *"Blue Plate" dinner special change daily; fruit-filled pancakes $6; E.J.'s Chicken Reuben $6.75; Dock's Key lime pie $3*

EDEN ROCK CAFE BLD Middle Eastern

(D13) 2325 Broadway (84th & 85th) 212/873-1361

F 7 / S 6 / A 3 / $13 MC V AE **TO/D**

A small, nondescript, inexpensive neighborhood spot that serves a surprisingly large array of Middle Eastern and Lebanese snacks and meals. Appetizers and salads, like tabouli, can be combined to make a full meal. "The #1 falafel in N.Y."

SPEC: *Baba ghanouj $3.50; Kibby $3.50; Meat shawrma $9.95; Shish kabab $9.95; Falafel platter $7.95*

EDGAR'S CAFE LD Italian

(D13) 255 W. 84th (B'way & WEA) 212/496-6126

F 6 / S 6 / A 6 / $15 Cash only **TO**

Named for Edgar Allan Poe, this eclectic Italian-style cafe offers an interesting array of tasty salads and sandwiches. But the real draw of this relative newcomer to the Upper West Side is the dessert menu—over 50 different cakes, pies, gelati and sorbets, many of them imported directly from Italy. "Cheap and busy. Such variety."

SPEC: *Focaccia w/goat cheese & bresaola $8.25; Chicken zingara $8.75; Edgar salad $8.25; Black forest cake $4.95; Plum tart $4.95*

Ernie's

ERNIE'S LD Italian

(E13) 2150 Broadway (75th & 76th) 212/496-1588

F 6 / S 6 / A 7 / $25 MC V D AE **TO**

Indistinguishable food, but the portions are huge and affordable. At night, a major meat market for singles. Maybe that accounts for the line of phones by the bar. "Bustling with energy, always something to explore on the extensive menu." "Quality of food and service has declined."

SPEC: *Bocconcini (fresh mozzarella, olive oil, oregano & basil w/garden greens & balsamic vinegar) $5.95; Capelli d'angelo $13.95; Grilled chicken $12.95*

FINE & SCHAPIRO LD Deli

(E14) 138 W. 72nd St. (Col & B'way) 212/877-2721

F 6 / S 5 / A 4 / $19 MC V AE DIS **TO/D**

This kosher, old-fashioned deli has been a mainstay on the Upper West Side since 1927, and it's more than likely the very same dishes served then are still on the menu. As for the service, it's as surly as a sour pickle, and frankly, we wouldn't have it any other way. Besides, where else could you find a chef named Irwin?

SPEC: *Gefilte fish $4.95; Stuffed derma $4.95; BBQ veal ribs $12.95; Chicken-in-the-pot $14.30*

FIORELLO'S ROMAN CAFE LD Italian

(F14) 1900 Broadway (63rd & 64th) 212/595- 53-30

F 6 / S 6 / A 3 / $34 MC V D AE

Wafer-thin pizzas, fresh pastas, and their famous antipasto bar help make Fiorello's one of the best dining choices in the Lincoln Center area. You can either choose to sit in the intimate dining room, the antipasto bar or, if weather permits, at the small outdoor cafe. The pre-theater crowd is always large, so reservations are advised.

SPEC: *Antipasto bar: vegetable $12.95; seafood $15.95; Pizzas $10-$12*

FIREHOUSE LD American

(D14) 522 Columbus Ave. (85th) 212/787-3473 Fax: 362-3004

F 5 / S 4 / A 4 / $15 MC V D AE **TO/D**

True to its name, this popular neighborhood spot (especially for young singles), is decorated with firehouse memorabilia and pictures of those fire engine chasing spotted dogs (we know, Dalmatians). A great place to meet for a drink before you head out for the evening, or a night cap as you wind down.

SPEC: *Onion rings w/blue cheese $3.75; Buffalo wings $5.50; Roasted chicken $9.95; BBQ ribs $11.95; Hot fudge brownie $3.50*

FISHIN EDDIE D Seafood

(E14) 73 W. 71 St. (Col. and CPW) 212/874-3474 Fax: 874-7182

F 6 / S 5 / A 6 / $35 MC V D AE DIS **TO**

Owned by the same folks who gave us Vince and Eddie's, this "healthy East Coast" seafood restaurant offers diners an airy, well-lit, atrium like room, as well as a casual, comfortable bar area. Our advice is not to waver too far from the simple, grilled fish, or you're likely to be disappointed. "Great oysters at the bar."

SPEC: *Chesapeake Bay crabcakes $11.95; Tuna & salmon tartar w/sesame, shiso & gaufrette chips $9.50; Northeastern bay seafood stew $19.95; Pan-roasted chicken w/garlic mashed potatoes $16.50*

FRENCH ROAST BLD French

(D13) 2340 Broadway (85th) 212/799-1533
See review on page 84.

GABRIEL'S BAR AND RESTAURANT LD Italian

(F14) 11 W. 60th St. (B'way and Col.) 212/956-4600

F 7 / S 7 / A 6 / $37 MC V D AE **TO**

A chi-chi spot in the shadow of the former Paramount building that serves up authentic Italian dishes to locals, Hollywood entertainment execs and gourmands. The decor is subtle and snooty, like the staff, and the wine list boasts hard-to-get Italian specialties. "Great Italian," gush diners.

SPEC: *Grappa cured salmon $12; Eggplant tart $9; Grilled chicken marinated w/buttermilk $21; Grilled tuna marinated w/fennel seed & lemon $26; Slow roasted kid w/white wine & rosemary $25*

0	1	2	3	4	5	6	7	8	9	10
disappointing		fair		good		very good		excellent		perfect

GOOD ENOUGH TO EAT BLD American

(D14) 483 Amsterdam Ave (83rd & 84th) 212/496- 0163

F 7 / S 7 / A 6 / $24   MC V AE   **TO/D**

One of the first neighborhood restaurants to serve "homestyle" cooking. The room is small and folksy, and if you're lucky enough to sit at the table near the front window, you can rest comfortably against pillows that cushion your back. "The best for breakfast—if you don't mind waiting." "Hearty breakfasts even better than mom's."

SPEC: *Grilled corn bread $3.50; Meatloaf $14; Roast chicken $14; Macaroni & cheese $9; BBQ pork chops $16.75*

HARRY'S BURRITO JUNCTION LD Mexican

(E14) 241 Columbus Ave. (71st) 212/580-9494 Fax: 580-4635

F 5 / S 5 / A 5 / $13   MC V   **TO/D**

A young, noisy crowd comes for the cheap, good "San Francisco" style burritos, and the 28 oz frozen margaritas. The salsa is topnotch and those burritos are, all things considered, a good replication of the California version you might crave when in New York.

SPEC: *Chicken fajita burrito $8.75; Non-dairy burrito $6; Vegetarian burrito $6.75; Flan of the day $3; Rice pudding $3.25*

HI-LIFE BAR & GRILL D American

(D14) 477 Amsterdam Ave. (83rd) 212/787- 7199

F 7 / S 6 / A 6 / $18   MC V D AE   **TO/D**

"Happy Days" with an art deco twist, is the best way to describe this hopping restaurant/bar, a favorite of those Upper West Siders into the bar scene. The food, American with a twist of Thai, is adequate, but that's not why most people go. It's the scene—complete with good-looking waitresses and singles on the make—and, perhaps, the martinis. "Pork chops are excellent."

SPEC: *Steamed dumplings $4.95; Potato skins w/cheddar cheese & bacon $4.50; Black angus "New York" sirloin steak $14.50; Crispy southern-fried chicken w/mashed potatoes $9.95; Pad Thai $10.95*

HOULIHAN'S LD Amer/Continental

(F14) 1900 Broadway (63rd) 212/339-8862

F 3 / S 4 / A 4 / $26   MC V D AE DIS   **TO/D**

What can we say about Houlihan's that hasn't already been said? Okay, so we'll say it again. The food is...well, it's a step above the fast stuff; but the prices...whoa! Very steep for what you get. "Love those desserts." "Food and service are lousy.".

SPEC: *Potato skins $7.99; Cajun chicken grilled sandwich $10.99; Caramel nut crunch pie $5.89; Chocolate cappuccino cake $5.99*

INDIAN OVEN D Indian

(D14) 200 W. 84th St. (Amst) 212/874-6900

F 6 / S 7 / A 6 / $15   MC V D AE DIS   **TO/D**

A small, neighborhood place on a tough block. But don't let the location deter you from this pleasant, family-run restaurant with an interesting and innovative menu. "Best West Side Tandoori." "Hot, hot, hot food."

SPEC: *Samosa $2.50; Aloo chat $2.50; Patra-Ni-Machi (pompano steamed in banana leaf) $11.95; Chicken Afghani $11.95; Mixed tandoori grill $11.95*

Indian Oven

IRIDIUM RESTAURANT & JAZZ CLUB   LD   American

(F14) 44 W. 63rd St. (B'way & Amst) 212/582-2121

F 5 / S 5 / A 7 / $34   MC V D AE DIS   **TO**

Entering Iridium is like walking into the world of Dr. Seuss.With its quirky, unconventional seating and decoration, it's toon town on the Upper West Side. Reports on the food are spotty, at best, but it's an experience. And the live jazz every night, featuring big names like Ellis Marsalis, T.S. Monk and Don Byron, along with an "All You Can Drink" jazz brunch on weekends, makes it a worthwhile trip. "Who needs bad food, surly service, and silly chairs?" "Great live jazz

SPEC: *Barcelona tasting (grilled Spanish octopus, chicken chorizo, manilla clams w/black bean, corn & tomato compote $9.50; Pan seared salmon $21.50; Florida red snapper $21.95; Striped bass $18.50*

ISABELLA'S   LD   Mediterranean

(E14) 359 Columbus Ave. (77th) 212/724-2100

F 7 / S 7 / A 7 / $21   MC V AE

Strategically placed on Columbus Ave., across from the Museum of Natural History, this is one of the better people-watching spots on the Upper West Side. So good, in fact, that it was immortalized when it was named in an episode of "Seinfeld," as being "too trendy." This may be true, but it doesn't seem to have deterred business, especially on weekends when it's difficult to get a table outside. "Best on Columbus strip."

SPEC: *Warm roasted asparagus w/shaved asiago & tomato vinaigrette $5.95 Grilled tuna $15.95; Hay & straw pasta w/grilled chicken $11.50*

ISOLA   LD   Italian

(E14) 485 Columbus Ave. (83rd & 84th) 212/362-7400

F 7 / S 7 / A 6 / $24   AE   **TO**

Another one of the numerous Italian cafes that line Columbus Avenue. It's so small you could almost miss it squeezed between all the other eateries. "Reliable. Wonderful salads/appetizers." "Keeps getting better and better."

SPEC: *Foccaccia nostra $4.95; Grigliata mista stagionale $6.95; Pollo alla griglia $12.95; Linguine alla smeralda $12;*

JACKSON HOLE   BLD   American

(E14) 517 Columbus Ave. (85th) 212/362-5177 Fax: 721-4613

F 4 / S 5 / A 4 / $12   AE   **TO**

This New York chain serves 28 varieties of reliable "Jurassic-size" burgers (okay, maybe not the beef burger tartare), and 27 varieties of grilled chicken sandwiches, as well as the conventional artery-clogging sides. The decor is clean and unimaginative. Prices are cheap. Some call the "steamed burgers," "the greatest in the city." For others, it made them "remember why I don't really eat red meat."

SPEC: *7-oz hamburger platters $6.70 -$10.80 (The Classic-bacon cheeseburger topped w/ham, mushrooms, tomatoes & fried onions)*

0	1	2	3	4	5	6	7	8	9	10
disappointing		fair		good		very good		excellent		perfect

JOE'S FISH SHACK · D · Seafood

(D14) 520 Columbus Ave. (85th) 212/873-0341

– / – / – / · MC V D AE · **TO/D**

Used to be Mi Chiamo? Now it's a seafood restaurant. You can tell by the fishing gear scattered throughout the place. Will it last? Or can we expect another change in the future?

JOHN'S PIZZERIA · LD · Pizzeria

(F14) 48 W. 65th St. (CPW & Col.) 212/721-7001
See review on page 86.

JOSEPHINA · LD · American

(F14) 1900 Broadway (63rd) 212/799-1000 Fax: 799-1082

F 6 / S 6 / A 6 / $27 · MC V D AE · **TO**

A trendsetter, Josephina was one of the first restaurants in the area to introduce dairy-free but flavorful food on an eclectic American menu. The offerings were so popular, that the owners spun off Josie's on Amsterdam which also serves dairy-free, ecologically correct food. "Healthy food that tastes good." "Great vegetarian entrees." "Inconsistent. Tries too hard."
SPEC: *Josephina caesar salad $6; Basil horseradish crusted salmon $17; Rigatoni w/free range chicken & sun dried tomatoes $12.50*

Josie's

JOSIE'S RESTAURANT AND JUICE BAR · D · American

(E14) 300 Amsterdam Ave. (74th) 212/769-1212 Fax: 873-3913

F 6 / S 6 / A 6 / $23 · MC V D AE · **TO/D**

Hip is the operative word here. Hip interior design. Hip menu. Hip service. Hip clientele. But how long before American/Eclectic is no longer hip? All foods are "organic" and prepared dairy-free. No question about it, Josie's is certainly ecologically correct, even down to the menu which is printed on recycled paper. Question is, why does healthy always seem to mean bland. "We wouldn't mind a bottle of hotsauce on each table."
SPEC: *Ginger grilled calamari $6; Portobello mushroom fajitas $11; Seared organic St. Peter's fish $14; Roast free range chicken $13*

LA BOITE EN BOIS · D · French

(F14) 75 W. 68th St. (CPW & Col.) 212/874-2705

F 5 / S 5 / A 4 / $31 · MC V D AE

The itsy-bitsy bistro located on a quiet corner offers fine cuisine at moderate prices. The brainchild of restaurateurs Allan Broussard and Jean-Claude Coutable, this remains a favorite among Lincoln Center clientele. The dining room is decorated with antique farm tools and bucolic paintings, giving it a rustic ambiance. "Good choice for Lincoln Center.".
SPEC: *Goat cheese ravioli $6.50; Homemade pate $5; Swordfish w/lobster sauce $20; Sautéed loin of veal $21*

LA CARIDAD   LD   Cuban/Chinese

(D13) 2199 Broadway (78th) 212/874-2780

F 7 / S 6 / A 5 / $11   Cash only

Formerly a hangout for taxi drivers from the Caribbean when it opened 20 years ago. Today, although the cabbies still come, so do countless other denizens of the neighborhood. And why the long lines? Because the food is hearty and the portions gargantuan, especially the monstrous pork chops smothered in garlic; the overflowing plates of rice and beans; the comforting, steamy bowls of soup. "Awesome food."

SPEC: *Ropa vieja $5.55; Pollo asado $5.35; Carne guisada (beef-stew) $5.35*

LA COCINA   LD   Mexican

(D13) 217 W. 85th St. (B'way & Amst.) 212/874-0770

F 6 / S 6 / A 5 / $15   MC V D AE DIS   **TO/D**

Fresh corn tortillas and flavorful sauces—mole, verde and salsa—help make La Cocina one of the better Mexican restaurants in the neighborhood. The room has high ceilings, prints of Frida Kahlo adorning the wall, and an attractive bar. "Great happy hour and even better margaritas."

SPEC: *Black bean soup $2.25; Chicken mole $7.95; Shrimp tequila $12.95; Fajitas $10.95; Burritos $3.99*

LE SELECT   LD   French

(D14) 507 Columbus Ave. (84th & 85th) 212/875-1993

F 6 / S 4 / A 6 / $27   MC D AE   **TO/D**

Yet another cafe on Columbus? You bet. But thankfully, this one isn't Italian, but rather a genuine French bistro with unique art deco interior, magnificent light fixtures, and a celestial staircase leading down to the....okay, restrooms. We know it's genuine because the owners, management and most of the waiters are French natives, which translates naturally into an "arrogant wait staff."

SPEC: *Onion soup $4.75; Canard roti, champignons vinaigrette au porto $16.25; Hachis parmentier (Shepherd's pie) $12.75*

LOUIE'S WESTSIDE CAFE   BLD   American

(D14) 441 Amsterdam Ave. (81st) 212/877-1900 Fax: 877-1863

F 7 / S 7 / A 6 / $30   MC V AE   **TO/D**

A neighborhood hangout with a loyal clientele. Instead of waiting in line at Sarabeth's and other more famous Amsterdam eateries, throw caution to the wind, dare to be different, and try breakfast at Louie's for a special treat. "Great for Sunday brunch." "Exceptional."

SPEC: *Wild mushroom ravioli $7.50; Sliced fresh mozzarella w/tomatoes, onion & basil $6.75; Steak au poivre $22; Meatloaf $14.50*

MACKINAC BAR AND GRILL   D   American

(D14) 384 Columbus Ave. (78th & 79th) 212/799-1750

F 6 / S 5 / A 6 / $24   MC V D AE   **TO**

Patterned after a country club eating hall, with its dark and woodsy interior — Mackinac is yet another top "people watching spot" on Columbus Avenue. The food is solid, though perhaps a little pricey. The weekend brunch is popular, especially during warm weather when the outdoor cafe is open "The prettiest bar in the city with a fireplace."

SPEC: *Spicy chicken broth w/roasted carrots, red onion, hominy $4.25; Mackinac pizzette w/mushrooms, goat cheese & roasted tomatoes $7.95; Pork chops $14.95; Grilled Gulf shrimp $17.95*

0	1	2	3	4	5	6	7	8	9	10
disappointing		fair		good		very good		excellent		perfect

JOE MAJOR

Main Street

MAIN STREET   D   American

(D14) 446 Columbus Ave. (81st & 82nd) 212/873-5025

F 6 / S 7 / A 6 / $35   MC V AE DIS   **TO**

The space is large, the portions are large and the noise is largest of all in this family style restaurant serving American homestyle cuisine. The food is hit or miss. Some call it "too bland," while others rave about the kind home cooking their mom used to make. Our advice: go with a lot of people and order different things. "Fun, solid, family-style dining."

SPEC: *Cajun popcorn shrimp $16; Mashed potatoes $7; Meat loaf $19; Chicken pot pie $19; Heathbar crunch cake $6.50*

MERCHANT'S   LD   Continental

(D14) 521 Columbus Ave. (85th & 86th) 212/721-3689 Fax: 929-1844

F 6 / S 6 / A 7 / $22   MC V AE

We're still trying to figure this one out. Is it a bar? Is it a lounge? Is it a restaurant? Whatever it is, it seems to work, probably because it's a bit of everything and somehow the mix works. There's a "warm" and romantic dining area; a separate lounge area with couches and a fireplace for more intimate conversation; and a bar area for people to mingle. "Grazing food." "Can't beat the martinis."

SPEC: *Special martinis $5.50-$12.50; Single barrel bourbons $5.50-$12.50; Grilled chicken w/sundried tomatoes $9.95 Baked chicken sushi roll $9.95*

MINGALA WEST   LD   Burmese

(E14) 325 Amsterdam Ave. (75th & 76th) 212/873-0787

F 6 / S 6 / A 6 / $16   MC V D AE DIS   **TO/D**

A subtle melding of Asian cuisines; Chinese, Malaysian, Indian, and Thai, combine to form the distinctive Burmese flavor. "Always top notch and bursting with taste." "The lunch special at $4.95 is possibly the best in the neighborhood." "Better than Burma."

SPEC: *Festival noodles & fish lemongrass soup $4.95; Tea leaf salad $5.95; Glass Palace chicken $8.50; Pork w/mango pickle curry $8.50; Mandalay nungi noodles $7.50; Thousand layer bread $2*

MISS ELLE'S HOMESICK BAR & GRILL   LD   American

(D14) 226 W. 79th St. (Amst & B'way) 212/595-4350

F 5 / S 6 / A 6 / $18   MC V D AE DIS   **TO/D**

Quaint and romantic, Miss Elle's, offering homestyle cooking (where else on the Upper West Side could you find a menu that includes Aunt' Sadie's chopped liver and milk and cookies?), is a favorite neighborhood meeting spot for actors and artistic types. Downstairs, there's a garden dining room. "Cozy dining rooms that make you feel right at home."

SPEC: *Meatza (English muffin pizza w/meatsauce) $3.50; Meatloaf $8.95; Pot roast w/carrots $9.95*

MUGHLAI D Indian

(E14) 316 Columbus Ave. (75th) 212/724-6363 Fax: 724-4224

F 6 / S 5 / A 4 / $24 MC V AE **TO/D**

We're used to the prices of Indian food in the East Village, so the price of an entree here, which averages over ten bucks, seems pretty high to us. But I guess we're paying for location, location, location. And if Upper West Siders crave Northern Indian cuisine, there aren't all that many options.

SPEC: *Vegetable pakoras $3.95; Jhinga balchoo $7.95; Sali boti $13.95; Rogan josh $13.95; Rasmalai $3; Gulab jaman $3*

MUSEUM CAFE LD Amer/Continental

(E14) 366 Columbus Ave. 77th 212/799-0150

F 5 / S 5 / A 5 / $23 MC V D AE **TO**

Not much has changed here since opening in 1976. Still serves those huge, popular salads that were so big in the '70s. It worked then and it still works now. Unlike so many other Columbus cafes, this doesn't have outdoor dining, but it does have a sunny enclosed cafe that overlooks the avenue.

SPEC: *Cornmeal fried calamari, spicy tomato sauce $5.75; Shrimp & crab meat potstickers $6.95; Museum Grecian chicken salad $10.95; Peanut chicken salad $9.95; Spaghetti w/spice grilled chicken $11.95*

Merchant's

NIKO'S MEDITERRANEAN GRILL LD Greek

(E13) 2161 Broadway (76th) 212/873-7000

F 7 / S 7 / A 6 / $32 MC V D AE **TO**

Owned by the proprietor of Big Nick's down the block, this new addition to Broadway tries to replicate the ambiance of a Greek taverna, complete with ethnic music and a TV set with videos of Mediterranean scenes. Throwing of plates, however, is definitely not encouraged. For some, the question remains, is "Big Nick reaching beyond his abilities?"

SPEC: *Grilled octopus $7.95; Dolmades yalangi $4.25; Rodos yuvetsi $11.50; Lamb shank Corfu & fettucine in a clay pot $13.50*

O'NEALS' BLD American

(F14) 49 W. 64th St. (CPW & B'way) 212/787-4663 Fax: 799-3659

F 6 / S 6 / A 6 / $29 MC V AE D DIS

One of the two models for the Statue of Liberty sits atop this ware-house turned restaurant. Mike O'Neal's spirit lives on, as everyone from celebrities to kids (who have their own special menu) are made to feel welcome. A good place to dine before taking in a performance at Lincoln Center. But some are nostalgic. "When the balloon flew away, O'Neals' should have flown with it."

SPEC: *Caesar salad $5.95; Onion soup $5.95; Broiled shrimp curry $17.95; Sautéed calf's liver w/bacon & onions $16.95*

0	1	2	3	4	5	6	7	8	9	10
disappointing		fair		good		very good		excellent		perfect

Ben Benson
Owner, Ben Benson's Steak House

"In addition to my obsession with the art of the steak, occasionally I indulge my love of Italian food. And when I want good Italian cooking, one of my favorite choices is **Il Toscanaccio**. Here I can always enjoy reliable, first-rate homemade pastas and veal."

OLLIE'S NOODLE SHOP & GRILLE LD Chinese

(D13) 2315 Broadway (84th) 212/362-3111 Fax: 362-3097

F 6 / S 6 / A 2 / $15 MC V AE **TO/D**

The Chinese version of a coffee shop. It's loud, it's boisterous and you can watch the dumplings being made from the front window. The soups are as comforting as ice cream...and much better for you.
SPEC: *Wonton roast pork soup $4.95; Steamed vegetable dumplings $3.75 Roast duck $6.25*

OTTOMAN CUISINE LD Turkish

(D14) 413 Amsterdam Ave. (79th & 80th) 212/799-6363

F 6 / S 5 / A 5 / $21 MC V DIS AE **TO**

One of the few Turkish restaurants in New York and the only one on the Upper West Side. Still feeling their way, but filling the restaurant nightly is a good indication that the Dumarkaya family, who run the place, know the right recipe for success. Turkish food is rooted in red meat, and here the lamb dishes are the standouts, as are the cold appetizers.
SPEC: *Kabak muneri $5.75; Sigaro boregi $5.75; Hunkar befendi $13.75; Sis kebap $14.75; Baklava $5.50; Kadayif $5.50*

PAPPARDELLA LD Italian

(E14) 316 Columbus Ave. (75th) 212/595-7996 Fax: 724-4224

F 6 / S 5 / A 6 / $24 MC V D AE

Yet another popular Italian restaurant on Columbus, this one serving Tuscany cuisine. Great spot for people watching at the outdoor cafe, and the dining interior is quite nice, what with wine bottles, baskets, and large plants scattered throughout. The food is reliable and the choices plentiful.
SPEC: *Crostini Rossi $3; Bresaola della valtellina $7.95; Pappardella Buttrea $12.95*

PATZO LD Italian

(D13) 2330 Broadway (85th) 212/496-9240

F 6 / S 7 / A 7 / $19 MC V D **TO/D**

Every Monday is "Pasta Specials" night for $6.95, at this popular Italian restaurant. The decor is sleek, yet casual, and the staff is friendly. Diners' comments include: "Inexpensive, but blasé." "Good location, ordinary pasta."
SPEC: *Grilled portobello mushrooms w/gorgonzola polenta $6.95; Pizzas from $6.95-$8.95; Grilled rib eye steak "Arrabiata style" $16.95*

PETER'S LD Continental

(E14) 182 Columbus Ave. (68th & 69th) 212/877-4747 Fax: 496-7466

F 4 / S 6 / A 4 / $25 MC V AE **TO**

A lively bar scene with soap opera stars and ABC employees keep Peter's bustling at lunch and after work. "Pretty setting, but only mediocre food."
SPEC: *Tex-Mex shrimp or chicken quesadilla $7.95; Pasta strudel $12.95; Chicken margarita $13.95; Calf's liver $14.95*

PICHOLINE　　　　LD　　　French

(F14) 35 W. 64th St. (CPW & B'way) 212/724-8585

F 7 / S 7 / A 7 / $39　　MC V D AE

This beautiful French Mediterranean neighbor to Lincoln Center is romantic and elegant. It's named for the variety of olives that are on every table, which give Picholine its warm, green theme. Their fabulous cheese cart is quickly becoming world famous (as is chef, Terrance Brennan), and be sure to choose a glass of wine from their award winning list. "Welcome dining in Lincoln Center neighborhood."

SPEC: *Organic mesclun salad $8; Ceviche of Spanish mackerel $9; Organic free range chicken $22; Moroccan spice loin of lamb $25; Coconut tuile cannoli $8; warm rhubarb streusel crisp $8*

PIPINA PRESTO　　　LD　　　Italian

(D14) 434 Amsterdam Ave. (81st) 212/721-9141

F 6 / S 6 / A 4 / $21　　MC V DIS　　**TO/D**

The classic trattoria-style interior, with art deco posters from France, Italy and the USA covering the walls should tip you off that you're in for classic, regional Italian cuisine. And you won't be disappointed. The food is reasonably priced and, even more important, good. The outdoor, elevated "porch" is a prime people-watching spot.

SPEC: *Filet mignon in Barolo wine sauce $17.95; Fettuccine verde con frutti di mare $13.95; Risotto pescatore $13.95*

PIU BELLO　　　　BLD　　　Pastry

(E13) 2152 Broadway (75th & 76th) 212/268-4400

F 4 / S 5 / A 5 / $9　　Cash only　　**TO**

Skip dessert at Ernie's and head next door to the newest pasticerria in the neighborhood for a cannoli and cappuccino. Piu Bello also serves sandwiches, quiches and other snack items.

SPEC: *Mini bun (ham, tomato, Swiss) $3; Whole wheat hero $5.95; Stuffed avocado $5.95; Napoleon, eclair, cannoli, & other pastries $2-$5*

POPOVER CAFE　　　BLD　　　American

(D14) 551 Amsterdam Ave. (86th & 87th) 212/595-8555

F 6 / S 6 / A 6 / $27　　MC V AE　　**TO**

The only place in New York where genuine, old-fashioned popovers are served. And while teddy bears may populate the seats, it's Upper West Siders who line up at the door and onto Amsterdam Avenue on weekend mornings, salivating for those delicious concoctions smeared with strawberry butter. "Fun for kids." "Comfort food."

SPEC: *Popovers w/strawberry butter 3 for $3.75; Taravari sandwich $9.25; Mad Russian sandwich $8.95*

PUCCINI　　　　BLD　　　Italian

(D14) 475 Columbus Ave. (83rd) 212/875-9532

F 8 / S 7 / A 5 / $19　　MC V AE　　**TO/D**

Small, unassuming neighborhood Italian cafe. Brick walls give it a country feel. Surprisingly good pastas at shockingly low prices. Good for just hanging out, reading your favorite magazines.

SPEC: *Anti pasti misto $7.50; Funghi ripieni pesto $6.25; Pollo parmeggiano $9.25l Fusilli alla putanesca $8.25*

0	1	2	3	4	5	6	7	8	9	10
disappointing		fair		good		very good		excellent		perfect

JOE MAJOR

Rain

RAIN D Vietnamese

(D14) 100 W. 82nd St. (Col. & Amst) 212/505-0776 Fax: 501-9147

F 7 / S 7 / A 7 / $26 MC V AE

Just what the Upper West Side needed: Another trendy restaurant serving trendy food. Oh, what's a poor Epicurean to do? It's a scene, that's for sure; but the food, a combination of Vietnamese, Thai and Malaysian, is undeniably good, even if the service, especially for larger parties, is spotty. The beer list is vast, but so is the noise level. "Haughty instead of hearty." "Surprisingly good for the neighborhood."

SPEC: *Charred beef salad $9; Vietnamese spring rolls $5.0; Sticky rice $3; Crispy whole fish $19; Fresh green curry chicken $12*

RANCHO MEXICAN CAFE D Mexican

(D14) 466 Amsterdam Ave. (82nd & 83rd) 212/362-1514

F 6 / S 6 / A 7 / $18 MC V AE **TO/D**

A lively eclectic crowd gathers here for the frozen margaritas served by the friendliest bartenders on the Upper West Side. The entrees are ordinary, but it's always a fiesta at the bar, so just plant yourself there, fill up on the chips and salsa, and keep sipping those margaritas. "Great music. Great nachos. Great fun."

SPEC: *Super quesadilla $5; Queso flameado (melted cheese w/Mexican sausage pico de gallo) $5.75 Enchiladas $9; Chile relleno $7.95; Sizzling fajitas $11.50; Homemade flan $3*

RAY BARI PIZZA LD Pizzeria

(E14) 201 Amsterdam Ave. (69th) 212/595-8400

See review on page 176.

RIKYU LD Japanese

(E14) 230 Columbus Ave. (69th & 70th) 212/799-7847

F 6 / S 6 / A 5 / $22 MC V D AE **TO/D**

Eating at Rikyu was formerly a tight squeeze, but the sushi was always fresh and masterfully prepared. Now, after a recent renovation, the sushi continues to be high quality, but the digs are much more comfortable. You might even want to take your shoes off. And for a pre-Lincoln Center meal, Rikyu's $9.95 specials are a steal.

SPEC: *Avocado sashimi $3.75; Salmon teriyaki $11; Rikyu Hamanabe (crab, shrimp, fish, vegetable in soybean broth) $10*

ROYAL CANADIAN PANCAKE HOUSE BLD American

(D13) 2286 Broadway (82nd & 83rd) 212/980-4131

F 5 / S 5 / A 4 / $18   MC V   **TO**

All day breakfast! This Manhattan branch flaps 50 varieties of jacks (from organic wheats to fresh fruits to peanut butter and banana) from dawn to dusk and shores you up with a darn good chocolate chip cornbread. Variations on the genre: hubcap-sized "baked" cakes could feed a family, and the innovative "womlet" an omelette topped waffle. "I don't like eating over-priced pancakes with Nirvana blaring in the background at 8 a.m." "Don't go with a hangover."
SPEC: *Cheddar cheese soup $3.50; 53 types of pancakes including chocolate chip, corn meal, potato, matzoh, and fruit $5.75-$15.75*

RUPPERT'S LD Amer/Continental

(E14) 269 Columbus Ave. (72nd & 73rd) 212/873-9400

F 5 / S 5 / A 5 / $12   MC V D AE   **TO/D**

So you want to have an inexpensive meal, but you crave "atmosphere?" Well, here you'll get the best of both worlds. The rather posh Victorian interior doesn't exactly go with the incredibly low prices, but somehow it works. The menu is surprisingly varied, the food acceptable, and even at these low prices there are plenty of daily specials to choose from.
SPEC: *Steamed mussels $2.95; Fried mozzarella sticks w/marinara sauce $3.25; Blackened or pan-fried catfish w/tequila salsa, rice pilaf & vegetable $6.95; Reese's peanut butter chocolate cake $4.50*

SALOON, THE LD American

(F14) 1920 Broadway (64th) 212/874-1500 Fax: 874-2083

F 6 / S 5 / A 6 / $30   MC V D AE   **TO**

One of the most famous outdoor cafes in the neighborhood offers a long stretch of tables where nosy diners can face the sidewalk and stare at Lincoln Center. It's the ultimate in people watching, though there are times that watching people on the street can dull one's appetite. And watch your back. Those black-clad waiters and waitresses on rollerskates can be hazardous to your health. "The waiters on skates get you to the ballet on time."
SPEC: *Grilled vegetable sandwich $5.95; Roasted red snapper $16.95; Grilled filet mignon $17.95; Angel hair w/shrimp & crabmeat $16.95*

SAMBUCA D Italian

(E14) 20 W. 72nd St. (CPW & Columbus) 212/787-5656

F 6 / S 8 / A 7 / $29   MC V D AE   **TO/D**

This family-style Italian restaurant rode in on Carmine's coattails. But surprisingly the food and prices are comparable to their competition. It's also far less hectic and easily fills the large space which was once a Chinese restaurant.
SPEC: *Fried calamari $12; Zuppa di mussels $10; Penne a la vodka $16; Veal chop Milanese $21.75; Tiramisu $5; Ricotta cheesecake $4*

SANTA FE LD Southwestern

(E14) 72 W. 69th St. (CPW & Columbus) 212/724-0822

F 7 / S 6 / A 7 / $28   MC V D AE

A loyal following of locals and ABC executives have kept Santa Fe thriving for almost 15 years. The food may be one reason, but southwestern ambiance, including a cozy fireplace, give it a romantic feel. "Adobe, 'hot' cuisine takes you to New Mexico."
SPEC: *Black bean soup $4; Spice beef tostada $5.50; Chicken chipolte $15.50; Charcoal grilled swordfish $17.50; Filet mignon fajitas $16.50; Apple crisp $4; Key lime mousse $5*

0	1	2	3	4	5	6	7	8	9	10
disappointing		fair		good		very good		excellent		perfect

SARABETH'S BLD American

(D14) 423 Amsterdam Ave. (80th & 81st) 212/496-6280

F 6 / S 6 / A 7 / $23   MC V D AE DIS

Lots of Polo shirts spill out onto Amsterdam Avenue on Saturday and Sunday mornings in anticipation of cute and tasty specials such as pumpkin waffles and Papa Bear and Mama Bear oatmeal. But it's not only the food that attracts them, but the bed and breakfast ambiance which lets us pretend that we're at a country inn and not in the heart of the cruel, gritty city.

SPEC: *Oatmeal $4.50; Goldie Lox eggs $9.50; Pumpkin waffles $8.25; Club sandwiches $10.25*

SENOR SWANKY'S LD Mexican

(E14) 287 Columbus Ave. (73rd & 74th) 212/501-7000

F 5 / S 4 / A 4 / $20   MC V AE   **TO/D**

They call it a "Mexican Cafe and Celebrity Hangout," but this is obviously wishful thinking since we've never seen even a celebrity look-alike lingering about. And the menu, which we admit is interesting, has items named for California, Florida, and Texas. But it's obviously all tongue-in-cheek, which is where you hope you can keep it while you eat. The food is pretty good and the atmosphere is much the same as it was when this was the Blue Moon.

SPEC: *East meets west wings $6.50; Chino Latino kabobs $6.50; Florida burrito $7.95; Fajita pita $7.75; Pollo limon $10.95*

SFUZZI LD Italian

(F14) 58 W. 65th St. (B'way & CPW) 212/873-3700 Fax: 873-1390

F 6 / S 6 / A 4 / $33   MC V D AE DIS   **TO**

Bustling at lunch, as well as pre-Lincoln Center performances, this is a popular hangout for ABC network executives, newscasters, and soap stars. And, for a national chain, the food is surprisingly good.

SPEC: *Calamari $7.25; Frozen Sfuzzi drink $5.75; Brick oven pizza 14.95; Romano crusted chicken $19.95; Tiramisu w/leghorn sauce $6*

SHARK BAR, THE LD Southern

(E14) 307 Amsterdam Ave. (74th & 75th) 212/874-8500

F 8 / S 7 / A 6 / $26   MC V D AE   **TO/D**

Rosie Perez at one table, Rodney Hampton at another, and Greg Anthony (before he was plucked from the Knicks in the expansion draft) sipping a Coke at the bar. This is a typical night at The Shark Bar, one of the best spots on the Upper West Side to hobnob with sports stars and musical celebrities. And the food ain't bad either. "Yams to make love to." "Fun and funky."

SPEC: *Honey dipped fried chicken $11.75; Georgia bark catfish $12.75; Peach cobbler $4.50; Sweet potato pie $3.95*

STICK TO YOUR RIBS LD Southern

(D14) 433 Amsterdam Ave. (80th) 212/501-7897
See review on page 253.

SUPERSTARS SPORTS & STEAK D American

(E14) 208 W. 70th St. (Amst) 212/877-6787 Fax: 877-6867

F 3 / S 4 / A 4 / $20   MC V D AE DIS

Formerly known as Lee Mazzilli's, but the ex-Met bailed out, hence the name change. Otherwise, it's pretty much status quo: a spacious sports bar with memorabilia and TVs in great abundance. Saturdays and Sundays in the fall and winter, it's jammed for football. Sports celebrities occasionally stop by. The food is your average sports pub fare.

SPEC: *Buffalo chicken wings $4.95; Cajun burger $9.95; Danish baby back ribs $14.95; Cajun chicken breast $11.95; Mom's apple pie $2.95*

TACO MADRE   BLD   Mexican

(D13) 2345 Broadway (85th) 212/873-0600 Fax: 873-7619

F 5 / S 5 / A 3 / $11   Cash only   **TO/D**

One of the leaders in the recent New York taqueria explosion...and one of the city's best. It's really nothing more than Mexican fast food, but it's a heckuva lot better than McDonald's.

SPEC: *Huevos con tocino $1.75; Chile verde $1.50; Tortilla sandwich $4.95; Quesadilla $5.50; Fajitas del rancho $8.95*

Tavern on the Green

TAVERN ON THE GREEN   LD   American

(F14) Central Park West & 67th St. 212/873-3200 Fax: 873-6405

F 6 / S 6 / A 8 / $45   MC V D AE DIS

One of N.Y.'s prettiest restaurants that has traditionally attracted large crowds, especially tourists. Current 3-star chef, Patrick Clark, has created dishes for Odeon and Cafe Luxembourg before Warner LeRoy lured him here in an effort to upgrade the restaurant menu. The virtues here are many: It's an eating/tourist emporium with gift shops and multiple private party rooms. There's a hard to beat brunch in the cafe overlooking Central Park.

SPEC: *Foie gras $16; Moroccan style barbecued salmon $26; Pan roasted Chilean sea bass $26; Grilled pork porterhouse $26*

TEACHER'S TOO   LD   Continental

(D13) 2271 Broadway (81st & 82nd) 212/362-4900

F 7 / S 7 / A 5 / $22   MC V D AE   **TO**

On a very busy stretch of Broadway, this is a place to imbibe and eat during breaks from Barnes & Noble's and Zabar's. The cuisine is an unusual and unpredictable mix of regular pub fare, continental and Thai specials. Beats us as to who came up with this mix, but it seems to work since they've managed to stay in business since 1970. "Don't miss the pork strips in peanut sauce." "Best value by far on the West Side."

SPEC: *Indonesian chicken sate $5.95; Classic Buffalo chicken wings $4.95; Chicken gai yang $9.95; Grilled K.C. strip steak $16.95*

TIBET SHAMBALA RESTAURANT   LD   Tibetan

(D14) 488 Amsterdam Ave. (83rd & 84th) 212/721-1270

F 5 / S 6 / A 4 / $15   MC V D   **TO/D**

Tibetan cuisine, though distinctive, is heavily influenced by the foods of China and India. This refuge on a battered Amsterdam Avenue block serves good, comforting, home-cooked ethnic food. "Pretend you're on a Himalayan mountain top in a Tibetan Monk's sanctuary." "The food served will nourish your body and enlighten your soul." **Closed: Every day from 4-6**

SPEC: *Ruthang momo $3; Dumplings stuffed w/potatoes $6.25; Chicken curry $8.25; Sha dofu $7.25; Deyshee $2.50; Bhatsa maghu $3.25*

0	1	2	3	4	5	6	7	8	9	10
disappointing		fair		good		very good		excellent		perfect

WEST 60TH – 86TH STREET

TWO TWO TWO   D   American

(D13) 222 W. 79th St. (B'way and Amst) 212/799-0400

F 8 / S 8 / A 7 / $41   MC V D AE DIS

Chef Frank Dalla Riva creates magic each night in the kitchen of this converted townhouse. The dining room is small, but beautifully structured, and a small smoking area near the bar is a place for those who like to puff before, between or after the sumptuous meal. A neighborhood restaurant so elegant and so good it should be savored for special occasions.

SPEC: *Two Two Two fish soup (lobster, tarragon broth, thickened w/melted leeks served w/seared tuna, salmon, focaccia & rouille) $10; Foie gras ravioli $14; Pan seared Atlantic salmon $25; Prime rack of lamb $34; Maple creme brulee $8.50*

VINCE AND EDDIE'S   LD   American

(E14) 70 W. 68th St. (Col. & CPW) 212/721-0068

F 7 / S 7 / A 8 / $39   MC V D AE DIS

There once was a Vince and Eddie, but as far as this "quaint, comfortable, and charming," restaurant is concerned, they are no longer, But their legacy lives on, with "wonderful" American cuisine, "perfectly prepared." The setting couldn't be nicer. "It's like dining in someone's townhouse."

WEST 63RD STREET STEAKHOUSE   D   American

(F14) 44 W. 63rd St. (B'way & Lincoln Center) 212/246-6363

F 6 / S 6 / A 4 / $44   MC V D AE DIS

Nice hotel dining with a heavy nod to "male bonding." Hence, a perfect place to treat a good "buddy" on his promotion. If the prices were a little better, there wouldn't be any problem with this Lincoln Center steakhouse offering reliable food. But they are a little steep.
Closed: Sunday and Monday
SPEC: *Maryland lump crabcake $10.50; Escargot $9; Prime Porterhouse for two $27 per person; 12 oz. center cut filet mignon $27*

WORLD CAFE   LD   Continental

(E14) 201 Columbus Ave. (69th)799- 80-90

F 4 / S 5 / A 5 / $30   MC V D AE   **TO/D**

A lively, casual, Upper West Side eatery that features reasonably priced well-presented and solid items such as burgers, sandwiches, salads and pastas. The main dining room is attractive, with light-colored stucco walls, and there's a cozy room with fireplace in back. A lively bar scene at night..
SPEC: *Crostini Gamberetti $7.95; Portobello salad $7.95; Semolina crusted red snapper $16.95; Rack of lamb $22.95; Lobster ravioli $15.95*

YING   LD   Chinese

(E14) 117 W. 70th St. (Col. & B'way) 212/724-2031

F 6 / S 6 / A 7 / $25   MC V AE   **TO**

Tina Ying is a charming, vivacious host whose colorful flair is reflected in the eclectic menu and the hip ambiance of her post-modern interior. This is one of the few Chinese restaurants with an outdoor garden. Truly distinctive in atmosphere and food, Ying also offers live jazz on Sunday.
SPEC: *Baby snow pea leaves $9.95; Crispy fried chicken wings $3.95; Orange duck $14.95; Sizzling hot wok $17.95*

WEST 87TH STREET & UP

BIRDLAND   D   Continental

(B13) 2745 Broadway (105th) 212/749-2228

F 5 / S 7 / A 6 / $19   MC V D   **TO**

This dimly lit supper club/jazz joint specializes in soulful, late-night acts, but also puts out reliable, if "too expensive," Southern meals. Tables are angled toward the stage. The Cajun-farmhouse menu will go more "down-home" in coming months, but that's hard to imagine as diners are already there for seafood gumbo, fish and ribs. Live jazz at brunch is soothing and "good," and homemade muffins and cornbread flow freely.
SPEC: *Louisiana shrimp boil $7.95; Creole macaroni & peas $8.95; Honey-dipped Georgia fried chicken $10.95; Pecan pie $4.95*

BLUE COLLAR CAFE   LD   American

(B14) 940 Amsterdam Ave. (106th & 107th) 212/864-9212

F 6 / S 6 / A 7 / $17   MC V   **TO/D**

This "earnest and imaginative" retro-bistro, tucked in a borderline Upper West Side neighborhood, attracts a casual, family crowd for "Fine Dining at Blue Collar Prices." Burgers, mashed potatoes, and chocolate mud cake to arugula, braised salmon, or Tuscan veal stew. "A breath of fresh air compared to the unbearable lines at E.J.'s."
SPEC: *Hot spinach salad $4.75; Roasted chicken w/two mustard glaze $8.95; Tuscan veal stew $9.95; Pecan pie $3.75*

JOE MAJOR

Boulevard

BOULEVARD   LD   American

(C14) 2378 Broadway (88th) 212/874-7400

F 5 / S 5 / A 3 / $26   MC V D AE   **TO/D**

The pig reigns supreme here, as evidenced by the porcine decorations scattered throughout this multi-level restaurant. As for the food, maybe it's not the best barbecue you'll ever have, but it's not bad for a Yankee establishment. Be warned: this is a kid-friendly restaurant—to some, it's "turned into a day care center,"— so you might consider bringing the earplugs.
SPEC: *Cajun popcorn shrimp $4.95; Crackerjack crawfish $5.95; Smoked BBQ salmon $14.95; Deep dish sour cream apple pie $4.75*

BROADWAY COTTAGE   LD   Chinese

(B13) 2690 Broadway (103rd) 212/316-2600

F 6 / S 7 / A 6 / $13   MC V AE

This popular spot happens to be one of the best run Szechuan restaurants in town. Though many call it standard fare, it's also "cheap and cheerful, you can get sloshed on the free wine." And though it can get noisy, it doesn't seem to bother its loyal following.
SPEC: *Szechuan dumplings $3.75; House special bean curd $6.50; Sesame shrimp $8.95; Prawns w/ young ginger root $8.95*

0	1	2	3	4	5	6	7	8	9	10
disappointing		fair		good		very good		excellent		perfect

BROADWAY COTTAGE II   LD   Chinese

(C13) 2492 Broadway (92nd & 93rd) 212/873-0221
See review on page 243.

CAFE MOZART   LD   Pastry

(C14) 70 W. 90th St. (Col. & Amst.) 212/678-7777
See review on page 226.

CAFE ST. JOHN   LD   Continental

(A14) 1018 Amsterdam Ave. (110th) 212/932-8420
F 6 / S 6 / A 7 / $22   AE   TO

A Mediterranean bistro that has "a unique alternative location," just yards from the Cathedral of St. John the Divine. This "well-kept secret," is airy and clean, with tile floors and giant, mahogany-framed windows which are open in summer to lend sunshine. Columbia faculty and neighborhood regulars fill the place evenings. Entrees are large enough to share if preceded by starters.
SPEC: *Normandy stew $14.75; Bouillabaisse $16.75; Gumbo $14.75; Louisiana crabcakes $15.25*

CARMINE'S   D   Italian

(C14) 2450 Broadway (90th & 91st) 212/362-2200
F 4 / S 5 / A 3 / $28   AE   TO

Carmine's tries to replicate old-time outer boroughs' Southern Italian restaurants. It's pleasing on the wallet, as platters are large enough for two or more. But the food suffers from mass production. Garlic may be the most pleasing herb on earth, but sometimes the chefs at Carmine's overload it to the point where diners suggest "bringing Binaca." Some call it "too much of a bad thing," deplore "the noise," and "hate the no reservations policy."
SPEC: *Zuppa di clams $14.50; Spiedini alla Romana $10.50; Chicken scarpiello $18.50; Linguini w/clam sauce $17.50; Chicken contadina $28.50*

COPELAND'S   D   Southern

(C20) 547 W. 145th (B'way & Amst.) 212/234-2357 F
F 7 / S 7 / A 7 / $26   MC V D AE DIS   TO

Southern food might be the cuisine of the moment, with downtown soul shacks sprouting on every block. But for the real thing go uptown, to Copeland's. There's a small bar and buffet area, a cafeteria adjacent to the dining room with paintings of musicians and scenes of Africa on the walls. Live jazz every night, and a gospel brunch on Sunday. The all-you-can-eat buffet is a steal, but make sure you leave room for their spectacular desserts.
Closed: Monday
SPEC: *Potato next w/creme fraiche & caviar $5.50; Pan fried chicken $9.50; Seafood jambalaya $16.50; Catfish $10.50*

DOCKS OYSTER BAR   LD   Seafood

(C13) 2427 Broadway (89th & 90th) 212/724-5588
F 7 / S 6 / A 6 / $30   MC V D AE DIS   TO

Though you may be tempted, it's best not to get too fancy here. Stick to steamed, broiled and froiled seafood, as "all else is mediocre, including actor wanna-be waiters." A bit pricey for the Upper West Side, and sometimes "crowded, noisy and rushed," but a good spot for special occasions." Sunday and Monday are New England Clambake Nights.
SPEC: *Steamers in beer broth $9; Maryland crabcake $8.50; Raw bar-oyster combo $13; Lobsters P/A; Imported sorbet $5*

FISH   LD   Seafood

(A13) 2799 Broadway (108th) 212/864-5000

F 6 / S 5 / A 4 / $22   MC V AE   **TO/D**

A reasonably priced fish house decorated in dark blue tones, lending it a decided deep sea feel. The fish is "fresh and served well." Clientele comes from the neighborhood or nearby Columbia.

SPEC: *Littleneck clams 1/2 doz. $4.95; Deep fried oysters $5.95; Rainbow trout $9.95; Pan seared salmon w/sun dried cherry butter $12.95; Steamed mussels & Littleneck clams over penne pasta $10.95*

FLORIDITA   BLD   Mediterranean

(E20) 3219 Broadway (128th & 129th) 212/662-0090
(E20) 3451 Broadway (141st) 212/926-0319
(A20) 4172 Broadway (177th) 212/928-06-53

F 5 / S 5 / A 6 / $15   MC V DIS D AE   **TO/D**

Spanish family diner chain with Harlem and Bronx locations serves reliable soupy rice, chicken and fish dishes in a shiny, antiseptic environment. Breakfast here is an especially reasonable treat. A takeout bakery showcases tempting desserts and homemade breads.

SPEC: *Rice w/shrimp $4.75; Shrimp stew $4.75; Chicken w/rice $6; Steak in sauce $8*

GABRIELA RESTAURANT & TAQUERIA   LD   Mexican

(C14) 685 Amsterdam Ave. (93rd) 212/961-0574

F 6 / S 5 / A 4 / $18   MC V AE DIS   **TO/D**

Authentic Mexican taqueria, but without the fast food trappings of the California-style version proliferating throughout the city of late. The light, airy, sunny room, along with colorful pastels on the walls and ceiling fans, makes it reminiscent of a tropical Mexican cafe. Patrons are a melting pot mix of neighborhood Latinos and gentrified yuppies. "Long waits" make some wish "they'd take reservations." Don't forget to try the excellent fresh fruit drinks.

SPEC: *Posole $6.95; Stuffed corn tortilla w/fried black beans, shredded pork topped w/marinated onions $3.25; Rotisserie chicken $8.95; Roast pork marinated $8.95*

GANDHIJEE   LD   Indian

(B13) 2667 Broadway (101st & 102nd) 212/932-1169

F 6 / S 7 / A 6 / $16   MC V D AE   **TO/D**

A remarkably quiet spot off a remarkably loud avenue, this underrated restaurant serves satisfying Indian fare with aplomb. The curries sizzle and the breads are especially tasty—all for reasonable prices. "The service is terrific," and "so's the food."

SPEC: *Samosa $2.25; Chicken chat $2.75; Chicken curry $6.95; Lamb or beef sabji $8.95; Murgi kebab $9.95*

HUNAN BALCONY   LD   Chinese

(B13) 2596 Broadway (98th) 212/865-0400

F 5 / S 6 / A 3 / $18   V D AE   **TO/D**

An Upper West Side institution. Although it offers the standard Chinese menu, including Cantonese and Szechuan classics, the quality of the food is "always dependable." Maybe that's why the restaurant boasts photographs of the owner and chefs with celebrities like Mike Tyson, Alan Alda and Jackie Mason. If it's good enough for them, it should be good enough for us.

SPEC: *Hunan flower steak $8.75; Rainbow prawns $10.95; General Tso's chicken $8.75*

0	1	2	3	4	5	6	7	8	9	10
disappointing		fair		good		very good		excellent		perfect

HUNGARIAN PASTRY SHOP BLD Hungarian

(A14) 1030 Amsterdam Ave. (110th & 111th) 212/866-4230

F 5 / S 5 / A 5 / $6   Cash only   **TO**

One of the oldest European-style cafes in New York. The tables are populated by coffee-sipping writers, poets, journalists and students from nearby Columbia University.

SPEC: *Cappuccino $2.25; Hungarian pastries $2; Croissants $1.30*

INDIAN CAFE LD Indian

(A13) 2791 Broadway (108th) 212/749-9200

F 6 / S 8 / A 4 / $13   MC V AE   **TO/D**

It's not much to look at—the decor of this "pleasant" restaurant will do little to please even the least discriminating eye. On the other hand, if you've got a hankering for "great Indian food for the buck," and you're not in the mood to trek all the way down to the East Village, Indian Cafe will fill the void.

SPEC: *Chickpeas noodles w/dice boiled potato $2.95; Tikka biryani $6.95; Chicken muglai $7.95; Kheer (rice pudding) $2.25*

LA ROSITA BLD Spanish

(A13) 2809 Broadway (108th & 109th) 212/663-7804

F 7 / S 5 / A 5 / $14   MC V D AE   **TO**

A small Spanish diner that serves the best cafe con leche around, along with an all-day breakfast of eggs and black beans and rice. Also, you'll find delicious grilled sandwiches at incredibly reasonable prices. At night chicken, steak and seafood in garlic and hot sauces are served with plantains, rice or bean dishes.

SPEC: *Tamales $2; Platana relleno $4.25; Beef stew $5.25; Ropa vieja (shredded beef) $6; Slice of fried king fish $6.25*

LEMONGRASS GRILL LD Thai

(C13) 2534 Broadway (94th & 95th) 212/666-0888

F 6 / S 6 / A 6 / $17   MC V   **TO/D**

It's decorated to replicate a tropical, Southeast Asia bungalow, with ceiling fans, dark wood interior and an open kitchen, Lemongrass serves authentic Thai food at remarkably reasonable prices. Diners extol it's "great, interesting food," but complain that it's "very crowded."

SPEC: *Satay chicken $4.95; Vegetable dumplings $4.95; Pork chops $7.25; Pad see yu (fried broad rice noodles w/Chinese broccoli, eggs & chicken or beef) $6.50*

LES ROUTIERS D French

(C14) 568 Amsterdam Ave. (87th & 88th) 212/874-2742

F 6 / S 6 / A 6 / $32   MC V D AE DIS

A small, cozy, French bistro "in a rustic setting," with a country interior and a great separate dining room in the back, perfect for those weekend têtes a têtes. If you're in a quandary as to which wine to order, just check the menu for suggestions as to what goes best with the entree you order. And if you have questions about the menu, "the chef comes out to discuss dishes!"

SPEC: *Assorted charcuterie & crudities $9.50; Mussels steamed in white wine & herbs $7; Bouillabaisse $22.50; Fillet of rainbow trout $17.50*

MANA   LD   Japanese

(C13) 2444 Broadway (90th & 91st) 212/787-1110

F 6 / S 6 / A 6 / $19   Cash only   **TO/D**

A cozy vegetarian spot frustratingly true to its cause. Decor and food are earthy. Put maple syrup in coffee and eat tofu mock meat or "scrambled eggs." Some thrive on it. The vegetable plate is well-seasoned, immense salads are served with flavorful tahini. Give us a turkey on toast and a diet Coke, but we still manage to give it a thumbs up.

SPEC: *Yuba $5; Yakko (raw tofu w/ponzu sauce) $5.50; Seitan stroganoff $9; Salmon corn chowder $14; Tofu pie $3.25*

MARY ANN'S   LD   Mexican

(C13) 2454 B'way (91st) 212/877-0132
See review on page 194.

MO' BETTER   D   Amer/Soul

(C14) 570 Amsterdam Ave. (87th & 88th) 212/580-7755

F 3 / S 4 / A 4 / $25   MC V D   AE   **TO**

In a neighborhood where Southern cooking and barbecue restaurants are popping up like Chinese noodle houses, this one lags behind the rest. The food is mediocre and the service "the worst ever.". However, the live music—Jazz, Funk, Soul, and R & B—is a definite plus, and perhaps the only reason to visit.

SPEC: *Chef's spicy wings $4.95; Catfish $13.95; Fried chicken $10.95; Salmon $15.95; Pork chops $12.95*

NACHO MAMA'S   LD   Mexican

(A13) 2877 Broadway (110th & 111th) 212/666-6187

F 6 / S 6 / A 6 / $14   Cash only   **TO/D**

Mexican burritos and classic margaritas make this a place enjoyed by everyone, including the University crowd. The extensive delivery menu makes this the place to order from to cater to your needs after a long day at school or the office, poker night, or a VCR flick.

SPEC: *Black bean soup $2.95; San Francisco-style chicken wings $6.95; Nacho Mama's burrito $5.95; Spinach enchilada $6.50*

POSITIVELY 104TH STREET   BLD   American

(B13) 2725 Broadway (104th) 212/316-0372

F 6 / S 5 / A 6 / $19   MC V AE DIS

An unpretentious restaurant that has three things going for it: decent food, friendly service, and bagels from H & H. In a neighborhood not particularly known for good restaurants, Pos. 104th is a haven for local writers, artists, and actors. Diners applaud the "bargain" prices, but say that sometimes it appears "no one's in charge here."

SPEC: *Arugula caesar salad $4.75; Country pate $4.785; Florentine ravioli w/puttanesca sauce $10.50; Blackened yellow fin tuna $12.75; Lemon angel food cake w/raspberry puree $3*

SAVANNAH CLUB, THE   D   American/Soul

(C13) 2420 Broadway (89th) 212/496-1066

F 8 / S 5 / A 4 / $23   MC V D   AE DIS   **TO**

This airy newcomer offers the down home cookin' that made Scarlett crawl back to Tara. An Alabama-bred mother-daughter chef team fry up chicken or catfish to die for, with gravy and all the fixin's. Friendly service. Generous portions. And excellent value. No pasta and sauce here!

SPEC: *Sweet potato fries $3.95; BBQ pork ribs $5.95; Catfish fritters $5.95; Mama's fried chicken $9.95; Sweet potato pie $4.95*

0	1	2	3	4	5	6	7	8	9	10
disappointing		fair		good		very good		excellent		perfect

TERRACE   **LD**   **French**

(F20) 400 W. 119th St. (Amst. & Morningside) 212/666-9490

F 8 / S 7 / A 8 / $45   MC V D AE   **TO**

There's a hike uptown to get there, but once you've arrived you'll be treated to one of the nicest views of the city north of the World Trade Center. The "sensational view" isn't the only thing that stands out. The food is "terrific," the service "outstanding," and the ambiance "perfect for a romantic evening."
SPEC: *Feuillete of seafood w/lobster sauce $13; Red snapper Adriatic style $25; Sliced breast of Muscovy duck and leg confit $26*

ZULA   **LD**   **Ethiopian**

(F20) 1260 Amsterdam Ave. (122nd) 212/663-1670

F 6 / S 6 / A 6 / $20   MC D AE DIS   **TO**

A cozy Ethiopian restaurant serving up traditional African cuisine to Columbia students, Harlem residents, and the Morningside Heights crowd. Diners ask for healthy Eritrean vegetarian dishes, but the pride of the house is lamb. African honey wine, and ten varieties of bottled beer make for a convenient trip to a faraway place. Late bar hours help make this "fun African."
SPEC: *Samabusse (beef, green chili & herbs) $4.75; Alitcha (lamb w/onions& green peppers) $8.50; Rum cake $2.95*

BROOKLYN

CAFFE BUON GUSTO   **LD**   **Italian**

(B27) 151 Montague St.   718/624-3838
See review on page 151.

HENRY'S END   **D**   **Continental**

(B27) 44 Henry St. (Cranberry & Middagh) 718/834-1776

F 6 / S 6 / A 3 / $28   MC V D AE

An award from the Wine Spectator in the window of a Brooklyn Heights restaurant? Yes, along with minimal atmosphere and food that would easily hold its own in Manhattan. Some call it "a jewel" with a "central-casting wait staff." While others wonder if they've "changed chefs" lately.
SPEC: *Blackened tuna salad $7.95; Bar-B-Q ribs $6.95; Boned duckling $16.50-$17.50; Soft shell crabs $19.95; Mud pie $5*

LA BOUILLABAISSE   **D**   **French**

(C27) 145 Atlantic Ave. (Clinton & Henry) 718/522-8275

F 6 / S 6 / A 5 / $24   Cash only

A "Paris comes to Brooklyn" bistro that has them lining up on the sidewalk. The decor is nothing special, but the menu certainly is. It's BYOB and diners should expect a weekend wait for dinner for the fresh Provencal-style seafood. You will be rewarded for your patience.

Doc Cheatham
Jazz Trumpeter

"When I eat out it's often at **Sylvia's**. It's the closest thing to home cooking I've found in the city. And the people make you feel like family."

MARCO POLO — LD — Italian

(D27) 345 Court St. (Union) 718/852-5015 Fax: 852-4515

F 5 / S 5 / A 5 / $27   MC V D AE DIS

Brooklyn's power elite favor this cozy spot where Italian special-ties reign and "service and food are as consistent as time." Taste snobs need not apply, but there is a warmth here decorators can't buy. A sunroom in fine weather; a working fireplace brightens the chilly months; and there's piano music nightly—the better to hold hands to, my dear. A party room upstairs jumps on special occa-sions.

SPEC: *Carpaccio de pesce spada $9.50; Spiedini alla Romana $7.95; Rack of lamb (for 2) $46.95; Bistecca ai Ferri $17.95*

NEW PROSPECT CAFE — LD — Southwestern

(E29) 393 Flatbush Ave. (8th Ave.) 718/638-2148

F 6 / S 7 / A 6 / $24   AE

This "cozy spot" has earned a faithful neighborhood clientele the hard way: with healthy, consistently tasty food and friendly service. Highlights includes a delicious organic free range chicken and numerous daily seafood specials.

SPEC: *Blackened duck and fontina fajita $6.25; Organic free-range chicken $12.25; Blackened catfish $12.25*

PATSY'S — LD — Pizzeria

(A28) 19 Old Fulton St. (Water & Front) 718/858-4300

F 7 / S 6 / A 5 / $15   Cash only   **TO**

Top 10 $0-20
Inexpensive

The line runs out the door and wraps around the corner on week-end nights. But it's worth the wait. Wood-fired ovens generate thin-crusted pizza with fresh buttery mozzarella and your choice of toppings. This is a "family place," and it can be "noisy." Some call it the "best pizza in N.Y., while others complain that "it's over-rated," and that "service is slow and inattentive." **Closed: Tuesday**

SPEC: *Pizzas $11- $22 (depending on size and toppings)*

PETER LUGER STEAK HOUSE — LD — American

(A30) 178 Broadway (Driggs Ave.) 718/387-7400

F 7 / S 6 / A 6 / $50   Cash only   **TO/D**

The attitude goes something like this: "We've been here over 100 years and we have this 'steak' thing down pat." Which makes one diner wish "they delivered." The choice is simple: Steak or fish. The only real question is "How do you want that cooked?" Almost universally considered "the best steak in N.Y," though some call it "overpriced." The neighborhood isn't great, but the steak is.

SPEC: *Jumbo shrimp cocktail $10.95; Steak for 2 $55.90; Fish of the day $18.95; Double loin lamb chops (2) $25.95*

RASPUTIN — LD — Russian

(B25) 2670 Coney Island Ave. (Ave. X) 718/332-8333

F 6 / S 6 / A 6 / $50   MC V AE

If you like late-night cabaret as a backdrop to Russian and French cuisine, and can stand the rude wait staff, you and Rasputin just might get along. However, at $50 to $65 per prix fixe dinner, some might resent a waiter suggesting that those with menu questions should order juice. That Rasputin, we say, is one mean rascal.

0 disappointing	1	2 fair	3	4 good	5	6 very good	7	8 excellent	9	10 perfect

RED ROSE, THE   D   Italian

(D27) 315 Smith St. (President & Union) 718/625-0963

F 6 / S 7 / A 5 / $17   MC V

A neighborhood find where the menu specialties stretch on to infinity. The service is good-natured and personal. The "great food" is unbelievably inexpensive. The atmosphere is cozy, and might make you believe, as it did one diner, "that the Godfather was in the corner." **Closed: Tuesday**

SPEC: *Zucchini marinara $4; Fettuccini Alfredo $6.95; Chicken picante served w/croquettes $7.50; Strawberry ice cream w/blueberry or peach cognac $4*

RIVER CAFE   LD   American

(A27) 1 Water St. (East River) 718/522-5200

F 8 / S 6 / A 8 / $58   MC V D AE

Buzzy O'Keefe's floating seafood emporium has some of the freshest fish in N.Y. In addition to the fabulous seafood, there's a great selection of other American food. It also offers a great view of Manhattan. The service staff is very friendly, hospitable and charming. It's expensive, but well worth a trip across the bridge for a romantic evening.

SPEC: *Prix-fixe menu: Pan roasted lobster w/cucumber linguine;Pan seared poussin breast w/foie gras corn caket; Pheasant steak w/grilled artichoke ravioli $58*

SLADE'S RESTAURANT   LD   Seafood

(B27) 107 Montague St. 718/858-1200 Fax: 858-1201

F 6 / S 6 / A 5 / $29   MC V D AE DIS   **TO/D**

A neighborhood haunt on the Height's main drag. This casual mecca now features a seafood menu and a raw bar. It's a local scene where heights-ians gather for weekend brunch, an after work drink, or to "hang" at one of Montague Street's outdoor cafes in season.

SPEC: *Seafood gumbo $4.95; Popcorn fried crayfish $6.50; Clam bake $17.95; Yellowfin tuna steak $17.95; Steamed sea bass $17.50*

TERESA'S   BLD   Polish

(B27) 80 Montague St. (Hicks & Montague Terrace) 718/797-3996
See review on page 72.

TRIPOLI   LD   Middle Eastern

(C27) 156 Atlantic Ave. (Clinton) 718/596-5800

F 6 / S 6 / A 6 / $21   MC V D AE

A popular Lebanese restaurant offering a creative shipboard decor complete with mural of coastal Tripoli to really get you in the mood. The "solid" menu is extensive without being expensive. Downstairs—where the food cost runs slightly higher— every Saturday there's live music and belly dancing. Reservations are a must.

SPEC: *Hommos B'tahini $4.25; Tripoli Maza (appetizer plate) $9; Shish kabob $13.25; Kibbee B'siniye $10.50; Milk pudding $3.50*

TUTTA PASTA   LD   Italian

(E29) (Garfield Pl. & 1st) 160 7th Ave. 718/788-9500
See review on page 95.

TWO BOOTS D Pizzeria

(F29) 514 2nd St. (7th & 8th Aves.) 718/499-3383

F 6 / S 7 / A 7 / $16 MC V D AE **TO/D**

Okay, okay, Cajun/Italian/Pizza doesn't sound particularly appetizing but take it from us, it works. Two Boots has a playful, Bohemian air about it, and serves an eclectic array of pizzas (ever had crawfish with extra cheese?) A great place to take the kids...but only if they'll let you tag along.
SPEC: *Jammin' jambalaya $10.95; Catfish Milanese $10.95; Pizzas (sm) $5.50-$9.75; Peanut butter sigh pie $3.75*

BRONX

ANN & TONY'S LD Italian

(A24) 2407 Arthur Ave. (187th St.) 718/933-1469

F 6 / S 6 / A 4 / $25 MC V D AE **TO**

In a neighborhood famous for its Italian food, Ann & Tony's has been a fixture since 1927 and has thrived for four generations. It's what eating on Arthur Avenue is all about. Forget the "tacky" decor, featuring mirrored walls, patterned tablecloths, greenery and year-round Christmas lights, and enjoy the food.
SPEC: *Hot antipasto $9; Pollo Ann & Tony's $14.95; Tripe $12.95;*

DOMINICK'S LD Italian

(A24) 2335 Arthur Ave. (187th St.) 718/733-2807

F 7 / S 7 / A 6 / $26 Cash only **TO**

"Stuff your face, and wish you hadn't." This family-style Southern Italian restaurant was one of the models for Carmine's and others of its ilk. No menus, no check. The waiter tells you what's to order and what to pay. "If only they were in Manhattan," yearns one diner. Long waits on weekends. But now there's an upstairs waiting room complete with bar to alleviate the wait outside in freezing weather. A restaurant with a heart. We love it! **Closed: Tuesday**
SPEC: *Linguini w/shrimp & calamari $15; Pork chops w/hot chili pepper $12; Steak $15; Veal Francese $12*

Mario's

MARIO'S LD Italian

(A24) 2342 Arthur Avenue (187th) 718-584-1188 Fax: 584-1100

F 6 / S 6 / A 5 / $28 MC V D AE DIS **TO**

Despite its Bronx location, Mario's has attracted celebrities like Clint Eastwood, George Lucas and Liz Taylor. Owner Joseph Migliucci treats his customers like family, whether you're famous or not. And the tuxedo clad waiters add a nice touch to the most famous restaurant in the Bronx's Little Italy. "The seafood salad and brick oven pizzas are treasures." **Closed: Monday**
SPEC: *Asparagus Fiorucci $6.75; Octopus salad $7; Spedini a la Romana $8.50; Zuppa di pesce w/ linguine $21.50*

0	1	2	3	4	5	6	7	8	9	10
disappointing		fair		good		very good		excellent		perfect

QUEENS

DAZIES   LD   Italian

(F34) 89-41 Queens Blvd. (40th) 718/786-7013

F 6 / S 6 / A 6 / $30   MC V AE   **TO**

This neighborhood favorite has served "decent" Italian food to families and couples for more than 20 years. Pasta is homemade and comes in more than a dozen varieties. Wines from France, Chile, Italy and Washington State round out the meal. A pianist or classical music accompanies meals.

SPEC: Clams oreganato $7.50; Spinach tortellini pesto $10.95; Pollo alla scarpariello $11.95; Scalloppine Armando $14.95

ELIAS CORNER   D   Greek

(B34) 24-01 31st St. (24th Ave.) 718/932-1510

F 8 / S 6 / A 6 / $24   Cash only   **TO**

Tucked under the subway, in the Greek enclave of Astoria, is Thebes native Elias Sidiroglu's restaurant. Long renowned for its "fresh and fragrant" fish dishes, each of which is on view in a glass butcher case in front—Elias doesn't offer menus. Its homespun environment, including taxidermed bluefish hanging on the wall, disguises what some call the "best grilled seafood in the city."

SPEC: Charred octopus $7; Seafood kabobs P/A; Snapper P/A; Grilled porgies $9-$12; Loukomides $3

GOODY'S CHINESE RESTAURANT   LD   Chinese

(A31) 94-03B 63rd Drive   (Booth & Saunders) 718/896-7159

F 6 / S 6 / A 4 / $14   Cash only   **TO/D**

This "traditional Chinese" draws diners all the way from Westchester with it's great dim sum and variety of other dishes. Known for its steamed soupy buns, the menu covers enough ground to keep both the timid and the adventurous coming back for more. The endearing staff and traditional decor make it well worth the trip from Manhattan.

SPEC: Steamed soupy buns $4.50-$6.50; Sautéed dried bean curd $7.95; Braised pork shoulder $11.95

JACKSON HEIGHTS DINER   LD   Indian

(E36) 37-03 74th St. (37th & Roosevelt) 718/672-1232

F 9 / S 8 / A 4 / $11   Cash only   **TO**

Snuggled in the "Little India" section of Jackson Heights, this "diner" offers an inexpensive selection of "awesome" Indian cuisine "in huge portions" from both north and south. In "spacious" quarters, the friendly staff is willing to help newcomers sample the many varieties of food. Some believe the atmosphere of 74th Street alone is worth the trip.

SPEC: Samosa $1.75; Vegetable pakora $1.75; Tandori chicken $6.75; Murg tikka makhanwala (broiled chicken in curry) $8

JACKSON HOLE   BLD   American

(C36) 69-35 Astoria Blvd. (70th) 718/204-7070

F 5 / S 6 / A 7 / $12   AE   **TO/D**

An original '50s highway diner, filled with antiques, including a cute jukebox loaded with Golden Oldies. Located on the way to LaGuardia airport, movie classics like "Goodfellas" and "Prince of the City," as well as many commercials, were shot here. And oh yeah, the burgers are "killers!"

SPEC: Baldouni style burger $6.20; Kaluba burger (fried onions, tomato, ham, melted cheese) $5.40; Chocolate cake $2.95

KARYATIS — LD — Greek

(D34) 35-03 Broadway (35th & 36th) 718/204-0666

F 6 / S 4 / A 6 / $31   MC V D AE   **TO**

"Eureka!" This traditional Greek restaurant is an international "hot spot" for visiting Greek politicos and celebrities, as well as those of a more domestic variety. The ambiance and "authentic" Greek food makes it "like being in Athens." Live Greek music is featured Tuesday through Sunday.

SPEC: Charcoaled octopus $6.95; Lamb stew $12.95; Baked shredded chicken in red wine, onions, green peppers, fresh tomatoes & Greek sausages $10.95; Baklava $4

LA PORTENA — LD — Argentinian

(E36) 74-25 37th Ave. (74th & 75th) 718/458-8111

F 6 / S 6 / A 5 / $30   MC V D AE   **TO**

Once a butcher shop, La Portena opened its "pleasant, authentic" Argentinian grill to the public in 1990, and has since been serving some of the most seductive cuts of meat in the city. Set in the international community of Jackson Heights, a walk along Roosevelt Avenue en route to a fine meal is half the fun. This is the Zabar's of steakhouses, so bring your appetite.

SPEC: Gaucho pie $1.50; Beef tongue vinaigrette $6.50; Tripe $14.95; Mixed grill $14.95; Sweetbreads $8

PEARSON'S STICK TO YOUR RIBS — LD — Southern

(F31) 5-16 51st Ave. (W. of Vernon Blvd.) 718/937-3030

F 6 / S 4/ A 3 / $18   MC V   **TO**

Pearson's serves Texas barbecue, a tomatoey and spicy sauce used on beef, sausage, hot links, pork shoulder, or chicken, served on homemade Portuguese rolls. For those fans of the vinegar based or "sweet and sour" North Carolina-style barbecue, chopped pork is also available that way. Special barbecues include a wild variety of game—whole pig, wild boar, alligator, venison, buffalo or rattlesnake—available periodically.

SPEC: Barbecued Texas beef sandwich $5; Barbecued sausage $12; Chopped barbecued chicken $13; Barbecued beef short ribs $8

PIER 25A — LD — Seafood

Top 10 $21-35

Moderate

(F31) 215-16 Northern Blvd. (215th & 216th) 718/423-6395

F 8 / S 6 / A 5 / $28   MC

Seafood restaurant of wide acclaim. Plentiful dishes of deliciously prepared fish gracefully distract from the diner-like surroundings. "Too expensive" it may be, but seafood ain't cheap, dearie…

RAY BARI PIZZA — LD — Pizzeria

(E33) 49-65 Van Dam St. (Corner L.I.E.) 718/361-9300
See review on page 176.

TERESA'S — BLD — Polish

(A32) 70-34 Austin St. 718/520-2910
See review on page 72.

TUTTA PASTA — LD — Italian

(F36) 108-22 Queens Blvd. 718/261-8713
See review on page 95.

0	1	2	3	4	5	6	7	8	9	10
disappointing		fair		good		very good		excellent		perfect

Water's Edge

WATER'S EDGE   LD   Amer/Continental

(E31)   44th Dr. on the East River   718/482-0033   Fax: 937-8817

F 7 / S 7 / A 8 / $48   MC V D AE

You'll get a breath-taking view of Manhattan and "the great sunset" from every seat in this luxuriously decorated, "sophisticated," first-class restaurant built on an old barge still floating in the river. The ferry ride over is "hopelessly romantic." The wine list, which is culled from a private wine cellar, is extensive, with prices ranging from $75-$650. And if you're looking for a place for a private party, try the top floor, where you can also have fireworks provided.
Closed: Sunday
SPEC: *Fricassee of wild mushrooms $11; Maryland crab & roasted pepper ravioli $12; Roast monkfish $23; Rack of lamb $29*

WATERFRONT CRAB HOUSE   LD   Seafood

(F31)   2-03 Borden Ave. (2nd St.)   718/729-4862   Fax: 937-9750

F 6 / S 6 / A 6 / $30   MC V D AE DIS   **TO**

So you want a romantic evening and you're dying to get out of Manhattan? Try hopping the 34th street ferry across the East River to the Crab House and treat yourself (and your date) to an evening here. There's a lovely dining room with antique collectibles hanging from the ceiling and adorning the walls. The only downer? Some claim the food "has gone down hill."
SPEC: *Clam chowder (New England & Manhattan) $2.75; Garlic crabs $14.95; Lobster tails start at $25.95; Double-cut primerib $14.95; Black angus steak $19.95*

ALPHABETICAL

BY CUISINE

AMERICAN /CONTINENTAL

SPECIAL INTEREST

BAR FOOD

INDEX
Business
BYOB
Dancing
Good For
Drinks

INDEX
Good Food,
Mediocre
Atmosphere
Great Views
Health
Menu

IN SPOTS

INDEX
People
Watching
Power
Scene
Pre-
Theatre

POWER SCENE

PRE-THEATRE

PRIX FIXE

SINGLES SCENE

SMOKING

Restaurants where smoking is allowed somewhere on the premises

SPORTS /PUBS

INDEX
Sports/
Pubs
Steak
Houses
Wheelchair
Access

STEAK HOUSES

WHEELCHAIR ACCESS

Most restaurants in New York City are wheelchair accessible–call for information.

Marcellino's

SPECIAL SERVICES

PRICE LIST

The following is a price list based on quantities of books ordered. Standard edition prices are for the books only. Custom edition prices include books with slip-cover jackets customized for your company or for yourself. The prices quoted are valid until 11/1/96.

Quantity	Standard Edition	Custom Edition B&W	2-Color	4-Color
1-9	$9.95	N/A	N/A	N/A
10-24	$8.95	N/A	N/A	N/A
25-49	$8.45	N/A	N/A	N/A
50-99	$7.95	N/A	N/A	N/A
100-249	$7.45	9.95	$11.45	N/A
250-499	$6.95	$8.75	$9.65	$11.45
500-999	$5.95	$7.45	$7.95	$8.95
1000+	Negotiable	Negotiable		

Additional 5% discount for reviewers.

For custom editions, the price does not include creation of camera-ready artwork or inserts. Shipping charges and tax are not included.

Order Card

☐ I want to take part in the Survey

Please send me _____ copies of the 1996 edition of
Marcellino's Restaurant Report 1996 New York at $9.95 each
plus shipping and handling*.

Name_____

Tel(_____) _____

Fax(_____) _____

Shipping Address_____

_____

_____

Billing Address (if different from shipping address)

_____

_____

_____

Send as a gift to:

_____

_____

_____

Please charge my:

☐ VISA   ☐ Mastercard   ☐ Diners Club
☐ American Express   ☐ Discover

Card Number_____

Exp. Date_____

Signature_____

Date_____

My check for $_____ payable to Marcellino's Guides
USA Inc. is enclosed

*Shipping & Handling Costs:
1-2   copies/$4.00   5-7   copies/$5.50
3-4   copies/$4.50   8-10 copies/$6.50

Please send your order to the address shown on the reverse side
or fax this form to 212/752-4101. Please allow 7 to 10 business
days for delivery.

Marcellino's
counts on you!

Fax this order card to 212/752-4101, or place it in an envelope with proper postage and return it to:

Marcellino's Guides USA Inc.
340 East 52 Street
Suite 7E
New York, New York 10022

Marcellino's

MAPS

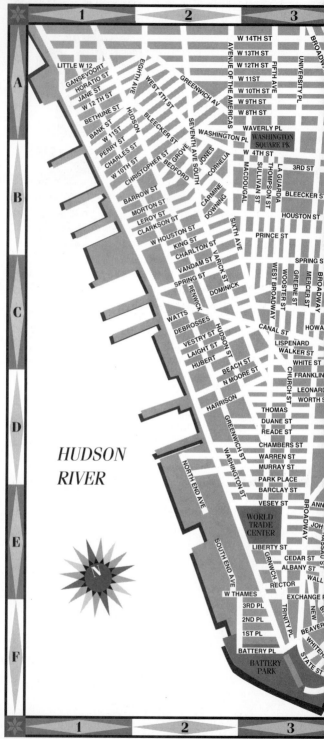

MAP NOT TO SCALE © 1995 MARCELLINO'S GUIDES USA, INC.

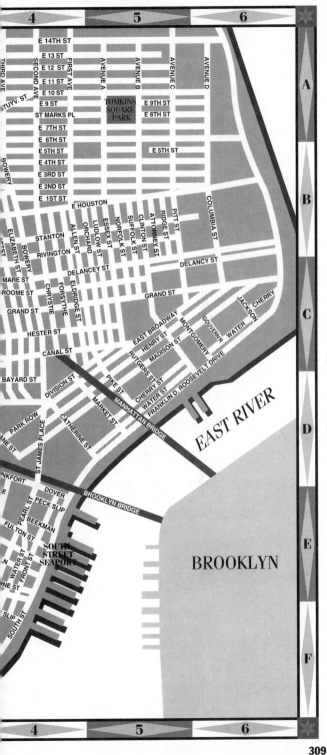

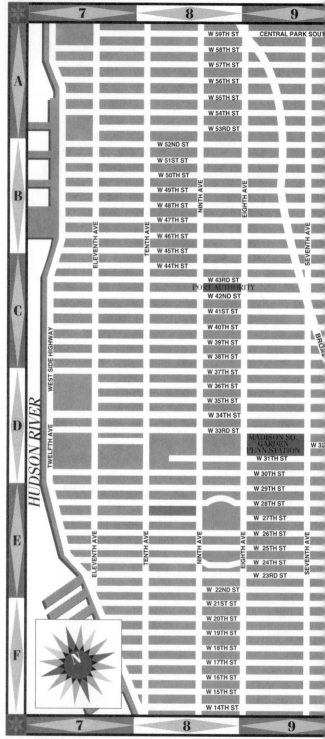

MAP NOT TO SCALE © 1995 MARCELLINO'S GUIDES USA, INC.

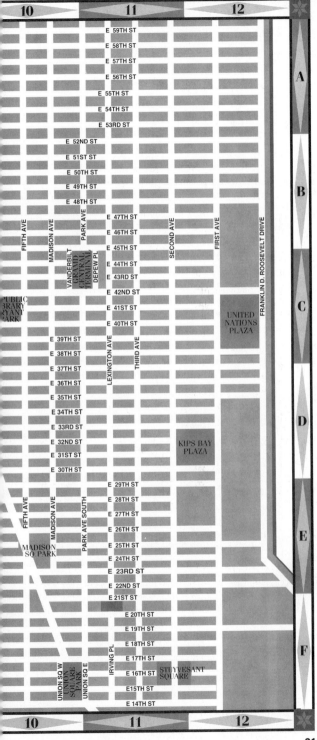

MAP NOT TO SCALE © 1995 MARCELLINO'S GUIDES USA, INC.

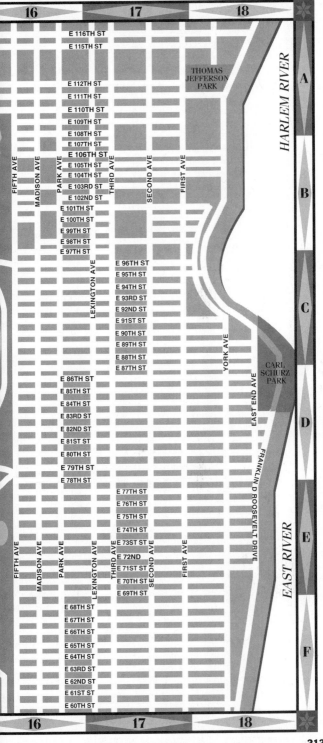

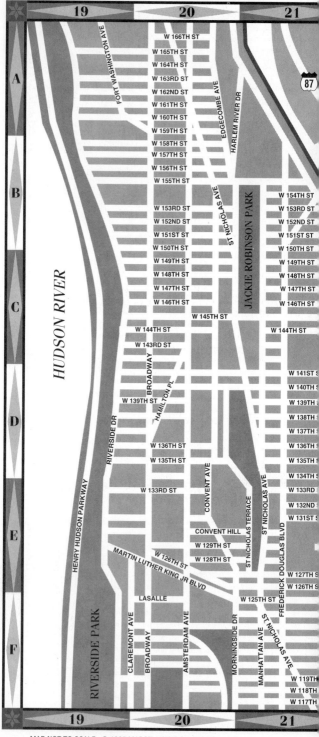

MAP NOT TO SCALE © 1995 MARCELLINO'S GUIDES USA, INC.

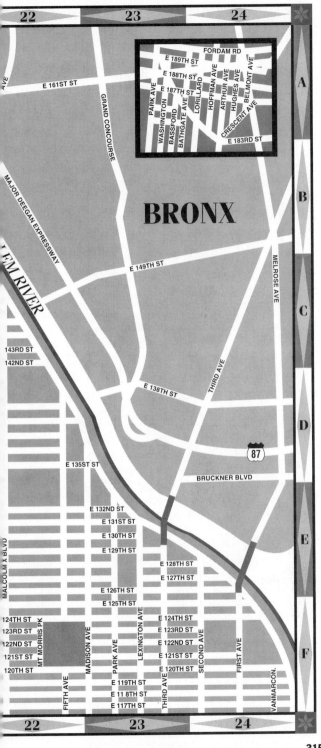

BRONX

FORDAM RD

E 189TH ST
E 188TH ST
E 187TH ST

PARK AVE
WASHINGTON
BASSFORD
BATHGATE AVE
LORILLARD
HOFFMAN AVE
ARTHUR AVE
HUGHES AVE
CRESCENT AVE
BELMONT AVE

E 183RD ST

E 161ST ST

GRAND CONCOURSE

MAJOR DEEGAN EXPRESSWAY

HARLEM RIVER

MELROSE AVE

E 149TH ST

THIRD AVE

143RD ST
142ND ST

E 138TH ST

E 135ST ST

87

BRUCKNER BLVD

E 132ND ST
E 131ST ST
E 130TH ST
E 129TH ST

E 128TH ST
E 127TH ST

E 126TH ST
E 125TH ST

MALCOLM X BLVD

124TH ST
123RD ST
122ND ST
121ST ST
120TH ST

MT MORRIS PK

MADISON AVE

PARK AVE

LEXINGTON AVE

E 124TH ST
E 123RD ST
E 122ND ST
E 121ST ST
E 120TH ST

SECOND AVE

FIRST AVE

THIRD AVE

FIFTH AVE

E 119TH ST
E 11 8TH ST
E 117TH ST

VANMARCON.

A
B
C
D
E
F

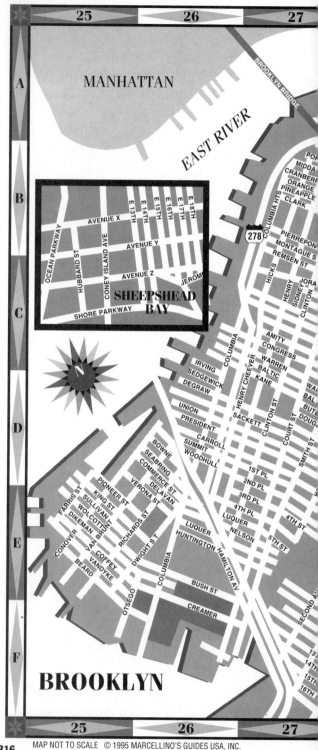

MANHATTAN

EAST RIVER

BROOKLYN BRIDGE

A

B

C

D

E

F

POP
MIDDA
CRANBERR
ORANGE
PINEAPPLE
CLARK

COLUMBIA HTS

278

PIERREPON
MONTAGUE S
REMSEN ST

HICKS

JORA
SIDNEY'S
CLINTON

HENRY

AVENUE X

E 13TH
E 14TH
E 15TH
E 16TH
E 17TH
E 18TH

OCEAN PARKWAY

HUBBARD ST

CONEY ISLAND AVE

AVENUE Y

AVENUE Z

JEROM

SHEEPSHEAD
BAY

SHORE PARKWAY

N

AMITY
CONGRESS
WARREN
BALTIC
KANE

COLUMBIA

IRVING

SEDGEWICK

DEGRAW

HENRY CHEEVER

CLINTON ST

COURT ST

WAR
BAL
DOUG.

UNION

PRESIDENT

CARROLL

SUMMIT

WOODHULL

SACKETT

SMITH ST

1ST PL
2ND PL
3RD PL
4TH PL

4TH ST

BOWNE
SEABRING
COMMERCE ST
DELAVAN
VERONA ST

PIONEER ST

KING ST

FARRIS ST
SULLIVAN
WOLCOTT

DIKEMAN

CONOVER

VAN BRUNT

RICHARDS ST

DWIGHT ST

COFFEY
VANDYKE

BEARD

OTSEGO

COLUMBIA

LUQUER

HUNTINGTON

HAMILTON AV

LUQUER
NELSON

5TH ST

SECOND A

BUSH ST

CREAMER

13T
14TH
15TH
16TH

BROOKLYN

BROADWAY

DRIGGS AVE

KENT AVE

JOHN ST
MARSHALL
PLYMOUTH ST
HUDSON
LITTLE
WATER ST
FRONT ST
YORK

GOLD ST

US NAVAL
RESERVE CENTER

NASSAU FLUSHING

B

278

RYERSON

PARK AVE

CLASSON
STEUBEN
GRAND

HALL
WAVERLY
CLINTON
VANDERBILT
CLERMONT
ADELPHI
CARLTON

MILLARY

HOYT
DUFFIELD

MYRTLE

LAWRENCE

WILLOUGHBY ST

FT.
GREENE
PARK

CUMBERLAND

WILLOUGHBY

FULTON ST

DEKALB

FT GREENE

C

LIVINGSTON ST
SCHERMERHORN
STATE ST
PACIFIC ST
DEAN ST
BERGEN ST
WYCKOFF

FLATBUSH AVE

S ELLIOT
S PORTLAND

LAFAYETTE

HANSON PL

S OXFORD

GATES

WASHINGTON AVE
ST JAMES
CAMBRIDGE

D

NEVINS ST

ST MARKS

ATLANTIC AVE

THIRD AVE

FOURTH AVE

PROSPECT
PARK

STERLING

ST JOHNS

FIFTH AVE

LINCOLN PL

BERKLEY PL

CARLTON

VANDERBILT

UNDERHILL

PRESIDENT

CARROLL ST

1ST ST

2ND ST

3RD ST

SIXTH AVE

GARFIELD PL

ST JOHN

LINCOLN

EASTERN PKWY

E

4TH ST
5TH ST
6TH ST
7TH ST
8TH ST
9TH ST
10TH ST
11TH ST
12TH ST

SEVENTH AVE

EIGHTH AVE

PROSPECT PARK WEST

PROSPECT
PARK

F

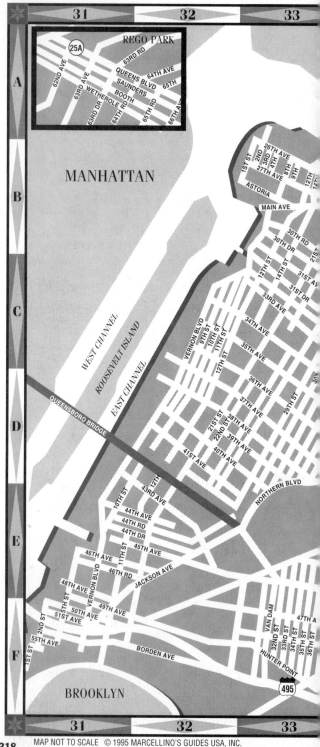

REGO PARK

25A

62ND AVE
63RD AVE
63RD DR
WETHEROLE ST
63RD DR
64TH RD
63RD RD
QUEENS BLVD
SAUNDERS
BOOTH
64TH AVE
65TH
65TH RD
66TH AVE

MANHATTAN

26TH AVE
1ST ST
2ND
3RD
4TH
8TH
9TH
12TH
27TH AVE
ASTORIA
MAIN AVE

30TH RD
30TH DR
31ST
12TH ST
14TH ST
31ST AVE
31ST DR
33RD AVE
34TH AVE
35TH AVE
36TH AVE
37TH AVE
29TH ST
38TH AVE
39TH AVE
40TH AVE
41ST AVE

WEST CHANNEL
ROOSEVELT ISLAND
EAST CHANNEL

VERNON BLVD
9TH ST
10TH ST
11TH ST
12TH ST
21ST ST
22ND ST

QUEENSBORO BRIDGE

NORTHERN BLVD

12TH
43RD AVE
10TH ST
44TH AVE
44TH RD
44TH DR
45TH AVE
11TH ST
46TH AVE
VERNON BLVD
46TH RD
JACKSON AVE
48TH AVE
5TH ST
50TH AVE
49TH AVE
51ST AVE
2ND ST
55TH AVE
1ST ST
BORDEN AVE

VAN DAM
47TH A
32ND ST
33RD ST
34TH ST
35TH ST
36TH
HUNTER POINT

495

BROOKLYN

MAP NOT TO SCALE © 1995 MARCELLINO'S GUIDES USA, INC.

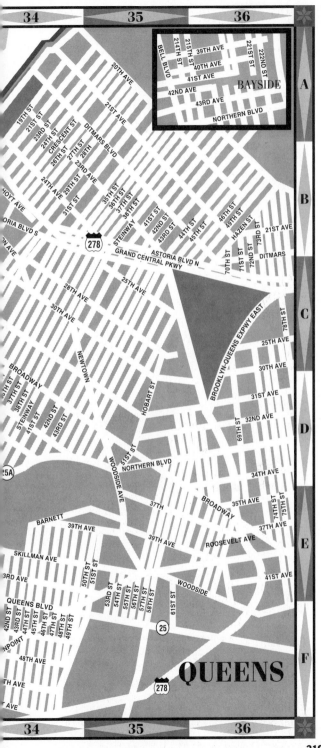

BELL BLVD
214TH ST
215TH ST
39TH AVE
40TH AVE
221ST ST
222ND ST
41ST AVE
42ND AVE
BAYSIDE
43RD AVE
NORTHERN BLVD

20TH AVE

19TH ST
21ST ST
23RD ST
24TH ST
CRESCENT ST
26TH ST
27TH ST
28TH
21ST AVE
DITMARS BLVD

HOYT AVE
24TH AVE
29TH ST
23RD AVE
31ST ST
35TH ST
36TH ST
37TH ST
38TH ST
41ST ST
42ND ST
43RD ST
4TH ST
45TH ST
46TH ST
49TH ST
HAZEN ST
21ST AVE

ASTORIA BLVD S
STEINWAY
ASTORIA BLVD N
70TH ST
71ST ST
72ND ST
73RD ST
DITMARS

278

ON AVE
GRAND CENTRAL PKWY

28TH AVE
25TH AVE

30TH AVE
NEWTOWN

BROOKLYN-QUEENS EXPWY EAST
78TH ST
25TH AVE
30TH AVE
31ST AVE

BROADWAY
37TH ST
38TH ST
STEINWAY
41ST ST
42ND ST
43RD ST

HOBART ST
69TH ST
32ND AVE
69TH ST

25A

51ST ST
WOODSIDE AVE
NORTHERN BLVD
34TH AVE

BARNETT
37TH
BROADWAY
35TH AVE
74TH ST
75TH ST

39TH AVE
39TH AVE
37TH AVE

SKILLMAN AVE
50TH ST
51ST ST
ROOSEVELT AVE

3RD AVE
WOODSIDE
41ST AVE

QUEENS BLVD
53RD ST
54TH ST
55TH ST
56TH ST
57TH ST
58TH ST
61ST ST

42ND ST
43RD ST
44TH ST
45TH ST
46TH ST
47TH ST
48TH ST
49TH ST
NPOINT

48TH AVE
25

TH AVE
QUEENS
278

NOTES